MEN AGAINST DEATH

PAUL DE KRUIF

~~~~~~

MEN
against
DEATH

~~~~~~

*The doctors tell us there are certain diseases
that are incurable. Do you know what an incurable disease is? It is one that the doctors
don't know anything about. The disease has
no objection to being cured at all.*
CHARLES F. KETTERING

~~~~~~

HARCOURT, BRACE AND COMPANY

NEW YORK

PRINTED IN THE UNITED STATES OF AMERICA
BY QUINN & BODEN COMPANY, INC., RAHWAY, N. J.
Designed by Robert S. Josephy

NOTE

ON SOURCES OF INFORMATION

~~~~~~

"Men Against Death" is based first of all on a detailed study of the original scientific contributions bearing upon the adventures of all the characters here recorded. This study has been supplemented by extended reading of the scientific reports revealing the state of knowledge (or ignorance) *existing in their respective fields before these men against death made their discoveries. A bibliography detailing all these scientific papers, bulletins and books would come to a list of nearly a thousand separate titles.*

Such a list, in a book which pretends only to tell the plain story of scientific adventure for plain people, would be swankish and punditical.

With the exception of Finsen, Schaudinn, and Semmelweis—who had passed on to the searcher's Valhalla long before this work was begun—the writer has known all of the principal characters of this book in person. His method has been to study the original publications of these characters, and then, equipped with this knowledge, to go to them personally to search out the intimate details of their adventures.

These details (*with the exception of those of Semmelweis who wrote naïvely and without restraint*) *rarely appear in scientific publications.*

By the use of this method of preliminary study followed by personal contact, the present reporter has tried to present the achievements of these death-fighters with an approach

vii

to the obscurely romantic way in which they actually happened.

This reporter wishes to thank Mr. Philip S. Rose, of The Country Gentleman, *and Mr. Loring A. Schuler, of* The Ladies' Home Journal, *for their constant support during the long years of preparation of this book. Their editorial insight had a great deal to do with the selection of its basic material. Its various chapters, excepting 7 and 8, appeared in a preliminary form in one or the other of these magazines and this made the collection of the basic material possible. From this material the book was then completely rewritten as a continuous story. Chapters 7 and 8 appeared in their present form in the* Forum.

PAUL DE KRUIF

May 20, 1932
Hungry Street
Holland, Michigan

CONTENTS

ILLUSTRATIONS

MEN AGAINST DEATH

PROLOGUE

I DON'T want to die. There are too many birds left whose songs I don't know, and it's going to take a long time to learn them.

Yet I cannot expect to live more than twenty years longer. As I begin this story of the deeds of men against death I am thirty-nine, and the actuarial experts look up from their slide rules and adding machines to tell me that fifty-nine years—slightly plus or minus—is as long as the average male American can expect to live.

But isn't there a chance that my men against death have found ways to help me, if I really follow their science, to trick the grim mathematics of the life-measuring experts?

I hate the thought of dying. It is too much fun fighting Lake Michigan's strong blue water. I want to go on cutting down more thousands of saplings to make barricades of sandbags and saplings against Lake Michigan when it tries to take our house at Hungry Street's end. Yet death is coming for me in a little while now, just as right now I'm watching it come to the brown leaves of the maples and the beech-tree's yellow leaves that drift by my windows this cold day in October.

I started across the bridge of life thirty-nine years ago last March, one of maybe a hundred thousand American mites born in my day and year. All of these years, all of this cohort of one hundred thousand, rich and poor, some reckless of death and others ridiculously hiding behind this or that health-fad armor, have been shot at by what lean-faced Karl Pearson calls the Marksmen Death.

Already thirty thousand of my brothers and sisters of March, 1890, have fallen, and of the chances of the seventy

3

thousand of us who are left, Karl Pearson has drawn a grim picture. It is simple as a child's scrawl. It is terrible as fate. It is called the L-x line of the Life Tables. It is only a thin streak going downhill on a chart and what are my chances as I stand, aged thirty-nine, on this downhill line? Up till now the downward course of that line has been gentle, but around age forty I have to begin to dodge shots of surer Marksmen Death, shooting like Davy Crockett himself, and oftener.

Here I am just beginning to learn a little about living, at the moment my path on this L-x line begins slanting down steeper. The ranks of my cohort thin faster. I've dreamt nights that I was on the steep slant of that line sliding down it like slipping down a rock face toward a crevasse with no life line. I haven't lived long enough yet to learn resignation.

So, mornings after the terrible dream I wake, thinking of the straight-trunked black oaks and the tough curly maples on this Lake Michigan shore waiting to feel the bite of my double-bitted ax.

And I remember the small but ever-growing republic of dear friends who believe in me, who would fight for me, who will give me the right steer through nasty situations I get into through my periodical fits of stupidity and silliness. . . .

Then I know I mustn't die. But how can I upset the predictions of my slide-rule executioners? Will I find tricks in the laboratories of the death fighters? I know I can't crawl back up old Karl Pearson's life line. Some day one of his Marksmen Death will get me. But somewhere I'll find tricks to dodge those marksmen for a long while yet—bar accidents.

II

So I've gone to the laboratories where the death fighters work, peer, probe, sweat, and argue and I've ransacked libraries through endless thousands of pages of their scientific reports—those drab reports that can suddenly turn as exciting as a trench mortar bomb bursting just over the parapet. There's plenty of good news. In the last eighty years life has been lengthened remarkably—on the average.

Babies born in 1850 could expect to live only thirty-five years while those born today have a gambler's chance to be still living at fifty-five, which is a great jump ahead and mighty encouraging for our present babies. But what have the death fighters done for the longer life chances of folks who are my age now, compared to the chances of folks who were my age in 1850? The answer to that question is not so pretty.

In 1850, people who were aged thirty-five could expect to live 25.3 years longer. Now from 1850 onward the real scientific fight against death got going. It was just then that honest Ignaz Semmelweis first found out how to keep death from sneaking into folks from outside—though he's never gotten proper credit for this most fundamental discovery. Then, right while Semmelweis was dying, crazy and forgotten, rose that brilliant band of microbe-hunting desperadoes. Pasteur at the head of them. In their ranks scraggly bearded little Robert Koch taught them precision and exactness. Inspired by these two rivals—who detested each other sincerely —scores of lesser death fighters tilted at this or that dangerous plague. They didn't confine themselves to trying to save babies. And yet . . .

After all these seventy-five years of sensational discovery, what have you? In 1850, folks who had lived thirty-five years had a chance to go on for 25.3 years longer. In 1925— the year of my thirty-fifth birthday—this figure had been pushed up to 25.4!

In spite of their daring, their sweat, their shrewd fixing and ingenious tinkering, the death fighters seem to have given longer life—just to babies.

III

Yet surely they have done more for men and women of my age than this miserable one-tenth of a year of longer life which the statistician's mass figures show? Surely individual lives of older folks have been lengthened? The death fighters I've known aren't worried by these pessimistic figures. They're statistical ignoramuses, thumbing their noses at L-x lines, and deep down in their hearts they know this:

That what Semmelweis, Pasteur, Koch, all their gang, have done to increase chances of human life in its early years, they themselves will do for folks in their prime. They know it is not intrinsically impossible to search out ways to check the slow hardening of our arteries. Some day some tinkering fixer will learn to stave off the gradual tiring of the muscles of our hearts. So they'll push death back and back . . .

But their failure up till now gives me warning not to let my hopes be pumped up by current life-prolonging promises. I'm from Missouri about life-lengthening experiments because savants are frail like all ordinary humans and their very eagerness to stave off their own passing may dim their sharp eyes, confound their common sense, and befog their scientific insight. Take Metchnikoff . . .

That fantastic man was the true pioneer of life-extension nonsense. About his phagocytes he'd been exact as exactness goes in our lamentably inexact microbe-hunting science, but near fifty, he began to be upset by life rushing by him and he turned himself into the first of life-extension's absurd model boys. We die too soon because we're poisoned by bad intestinal bacilli—that was his hunch and he set out to prove it on his own person with a sustained if idiotic courage for twenty years.

He neither drank nor smoked. Even when he felt fine he had himself probed, punched, and ransacked by the keen-

est diagnostic pooh-bahs of the faculty. He was always bending over microscopes and peering at test-tubes examining
his own blood and excretions, and bakers were amazed when
he insisted his rolls be sent him wrapped in sterilized paper
to keep out life-shortening microbes. Further to confound
these evil microscopic beings he guzzled gallons of sour milk
teeming with what he fondly thought were life-prolonging
bacilli from Bulgaria. He was so hygienic he was miserable
and died one year past seventy.

Yet the air is full of these see-your-doctor-every-six-months
notions. I am advised to be like the Chinese who pay their
doctors to keep them healthy, but when I consult the largely
idiotic jumble of superstitions that makes up Chinese medical science I can only wonder how Oriental doctors do it.
And when I think of the subtle protoplasm that goes to make
my body and of the enormous ignorance of medical science
regarding it, I wonder how physicians can pretend to overhaul me as garage men overhaul and recondition a worn
motor. Yet they hint at longer life for me if I'll let them
overhaul me when I feel fit and husky.

I wonder. I send for prospectuses and am impressed by
the formidable list—almost a Who's Who of medical great
men—of searchers who sponsor this life-extending commerce.
I study statistics that prove how I'll defer dying if I worry
while I'm well. I must bow to the actuarial eminence of
Doctors Knight and Dublin. Their figures show that the
death rate of well folks who go to have themselves periodi-
cally percussed and tested is lower than the rate of dying
of the foolish masses who so long as they feel well don't
worry. I am not competent to question the accuracy of this
compilation. Yet the number of the human animals in-
volved in this life-extending experiment is still so small that
my common sense says the whole business may well be happenstance.

"Oh, yeah," is still my answer to the blandishments of life-extension advertising. And yet . . .

It is all confusing. Other equally reliable physicians think these health assays are poppycock that may turn folks who feel fine into whining hypochondriacs denying themselves good food, strong drink, and other robust pleasures for fear of ten points too much blood pressure or traces of albumin in their urine.

The old heart-mender, Mackenzie, always held it is the man himself who knows first when he is sick. He said it is our own bodies, by causeless tiredness, by pain, that tell us first when it's time to go see our doctor. Our bodies flash the danger signals long before expensive gadgets like the X-ray or the electro-cardiograph reveal there's anything at all the matter. None will deny that Mackenzie was a master observer of the first signs of peril in healthy folks for whom death had started stalking. And yet . . . ?

IV

What of the gland wizards? Can their knife magic help me? By certain intimate surgeries they promise to stoke up my energies. By bold and curious experiments they claim they believe they've stretched out the life-span of rodents dilapidated and near dying. The Austrian Steinach is one of these gland masters and surely since his researches are printed in the austerest scientific periodicals I would be impudent to question their exactness.

With his scalpel Steinach caused male and female rats to trade their sex glands and what then happened was fantastic. The male white rats lost their manliness and became clinging vines and gentle. You'd have sworn the females were trying to set up housekeeping as fathers. Now, if such a fundamental change is possible . . .

Enraptured, Steinach picked out two white rats, brothers from the same litter. They were old fellows, moth-eaten with age and in the last degree senile. The records showed they had reached twenty-six months of age. Of these two rat brothers, Rat A was always drowsy. He doddered and had grave trouble to keep open his rheumy eyes. The state of Rat B, his brother, was still more lamentable, so bad, indeed, that Steinach said it was not even worth while to take his picture. Now the experiment . . .

Steinach's scalpel gleamed and here was Rat B—awake from his anaesthetic—and strangely modified. Steinach the gland master had tied off the ducts that lead from poor old Rat B's sex glands. Would certain cells of these sex glands now regenerate, pour their life-stimulating hormone into their doomed owner's body?

In two months Brother A—not operated—had gone to his reward. But while Rat A was dying, a weird awakening, a seeming setting back of the hands of life's clock, occurred in operated Brother B's carcass. Dr. Pearl, relating this experiment, says that operated Brother B now presented a perfect picture of lusty young rathood. In every way he was vigorous, and outlived Rat A by eight months in all, and reached the age of three years before he finally died.

Had Steinach actually made the down slant of the L-x line less steep—for rats?

There was a little catch in his experiment, if he had only looked up the records. There he would have found there are plenty of white rats who live for forty months and longer, with no operation, without any rejuvenating monkey business whatever.

v

Just the same, life stuff is immortal. I'll admit my discouragement after wading through all this moralistic-hygienic quackery, through dubious and premature statistics, through this comic-opera science of rejuvenation by the glands of ring-tailed monkeys. These things depress me and my eyes turn toward the brown and yellow leaves wavering

down from the maples and the beeches by my window. No
. . . the fight to prolong human life, to iron out the fateful
down slant of the L-x line . . . that fight is a thousand
times more subtle, more dangerous, more difficult a job than
this life-extending, gland-rejuvenating, pseudo-scientific ballyhoo tries to make me believe. . . .

But the life stuff I'm made of *can* live forever. And every
death fighter worth his salt knows this, believes it, and may
take heart from the awesome grandeur of that thought. It is
when I go back to the obscure outlandish dabblings of the
diggers in the very sub-cellars of biology that I forget the
L-x line and don't see brown and yellow dead leaves falling.
I stand again in the paper-strewn workroom of atheistical old
Jacques Loeb. He was a kindly man whose fierce gleaming
black eyes six years ago stopped looking into life's begin-
nings.

In imagination I can see him at Woods Hole, restless as
always, nervous, pacing up and down his laboratory. For a
moment he forgets his sarcasms against his fellow scientists.
He forgets his dreadful philosophy that says all life may as
well as not be a godless accident. He stares into a little dish,
shaped like a finger bowl, in which are the eggs of that miserable marine animal, the sea urchin, who makes up for her
insignificance by bearing the grand name of *Strongylocen-
trotus purpuratus.* He knows those eggs will surely die if
they're kept in their natural element, sea water, for only
twenty-three hours.

He dabbles. Days pass with Loeb dabbling. Still batch
after batch of those eggs go on dying in a day or even sooner.
He keeps on dabbling.

By some topsy-turvy logic, with a little pipette, this dark-
eyed Loeb feeds new batches of these urchin's eggs a bit of
that most deadly poison, cyanide of potassium. It is like
mediaeval magic, incredible. The eggs live, not for a day,
but two days, go on living for seventy-five hours. Three

times their natural term of life they live in this bath of poison. Then, touched by the sperm of the father sea urchins, they actually develop into husky larvae. So Loeb lengthens life—by chemistry.

He goes on dabbling. Who before him had ever dreamed that the egg of a sea urchin could awaken to form new life without the fertilizing touch of that other living thing, the sperm of the male? Surely this is beyond man's meddling, even the most diabolically ingenious would not attempt it. And what, anyway, can this have to do with the foredoomed death of the bodies of men, or any other animal? Loeb bends over his eggs in the finger bowl. He putters with them, no different from a housewife anxious to improve her sauce or gravy. . . .

He soaks those sea urchins' eggs in a little butyric acid— the acid that gives the smell to rancid butter. He washes them gently. He puts them in sea water and then in water a little saltier than the water of the ocean. He adds no sperm at all. Surely these eggs must die?

Instead of dying, these eggs begin to segment, to develop, and at last grow into a multitude of gayly swimming sea urchin children—completely fatherless. Death is a chemical thing. It can be tricked. It can be downed and life can go on to develop more life—by chemistry.

I know it's a far cry from chemically immortalized eggs of a sea urchin to my own inexorably senescent, my slowly dying bones and muscles. But nobody can deny me the right to grasp at straws, to be encouraged by knowing that length of some sorts of life—no matter how humble—can be controlled by men.

VI

I wander through laboratories, mull through reports in still libraries, and find news much more encouraging than this. I come to the strange experiments of Jacques Loeb's less famous brother, Leo. Leo Loeb knew—like any boy or girl brought up in the country—that when animals die all parts of them don't die at once. Bash in a snake's head no matter how thoroughly . . . his tail will go on moving, won't die, as the old saying goes, till sundown. A turtle's heart goes on strongly beating long after the rest of the unhappy creature would be declared dead by any coroner.

Now Leo Loeb stuck the surviving tissues of I don't remember what animals into test-tubes, into a suitable soup, such as nourishes delicate microbes. Those tissues not only kept on living, but they grew. Loeb's first crude dabblings were made exact and absolutely easy to reduplicate by the obscurely famous biologist Ross Harrison of Yale—who shies at publicity and is never seen in the rotogravures of the Sunday newspapers.

Now this strange keeping alive of tissues of beasts' bodies in test-tubes and dishes started a pack of scientific hounds off on a strange hunt. The most famous of these hunters was Alexis Carrel, the Frenchman and winner of the Nobel Prize, the surgeon who first stitched arteries together and kept blood flowing through them. His name is known to millions where thousands know the names of the trail-blazing Jewish brothers Loeb—and where dozens have heard the name of Ross Harrison.

It's better than seventeen years now since Carrel started a wee bit of the heart muscle of a chick to growing—away from that chick—in a highly special nutritious soup. Carrel's experiment is certainly a strange one when you consider how different is his philosophy from that of the God-defying Jacques Loeb. Loeb would be the first to question God's law that men and all living things are . . . mortal. Carrel is a Roman Catholic. . . .

Now the genial smiling Alexis Carrel and his faithful scientific slave, Ebeling, go on lifting bits of this living chicken heart from one dish of soup from which it has got its nourishment to another dish of new soup which will renew its growing. Day after day, month after month, year after year, Ebeling has tended this mysteriously beating bit of chicken heart muscle. Year after year Ebeling, dark-haired, with lean face above his severe white-collared uniform, has guarded and brooded over this rhythmically beating bit of barnyard fowl in Rockefeller Institute over the East River in New York City. When I knew him, Ebeling had next to no vacations on account of this outlandish detached living morsel of chicken. For seventeen years now it has lived, new healthy cells growing to take the place of old ones dying. . . . Potentially *immortal* . . .

Why shouldn't that bit of chicken heart go on beating for seventeen hundred years? It would, if there were succeeding generations of Carrels and Ebelings quixotic enough to tend it. For a moment I forget the dead leaves falling. I think of the life of the average chicken. I remember what Raymond Pearl has written about the length of life of chickens, and of the many learned things that Pearl is, he is a learned chicken husbandman. I learn that the average expectation of life of the ordinary barnyard fowl is hardly more than two years. The longest-lived chicken races can hardly expect to live more than four. Pearl has never been able to keep the toughest Barred Rock alive for longer than seven years.

And here Carrel and Ebeling have kept a chicken's heart muscle living better than nine times its owner's expectation of life.

Here is a fragment of life, not low and miserable like that of the sea urchin, but fairly high up among living creatures. So long as there are living human guardians to tend it, there's no reason why it can't live forever. This makes me forget the steep slant of Pearson's L-x line down which I'm sliding, slipping. I look into the future thrilled by the portentousness of this grotesque experiment. It is not only the heart muscle of young chicks that Carrel and Ebeling can keep living in their glass dishes. They've grown—apart from their original owners—a great assortment of the tissues of guinea-pigs and dogs and even humans. On wild days with northwest gales, when I have to lug sandbags in the swirl and smash of Lake Michigan's breakers, my breath shortens quicker than it would have done ten years ago. That's my heart muscle—growing old.

But I pick up a two-hundred-pound sandbag and laugh, getting a lift from knowing that, in spite of my own sure mortality, the stuff this ageing blood pump's made of *could* live on forever.

Aren't too many of our men against death too pessimistic? Shouldn't they believe more in the fundamental toughness of the life stuff they fight to make stay living? Can't we all take heart from deep-seeing Jacques Loeb?

Loeb, who dreamed over the mighty fact of life stuff staying alive after it's removed from the animal it was part of, wrote: "This points to the idea that death is not inherent in the individual cell. Death is only the fate of the more complicated organisms in which different types of cells and tissues are dependent upon each other."

If that is so! Remember, Loeb was never a man to kid himself into unjustified hopes of any immediate or dramatic life-extension. But Loeb writes further:

"In this case it seems to happen that one or certain types of cells produce a substance which gradually becomes harmful to a vital organ like the respiratory center. . . ."

With new heart I tug at another sandbag. Won't some unknown, some still unborn searchers, somewhere, trap one or all of these suicidal poisons?

Fierce-eyed old Loeb completes his argument: "The mischief of death may then be traced to the activity of a black sheep in the society of tissues and organs. . . ."

I grunt and laugh and hurry with my sandbag toward the

surf's strong undertow. Won't a hare-brained laboratory adventurer sometime show how to turn Loeb's black sheep white?

VII

There is many a searcher that will give my hopes a great laugh. Aldred Scott Warthin was my old teacher of pathology and I dreaded and in many ways admired him. He had an immense experience of thirty-eight years at the autopsy table in the dead house. One of his last works was his brilliant book, "Old Age," written while the muscles of his own heart were insidiously tiring, and in it he showed me how my dreams of longer life for men were tommyrot. Warthin was still stocky, healthy, ruddy and a joy in life showed out of sparkling eyes. He knew how to laugh and could not be called pessimistic. Yet he was a strange mixture of poet, part cheerful, part grim, and laid down this law:

Death is the inevitable consequence of all life.

From a life of assisting at the tragic study of babies dead before they were born, from peering into the bodies of old men and women marvelously preserved—but dead—at eighty-five or ninety, Warthin drew this conclusion:

Death begins at the very instant of the mystic union of the egg of the mother and the sperm of the father. At that very moment the vital clock that's to become the baby's body is wound up to its maximum charge of energy. The moment the sperm merges with the maternal egg, it loses its lashing whip that propelled it toward its goal. It's that way with everybody: it was so with me. Before I was born I lost my gill slits and at birth the soft downy covering of hair that protected me in my mother, died and was shed. Before I was eight my milk teeth died and came out, and in my adolescence my thymus gland had fulfilled its mysterious purpose and died.

Warthin, who is a kind of exultant observer of death,

proves to me that the involution of death goes hand in hand in my body with the evolution that is growth and life. It is awesome, utterly inevitable. Parts of me have died to let the rest of me live more completely: so at last all of me must die to make room in the world for new cohorts of humans born after my cohort of March, 1890. I must make way for my children. Only through my children—cold and grim consolation!—have I any chance for longer life. . . .

Unanswerable—yet I rebel at Warthin's terrible philosophy. He is deeply learned. But he has spent his working life in the dead house and peering at thin prettily colored slices of dead men and women through his microscope.

The words of that slow-spoken mountain of a man, Raymond Pearl, come back to me to give me courage again. Pearl is an arch-measurer of the length of human life. He is a student of the forces of death. His chuckling, stuttering sarcasms are devastating to life-extension advertisements. But, toward the end of his book, "Biology of Death," Pearl tells me:

Natural death is not an inevitable consequence of life.

I take that for my secret slogan. Lake Michigan's waves wash round my bare legs. They clutch at the sand dune back of me. They keep reaching for our house. My heart pounding, I reach for another sandbag.

VIII

Alas, this slogan I've got from Raymond Pearl can give me hardly more than a gleam of hope, surely no hope whatever for longer life for myself. He gives me plenty of reasons why the length of my own life is foredoomed.

"What determines," Pearl asks, "that John Smith shall die at fifty-eight while Henry Jones lives to the obviously more respectable age of eighty-five?"

For a good part of his life Pearl has been probing into the exact longevity records of animals high and low—from beings as miserable as that genus of beetles called *Blaps* to creatures as sublime as the cotton-wrapped princelings and preposterous duchesses of the royal families of Europe. He fusses with, sorts out, distills, and refines this jumble of figures into a plain proposition that is understandable, that sounds sensible. . . .

"Men behave in respect of their duration of life not unlike a lot of eight-day clocks cared for by an unsystematic person, who does not wind them all to an equal degree, and is not careful about guarding them all from accident. . . ." It is a nice description of a careless God.

"Some," Pearl says, "he winds up fully and they run their full eight days."

I take it that by these, Pearl means those of my cohort of March, 1890, who will still be clinging to the L-x line in their eighties. I mean to be among them—but will I?

"Others," Pearl says, "he winds up only half way, and they stop after four days. . . ."

I ask what's at the bottom of this seeming unfairness of the negligent Great Winder of vital clocks. Old Alexander Graham Bell gives me an answer. That versatile old tinkerer wasn't satisfied to invent the telephone, to fuss with box-kites, to make experiments in flying. To the very bottom of his own L-x line he stayed curious, kept working. At the last he buried himself in a maze of computations in the genealogy of the remarkable family, Hyde, of which the exact date of birth and death of 1,606 males and 1,352 females, is known.

Bell boils it all down to these grim facts:

Hyde fathers and mothers who lived to eighty and past, had children who averaged a life of fifty-two years.

Hyde fathers and mothers who died under sixty, had boys and girls whose average life-span was only thirty-two and eight-tenths!

Pearl sums it up with this gag: "However the matter is taken, a careful selection of one's parents in respect of longevity is the most reliable form of personal life insurance."

And who can select them? And what are my own hopes then? My parents and grandparents have left me no very brilliant legacy of long life. But these are only statistics. I remember that there are lies, damn lies, and statistics, and that wisecrack comforts me a little. Then Pearl downs me again by his curious experiments with that little red-eyed, brown-bodied fruit fly, the *Drosophila melanogaster,* those delicate inoffensive wee beings you'll find in all haunts of home-brewing.

Pearl turned himself from a chicken-raiser into a fly-husbandman, inbreeding countless thousands of these miserable creatures in milk bottles whose bottoms were covered with gelatinized pudding. There's something grotesque about this giant Pearl bending for so many years over bottles marrying fly brothers to fly sisters. But after years of exact counting and recording of the birth and the passing of millions of the offspring of these brother and sister wives and husbands, where Pearl has married short-lived husbands to long-lived wives and vice versa, he comes out of his laboratory sure of this . . .

That long fly life is inherited in that exact three-to-one arithmetic first discovered for tall and dwarf peas by the famous monk, Mendel.

It's well known that many a scientist has fallen into deplorable error by trying to make what he's found from experimenting with animals, apply to human beings as well. It would be easy for me to wisecrack that vinegar flies are a mighty long way from human. Yet everyday observation and common sense are on the side of Bell and Pearl when Pearl sums the whole sad business up:

"We may safely conclude that the primary agent concerned in the winding up of the vital clock, and by the winding determining how long it shall run—is heredity."

All right. But what exasperates me with Pearl is that he is so confoundedly resigned about it. To my face he has denounced me for an ignorant boy when I urge that men against death should fight this horrid inexorable. I know science is on Pearl's side and all I've got is the will—probably idiotic—to trick this legacy of my ancestors. Can't I trick this heredity—a little?

IX

While heredity may be the *primary* agent in determining how long I can live, yet nobody but the most lop-sided extremist would maintain that the winding up at the start, of my vital clock, is everything, and the influence of the world around me nothing. Even though my own particular gang of Dutch ancestors has left me only a fair chance of long life with a vital clock not wound to the maximum tightness, can't I control the speed of its running down?

For example, there is that pretty awful experiment the biologist Slonaker made with white rats—putting four of these little fellows near the beginning of their lives into a cage that kept revolving—always revolving like a squirrel cage. The cage had a mileage-recording odometer hooked up to it and these four unfortunate rats just had to spend their lives—running! These four perpetual Marathoners had three lucky brother white rats living in another cage right beside them, eating the same food exactly, exposed to all the same conditions of life, precisely, except they only made *their* cage revolve when they themselves felt they needed a little constitutional.

The four rats doomed to lifelong sprinting covered 5,447 miles and lived an average of twenty-nine months, point five. The three brothers who ran just when they wanted to lived on the average to the ripe rat old age of forty months, point three.

Maybe I'd better not spend myself so. I know I am too vain of my physical prowess. I'd better cut down the speed on my two-mile swims. When Lake Michigan threatens our sand dune again, instead of violently trying to lug all the saplings and sandbags myself, can't I get friends to help me? Shouldn't I act my age?

Of course this experiment with seven white rats isn't enough for anybody to found a rule of moderation upon. But Slonaker's not too kind experiment isn't all I've got to go by. I remember the experiments my old voyageur friend Jack Northrop did for Jacques Loeb. This Northrop looks like nothing so much as a Viking and it's ridiculous when you think of him fussing with little fruit flies. (In his heart he holds his potato-farming to be as dignified as his laboratory searching. He'd rather hunt or fish salmon than search or farm potatoes. He is altogether my ideal of a man of science.) But Northrop tended and nourished different batches of these little bugs—all their lives long—in flasks, with each crowd living its whole life at a different temperature. He kept one batch in a cool place with temperature regulated to just 10° Centigrade, and other batches at warmer and warmer temperatures all the way up to Centigrade 30. You see, Northrop's boss, Jacques Loeb, had what amounted to an almost lifelong obsession that he could prove every kind of living thing to be nothing but a machine—a physico-chemical machine, soulless! What were these fruit flies, Loeb asked with a sardonically atheistical chuckle, what were they but so many little bundles of chemical reactions?

Wouldn't a hotter and hotter life make those reactions go faster and faster the way chemical reactions are speeded up by heat in a test-tube? Wouldn't these batches of flies live faster and faster—and therefore shorter and shorter—the hotter and hotter?

That's just what happened. From the egg to the day of their death, the coolest, 10° Centigrade, flies lived on the

NORTHROP—"*In his heart he holds his potato-farming to be as dignified as his laboratory searching. . . . He'd rather . . . fish salmon than search or farm potatoes.*"

average to the ripe, the enormous fruit fly age of one hundred twenty-seven days and a half. It was almost exactly as if you could produce at will, families of humans living that many years! But the warmer the shorter—it was really mathematical—and the warmest flies living at 30° Centigrade, passed their sad lives flying frantically round their flasks, going the pace that kills, living an average life-span of no more than twenty-one days, point five.

I'm glad there's enough human freedom left to keep us out of the hands of enthusiastic experimenters like Loeb and Slonaker, though I'll admit it's folly to generalize about the effect of rate of living on the length of life from a half dozen rats or a few million fruit flies. To prove finally that we humans can live gently and so lengthen our life-span I suppose they should put gangs of us in enormous squirrel cages, running, running. We're lucky our financial and political tyrants aren't passionate enough about science and truth to do it. Meanwhile—and this is the next best thing to actual experiment—Raymond Pearl has dug up some fairly exact records showing how sure it is that the harder you live the sooner you die.

What made Pearl's work possible was a statistical system of the Registrar General of England and Wales, in which, along with the death rate of "occupied males" in those countries, their occupation is recorded along with the time of dying. Pearl took a whack at sorting out these vast records— of all English workers, from men with the cushy job of curate in the Church of England, all the way up the scale of bread-winning to coal heavers and puddlers of steel. Pearl was after just one answer: *Does intensity of physical labor affect length of life?*

It was a tough job for Pearl to sort out all the hundreds of different kinds of bread-winning into groups of harder and harder physical work, but he came out of it finally with five great groups, five for indoor and five for outdoor labor. The soft-job boys—like the curates and college professors—made up Group I, with men in each group made up of harder and harder workers up to Group V, whose members really had to sweat for their food and shelter.

Pearl ruled out all deaths due to occupational hazards. Keeping those deaths in would have falsified the whole picture because it's obviously not quite as safe to be a coal miner as to hold down a job as the Duchess of Plushbottom's secretary. He ruled out all accidental deaths of any kind. Being flattened out by a truck has no relation to whether a man is a coal heaver or—as Pearl says—"a delicate curate whose most strenuous physical labor had been an occasional hard-fought game of croquet."

The story coming out of the graphs and curves made from Pearl's calculations is pretty striking, and sad. It's difficult to kill a man by hard work before he is forty. But after that his rate of living begins to get in its licks. Take the two extremes, Group I whose members have sinecures and are likely to have calluses where they sit down, and Group V whose members have calluses on the palms of their hands. It's a tough story for the Group V toilers, who are past forty, and on the steep down slope of their L-x lines. From age forty-five to fifty-four their death rate is thirteen percent higher than that of the soft-job boys of Group I. Between fifty-five and sixty-four the difference is nineteen percent.

It seems mighty likely that the lives of the great mass of the world's hard workers are shortened—in proportion to the drudgery they do so that the rest of us may live easy. Now my half-day sandbag totings and tree choppings make me red in the face, ashamed, because I'm only a dilettante worker, able to go on or off the job when I want to. I understand now why good old Joe Nederveld—we used to call him the Commodore—used to get huffy at me when I was a youngster, digging ditches with him as straw boss. I never gave my L-x line a thought then. I was cocky. My life sap

was then at full turgor, and I used to keep two shovels of
dirt in the air most of the time. I was vain of my strength
and scornful of old Joe. Joe worked mighty slow always taking it easy.

I understand now. He was just slowing down his vital
clock . . . by instinct. He had to live his whole life long
by that work. Like everybody he wanted long life. Joe Nederveld's instinct makes me much more certain about Slonaker's
rat science, Loeb and Northrop's fly science, and Raymond
Pearl's beautiful statistics.

I begin to see now why the men against death are having
such a tough time making the L-x line *for the mass of man-
kind* go down less steeply. It's the millions who've got to do
the more or less hard physical labor even in middle life and
in their old days . . . or starve. It's those millions, not us
white-collar thousands—who make up the death rates in the
vital statistics.

The hope for longer life for those millions comes not from
the doctors, then, at least not as much from the men against
death as it comes from inventors, engineers, who are more
and more making machines do the drudgery. . . .

Meanwhile, taking lessons from the science of Slonaker
and Jacques Loeb and Pearl and Joe Nederveld, I'm going
to try to relax, to slow down my rate of living. I know I'm
selfish. When I think of my brothers the toilers I feel like a
miserable slacker. I realize *everybody* should do his share of
hard toil. Then nobody would have to spend his whole life
at it. That makes me detest my soft job as a reporter. So far,
not having guts to conquer my selfishness, I try to soothe
myself with sawing and wood-chopping, thereby kidding myself I am doing my part of the world's real labor. But even
at those jobs—selfishly wanting to live longer—I'm going to
take it easier.

To live longer I'm going to heed the saying that was true

long before there were smart men like Loeb and Pearl in the laboratories. I'll remember you can't burn the candle at both ends.

x

Anyway, surely the death-fighters have found ways to give me a chance to lengthen my life from age forty onward. Already they've made discoveries that will check or even abolish some of the ills that might put sand in the works of my vital clock after forty. These victories of theirs have failed so far to show up in mass vital statistics. But isn't that because the mass of humanity is too poor to pay for the thorough application of all the death-dodging devices that men against death have discovered already? And isn't it partly because the rank and file of physicians haven't had the time —or the inclination?—to keep up with the march of death-fighting discovery?

Even if the world were Utopic, if everybody had enough to pay for the very best care from the smartest doctors and if all doctors were as smart and unselfish as the best ones are now, how much would the lives of the mass of us be lengthened?

The economist Professor Irving Fisher has written a book on "How to Live"—which is what I want to learn how to do —and he sent, not so long ago, a list of ninety diseases to a picked group of keen doctors. What Fisher wanted to know from these authoritative big shots was this:

What percentage of deaths due to each of these ninety diseases do you think could be prevented, Doctor?

The eminent doctors replied with surprising honesty. They wrote their answers from the tragic answer zero death preventability for cancer to the amazing, hopeful estimate of 75 percent death preventability for t. b. of the lungs. Fisher then employed a smart actuary, Forsyth, to add all these life-saving estimates up, and average them and reduce them to years of life-prolonging. Forsyth calculated mortality tables basing them on the mortality experience of the U. S. Registration Area for eleven years. He assumed that all the life-saving that these doctors said they could do was actually being done. . . .

Alas! With all that prevention going full blast on everybody, and assuming—fatuously!—that an unemployed man was getting as good care as our expensively preserved Mr. John D. Rockefeller, *only thirteen years would be added to our life expectancy.*

That's grim. It's grimmer when I remember Pearl's sardonic gag that I could add maybe twenty years to my life-span if I had been allowed properly long-lived father and mother and grandmas and grandpas. . . .

Yet there's hope, as you'll see from the deeds of men against death whose story this book tells. Life-prolonger Fisher's eminent doctors—honestly—put their chance to prevent death from cancer at zero. Yet surely they must admit that some lives have been saved by the knife, by X-rays, by radium. And the fundamental mystery of why this or that tissue of our bodies goes suddenly bolshevik, killing us, might be discovered tomorrow. Surgeons report this curious fact. . . .

Now and again a malignant tumor that they were sure was going to be fatal, suddenly begins to get smaller, to fade away, and at last disappears altogether, by itself, with no treatment, spontaneously! There's a clew to the cancer mystery. As sure as tomorrow's sunrise, some plain surgeon in the operating room or some unknown threadbare youngster sweating in a cubby-hole of a laboratory will trick the human body into telling its secret of how it cures its own cancers—occasionally. It will have to be some man like Minot, with eyes sharp enough to penetrate the obscurity of the obvious, with guts enough to know that no scourge is incurable. Only a few years ago pernicious anaemia was as enigmatic as cancer, and more invariably fatal. But, as you'll read in these adventures of men against death, Minot bit the knots of that riddle. . . . And against cancer there will rise fighters like Minot.

So with Bright's disease. I know I'm coming to the age where that Marksman Death begins to shoot at me. But will its cause always remain as mysterious as it is now? Will there always be the jumble of theories about how to prevent or control it—the mix-up that confuses me now?

Some of these theories have a taint of what seems to me to be moral admonition rather than science. Kidney disease —such theories hint—comes to you, or gets worse in you, when you do things that are fun for you. To dodge the Marksman shooting at my kidneys, should I go on a low meat diet? I loathe the thought of not having my stiff whisky and water after a raw day of fighting Lake Michigan's cold surf and the thought of not having beer with my Beethoven disgusts me. But I'd make these sacrifices and embrace the dietary habits of a cow—if I were sure that doing so would prolong the good health of my kidneys.

But the men against death don't know.

Yet . . . a few years ago, the control of severe diabetes seemed hopeless too. Then Banting—an ex-farmer boy, unknown, laughed at by highbrow professors—found insulin. You'll read in this book of men against death how his mulishness, his absolute ignorance of a whole list of impossibilities, carried him through to it, and some such man will come to untangle the riddle of Bright's disease.

It's night and that savage northwest gale is still shaking our little house. The days during the writing of this story have been dreadful, what with the great storm of the 22nd of October tearing away ten feet of our bluff and ripping to tatters the sandbag and sapling barricade we had toiled at all summer, and what with the car-ferry *Milwaukee* lost with all hands just west of us. Here I've been trying to be optimistic but tonight sinister old Lake Michigan is reminding me of nature's ruthlessness, of all men's littleness. Against all death we putter but are fundamentally powerless.

Our little house trembles at the booming smash of the surf below us and I look out into the blackness and think of the Marksman who shoots at my heart muscle. Of course old James Mackenzie the heart-mender does console me a little. He's taught me not to be scared at small flutterings of my faithful blood-pump, of inconsequential irregularities for which doctors used to turn folks into invalids for life. If my heart muscle's badly hit by the Marksman or if he's succeeded in shooting a leak in my heart valves, Mackenzie has taught doctors how to prescribe the foxglove tea that will give the old engine new pep and wallop, and he's shown how I can save my heart muscle without drugs at all but by sane sensible living. But will some genius like Banting or Minot ever come to check for long years the gradual tiring of all hearts? I doubt it. And yet to the death-fighting brotherhood nothing's impossible. . . .

XI

The gale has stopped shaking our house and the boom of the surf is lower and less threatening and between the trunks of our two great beech trees and through the grove of young oaks and maples there's a faint gold-yellow streak low down on the eastern sky. It is morning. Life is good. Hope surges. I think of the strange power in my life stuff, in all protoplasm to remake itself, at least partially, after it's been damaged, of its power to *adapt* itself to this or that danger. Lifefixers are just beginning to scratch the surface of the mystery of this marvelous adaptive power.

You know examples of it. A man gets tuberculosis of one kidney. The surgeon cuts the kidney out of him. The other kidney promptly gets bigger and easily does the work of two. Microbes fasten themselves on a woman's heart valves. They start leaking. Then the heart's muscle swells mysteriously, gets stronger, and may carry her through to a fair old age. Or typhoid bacilli sneak into you. With no help from a doctor your body starts a new chemistry stewing inside you— a great stoking up of a fire of life that shows itself in a raging fever. That's just your body adapting itself to the presence of the typhoid marauders. Yet for centuries physicians have fought fevers, always tried to cool them, have never thought fever was friendly. Their fear of fever was so universal that, plugging through our best history of medicine, by Garrison, I find not one hint that fever might be friendly. . . .

I think the most exciting yarn this book of men against death will tell is the story of a strange lone wolf of a man in Vienna, Julius Wagner-Jauregg. He thumbed his nose at the medical dogma of the badness of fever. He took a terrible chance after thirty years of wanting to do it, and at last burned that most dreadful, incurable insanity, general paralysis, out of doomed ones by fevering them with malaria. You'll read of his disasters and the danger of the desperate business, but then comes the story of how Willis R. Whitney —not a doctor but only an engineer-physicist—discovered an electric fever that is safe, and marvelously controllable.

You'll understand how Whitney's safe harnessing of this fundamental adaptive force of our bodies is going to be used to help conquer one of those most dreadful of the ills that plague us. That's only a beginning of what the friendly fire of fever will do for us—now that at last we can use it safely.

XII

The sun is up now and the nut-hatches are running down the beech tree trunk and sounding their raucous cheerful yank-yank-yank and two chickadees are fighting a sham battle over suet tacked to the maple tree just outside my window and all round the sun, weak though it is in November in Michigan, has started life stirring. There's my best hope of all, better than surgeons or physicians or any men against death—best of all is the oldest doctor of all, Old Doctor Sun.

I forget my sadness at the slow groping progress the scientists, the organized brotherhood of men against death, in their job of making the down slant of the L-x lines of all of us more gentle. This sunny morning I remember what three amateur men against death, my three honorary uncles, have taught me in my quest to grow old very slowly and stay young very long, by life in the sun and the open.

Their death-fighting tricks are humble and much more instinctive than rational. They're backed by no impressive statistics of life-extension. My own hope to march down to the last extreme bottom of the L-x line of cohort of March, 1890, strong, tanned, and in reasonably sound mind and healthy . . . that hope comes from watching the way of living of these three uncles. Each one would snort at being called a scientist or a death fighter, yet each is a man against death, unscientifically, and with no big-word rigmarole, but just instinctive, primitive.

These three old men who honor me to let me call them uncle are extremely young for their age. That's the very first thing that struck me about them, and the next was that they are men of nature who've lived their lives long in the air of outdoors and the sun. Their ancestors were not particularly long-lived. When they were kids they didn't have phenomenally sound constitutions. But constitution—I know you'll say it's only hereditary!—has poured into all of them throughout their lives, wet as they've been with cold water, shivering as they have done with damp raw winds, burned as they've been by the life-giving flame of the sun.

They seldom get colds. You don't hear their breath bubbling bronchitically. They're not attacked by pneumonia, even when they've undergone such exposure that you'd bet a hundred to one that the pneumococcus would get them. That cursed bug is possibly in each and every one of their throats this minute. But they don't know it and the robust chemistry of their tanned hard bodies is enough to laugh off the attack of the most virulent microbe.

Right here the doctors will interrupt me. They'll say oh, yes . . . just a business of ultra-violet irradiation, an old story. I'll answer, You bet it's an old story, as old as our human race when it was nomadic and primitive and getting itself killed off by saber-toothed tigers instead of by measly bacilli and spirochetes. The doctors will reply that there's now a highly developed science of ultra-violet death fighting and that they themselves tell their low-resistant threatened patients they "should get some sunshine." That's the devil of it. Ninety-nine out of every hundred doctors are just that perfunctory and vague about their dosing of sun—which is more powerful, for good or bad, than any drug in their pharmacies.

Of course this book will tell the marvelous doings against death of the sun-wizard Rollier on his mountain side in Switzerland and of that tragic Dane, Niels Finsen, who in the fogs of Copenhagen tricked unfriendly nature by using the sun-like energy of the carbon arc light to give doomed folks' bodies the strength they hadn't got by heredity. But the trouble is that this scientific use of Old Doctor Sun and machine sunlight is only just in its beginning.

Meanwhile I go to school to prolong my life to my three unscientific uncles. George Hebden Corsan is nobody knows how many years past seventy. His arms and his face and a good part of his body are dark and tough like old leather. He is a swimmer who can make my crawl-stroke look foolish. He finishes easy with me panting at the end of a mush across country of any length you'll name.

Chase Osborn, too, has cheated the Psalmist's limit of three score and ten. His face looks like that of an extremely well-baked old chief of the Chippewas. From May till November around four every morning he jumps off the bank of his island, Zheshebe Minis, into St. Mary's River whose water is so cold it almost gives you a headache to look at it.

Jack Miner is well on in his sixties. He is not dark brown but only brick-red freckled. He can wheel a seven hundred pound load of wet clay along a narrow plank in his brick factory without a grunt or a wobble and running me around over his bird refuge for miles he hardly breathes faster at the end of it.

All their lives these uncles have been renewing the adaptive power of their protoplasm, never thinking of it. They all of them know other white men who've lived Indian lives just as they have and the fire of life still burns strong in all of them despite their position way down their L-x lines.

I know old Sachem Osborn must die some day, and so must Corsan the bird man, and so must the brick-red maker of bricks and tamer of the Canada Goose—Jack Miner. But the great point is they go toward their last days, so young! They might pop off tomorrow. They may not reach eighty. They may live to be ninety smelling the smoke of campfires built from wood they've warmed themselves chopping.

They're civilized barbarians, curious mutants from the race they've sprung from—chained as that race now is to its white soft civilization. I aim to be like them.

Of course I have hopes for some slightly longer life that will come from the deeds of the men against death . . . whose indomitable spirit this book will record.

I pin greatest hope for long life on the unbookish wisdom of my three uncles.

BOOK I
THREE DOCTORS

I. SEMMELWEIS

SAVER OF MOTHERS

─────────────────────────────

Isn't it nonsense to suppose that the fight against death must be fought first in laboratories away from the bedside and first by academic scientific men rather than by doctors? Semmelweis was first of all a plain doctor afire to find the safest way to help mothers have their babies.

─────────────────────────────

A JUST history of all the deeds of all men against death is beyond any one man's time or talent. In the comprehensive medical histories that I've seen, medical politicians and scientific stuffed-shirts are often given as much space and sometimes more than the real pioneering men against death. I have only tried to find out what kind of men a few of the best of these men against death were, and by what luck or accident, and by what kinks of character, each one of these few overcame his own particular impossible.

Semmelweis is the first of my trail-blazers. If you ask who on earth is this Semmelweis you'll not be showing mere layman's ignorance. During the past year out of ten intelligent doctors I've asked about Semmelweis, only one had more than a dim recollection of that strange Hungarian's name.

He was a tragic and I must admit in some ways a deplorable man, but among all death fighters certainly one of the most profoundly original. He was only a plain doctor afire to find a safe way to help mothers have their babies. Finding it, Semmelweis proved—long before Pasteur and way ahead of Lister—that death is not generated always inside our bodies but can sneak into us from without. For the first time in human record he proved how certain deaths can be kept out of us.

Years before Robert Koch finally proved that microbes can be murderers, Semmelweis devised a simple trick to scotch the attack of certain of these sub-visible assassins . . . of whose very existence he was ignorant. Yet today's saddest medical scandal is the needless death, every year, of more than seven thousand American women from childbed fever— which was the ill for which Semmelweis found an almost perfect means of prevention.

It's all of eighty-five years now since this unhappy Hungarian showed the way to block these microbe marauders, led by the terrible hemolytic streptococcus that today kills one out of eighteen of all American married women dying between ages fifteen and forty-four. Not wanting to die, this example of the neglect to use a truth like the one found by Semmelweis, makes me wonder whether it's more science we need, or a more thorough and honest use of what's already known to us. . . .

In more ways than one this story of Semmelweis is a sad example to all of us who are taxed to support the medical science and practice that is supposed to keep us living. The way Semmelweis was fired from his job in Vienna for making his mother-saving discovery is one of the dirtiest blots on the whole record of medical science. His trouble was that he was too forthright and honest. Even when he'd bitterly gone back to his home town of Budapest and proved his trick of keeping this death out of mothers, proved it over and over, even then, all over Europe, obstetrical highbrows kept giving him the horse laugh, while all over Europe young mothers in the bloom of youth went on needlessly dying. . . .

At last, Semmelweis wrote his marvelous, half-mad masterpiece, now forgotten, that roared at the doctors of Europe: "The murder must stop!" Then they began to listen.

SEMMELWEIS—"*The murder must stop—*"

Today in our country . . . with the exception of Chile
and maybe one or two others, the death rate from childbed
fever is higher than that of any civilized land and so today our
mothers still go on dying and so here is the story of Semmelweis.

II

Before he reached voting age Semmelweis showed what a
bull-headed young man he was. Baptized with the comical
first name of Ignaz, his Budapest merchant father, in 1837,
had sent him to Vienna to study law. One chance visit—it was
only a lark—to an anatomy demonstration with a medical
student pal made Ignaz pitch his lawbooks out of the window
and sign up for the study of medicine.

He was husky, with bright wide-open eyes. He was a real
Hungarian, an enthusiastic tripper of the light fantastic, and
his friends shortened Ignaz to the nickname of Nazi, and he
was gay as they know how to be gay in Vienna. He was one
of those young men you'd say would come to no good end
and then he contradicted all that by choosing the then most
tragic of all medical specialties—obstetrics. Then, a proud
young M.D., he began helping mothers have their babies in
the notorious First Maternity Division of the Vienna General Hospital, in April, 1844.

This month in that Division thirty-six out of two hundred
and eight mothers died—of childbed fever. Having a baby
there was only a little bit safer than having the worst form
of pneumonia.

Among the frock-coated Herr Professors and their bright,
big-word-using, yes-man assistants Semmelweis was unique.
They all thought he was peculiar because he couldn't get
used to those young women dying. It kept gnawing him.
They were charity cases, waifs, poor girls who'd become
mothers most of them without benefit of clergy, but for Semmelweis they were, even so, human beings. Hopeful, he began
helping them through the long hell of having their first ba-

bies. He'd leave them tuckered out but flushed and lovely in the happiness of cuddling their own new mites of life close to them. . . .

Two days . . . and here and there in the ward the flush of happiness deepened to the sinister rouge of raging fever. Three days . . . and Semmelweis shuddered hearing their tender words to their babies cut short by their moans at a new pain deep in them. "You'll come out of it, never worry," he would tell them and more and more he knew he was lying when he cheered them so.

Dry-tongued they looked up at him with anxious faces, and they begged for water, a little water, always more and more water. He tried to smile their worry away while he felt their pulses that grew faster, faster, faster, threadier, and at last, uncountable.

Four days . . . and here was Semmelweis still kidding them, asking them the names of their babies to cover up his horror at the strange, blue-violet spots beginning to show on their feet and hands. It was sad to watch their faces already waxy and good to hear their pale lips murmur: "Better now. Much less pain now, Doctor. . . ."

He turned his face from them to hide from them that he knew this was the merciful presage of death.

So during the next two years, 1844 to 1846, Semmelweis watched them die in bunches, whole rows of them often, and you'd have thought he'd have got over its galling him— just as his chief, old Professor Klein had got over it. Instead it bit him deeper and deeper and with an immense lack of tact Semmelweis kept bothering old Klein about it, annoying that good old man with fool questions. Old Klein would have loved to see more of these young women live to enjoy their babies—but what to do?

Old Klein had taught Semmelweis what other professors had taught before him, having learned it from still earlier professors who had learned it from their professors—that it was an invisible miasm that killed these mothers. It was an unknown epidemic influence of an atmospheric-cosmic-telluric nature, all pervading, inexorably sneaking into them, poisoning them, killing them. Old Klein was the tail-end of a long tradition of ducking responsibility. I'll admit he was a fatuous old man, but in this fatuity he was in highbrow company because this balderdash was believed by the most learned obstetricians of Europe.

It had the backing of terrifically learned little Rudolph Virchow who was already on his way to be the pope of European pathology.

Now with the digging up of one little fact Semmelweis reduced this theory of childbed fever to nonsense. Here in Klein's First Maternity Division four hundred and fifty-one women had died in 1846—in this one year. Next door—with the same entrance hall—was the Second Maternity Division, *with deaths five times fewer.*

If this miasm, this atmospheric-cosmic-telluric influence pervaded everything, why didn't it pervade the Second Maternity Division? Semmelweis began getting annoying pointing it out, kept getting nasty asking and asking about it. He didn't take any particular credit for seeing this peculiar difference in deadliness between the two divisions. He'd only learned it from poor pregnant women themselves. Admissions to the two divisions took place on alternate days, Sunday for the first, Monday for the second, and so on. . . .

It was notorious, everybody knew it, even old Klein was aware of it, how those poor women schemed, cajoled, even tried to hold off their labor pains to get to be admitted to the safer Second Division. It was annoying how they'd cheat and lie to get in there. Many a one of them, finding she'd miscalculated and got into the fatal First Division, had fallen to the floor and grabbed Semmelweis round his knees sobbing: "Doctor, let me go home. . . ."

Semmelweis got sarcastic. He bedeviled old Klein and

began laughing bitterly in the Viennese coffee houses and wine-shops asking how come that this deadly atmospheric-cosmic-telluric influence worked only Sundays, Tuesdays, and Saturdays?

III

Professor Klein in spite of all this ragging did actually appoint Semmelweis to full assistantship in 1846. He had to. It was the talk of the medical faculty what a worker this former gay blade now was. Early mornings before the stoves were lighted you'd find him, scalpel in hand, in the deadhouse, bending over the body of a mother who the evening before had left her five-day-old baby for always. So the exact, devastating picture of the havoc of childbed fever inside these women—hundreds of them—burned itself into the Hungarian's brain.

From the deadhouse he'd then hurry, along with the students who'd been helping him, to the First Maternity Division and with a smile that was a lift for the young women in agony he'd go at examining them with deft, gentle fingers to see just how near they were to having their babies. Behind that smile he kept mulling over the dreadful contrast of his continual alternation between death and clean new life—that life whose coming had one chance in five of bringing death in its wake again.

Even here the autopsy room seemed to follow him. Its subtle aroma, faint but dreadful, seemed to cling to his clothes, even his carefully washed fingers. But Semmelweis didn't care about that. He was even proud of it. That smell of the deadhouse sticking to them was a sign they were workers, real investigators, he used to tell his students.

In that First Maternity Division the mothers went on dying, as many as thirty out of every hundred in some terrible months. Old Klein stayed conveniently away from it and it was all up to Semmelweis and as he walked through the wards he had to take it on the chin, feeling the contempt of the nurses, even the scrub-women. He was sorry he'd been so openly sarcastic about it because the scandal of it had now seeped generally through all the Vienna coffee houses. Citizens even began saying something should be done about it. So a commission was appointed and you know those commissions. . . .

The commission was a committee of distinguished, footling, old medical gentlemen who knew they had to blame something so they blamed overcrowding—though the safer Second Division actually housed more women on less floor space. From their armchairs these pooh-bahs decided that the cause of the frightful childbed fever mortality was, in addition, the rough way the doctors and the male medical students examined the women in labor. The safer Second Division was run by midwives, women, therefore gentler. . . .

Semmelweis laughed. This armchair, committee science! Doesn't every baby getting itself born damage its mother far worse than any examining hand? Then why don't *all* women die from bearing their babies?

He had to admit to himself he was near the end of his tether. Evening . . . here he's slumped in his chair in his little office. He sits up. What's that?

Away down the corridor he hears a faint tinkling. It gets louder, coming nearer and swells at last into an ominous ringing. God! It's the priest again. Now past his door goes a little procession—the priest solemn in his robes with a lay brother hurrying ahead of him ringing the death bell.

It is the procession of the Last Sacrament. It is the fourth one this day. Semmelweis buries his head in his arms, stuffing his fingers into his ears to try to shut out the tinkling tolling of that damned bell. . . .

He sits up. Wait. Here's a chance experiment. It is one of the thirty more or less idiotic theories of the cause of childbed fever that fear is the cause of it. In the First Maternity Division the priest with his dreadful bell had to march through five rooms past women in labor—imagine the effect on them!—to get to the death room. While, in the Second Division it is so arranged that the priest can go straight to the death chamber from outside. . . .

So, in the name of humanity, Semmelweis begged the holy man to stop his processions, put by his bell. The priest granted it. . . .

Yet the mothers in the First Division went on dying.

But the bell kept ringing in his head, urging Semmelweis on. Here was a chance for another experiment. In the safer Second Division it was the practice of the midwives to have the women lie on their sides to have their babies. In the deadly First they were delivered lying on their backs. Semmelweis changed it to the side position.

The women went on dying.

"I was like a drowning man grabbing at straws," he wrote. "Everything was questionable, everything inexplicable, only the great number of dead was an undoubted actuality."

IV

Then he was fired. Breit had been assistant before Semmelweis and now Breit wanted his job back. Breit wasn't so upset by all these women dying, and didn't keep pestering Professor Klein about them, and so Klein reappointed Breit and Semmelweis got the gate. Semmelweis spent that whole winter learning English, planning to go to England and Dublin to find out why it was they had so much less child-bed fever in the lying-in hospitals there. Then Breit landed a professorship in Tübingen and Semmelweis got the offer of his job back. You'd have thought he'd have been too proud. . . . But he took it.

Semmelweis whirled back into his work in the First Maternity Division after a little vacation in Venice. He dug back into it feeling like a fighting-cock, saying that Venetian art had healed his half-mad brooding over the dirty deal he'd got and over his not being able to find out why those women went on dying. He'd hardly got his coat off in the dead-house when they told him his friend, the pathologist Kol-letschka, had just been buried—dead from blood-poisoning from a careless student sticking him with a knife at an autopsy.

At an autopsy!

Wait, let's see. Yes! Quick. . . . Semmelweis must see the report of Kolletschka's post mortem. His fingers shook hold-ing the pages. Yes . . . absolutely! What a blind blockhead he'd been. Blood-poisoning . . . into Kolletschka by a knife in the deadhouse. Blood-poisoning . . . what else but blood-poisoning was childbed fever?

How stupid he'd been! How often Semmelweis had peered into the inflamed insides of women dead of childbed fever? Oh . . . absolutely. They were the same. No doubt of it.

It got hold of him in a flash that was more than a thought in his brain, that was rather a wild sure feeling he felt from his head down his spine to his heels. The wound of the stu-dent's knife slip had carried the invisible cadaver poison into Kolletschka. Wound? Of course! Every mother having her baby—the whole inside of her womb is wounded. And the cadaver poison . . .

How did that get into the mothers? Now it was clear to him, shaking him to the soles of his shoes. It was himself, and his students, who'd been carrying it there. Month after month every day hadn't he led his students straight from the autopsy table to the maternity? They'd washed their hands, yes—but what of that faint aroma of death on them, hours after?

Hadn't he, Semmelweis, fool that he was, been proud of that aroma, boasting it showed what autopsying busy bees they'd been?

Then, with that invisible poison on their hands, he and his students, right into those mothers, examining . . .

He himself was the killer.

Much quicker than these poor words can tell it the whole horrible, marvelous truth was all through him. This was why the Second Maternity Division was safer:

The midwives didn't do autopsies.

This was why girls in the bloom of their youth having their first babies were most often stricken: because their labor was long. And the longer their labor, the more often they were examined, by *his* hands, carrying death. This was why mothers who had their babies ahead of time, even in the street before reaching the Maternity, were safer. Because they weren't examined at all.

Like the man he was he faced it. He was the killer.

v

If we, today, with our seven thousand mothers a year dying, if we older ones facing all of old Karl Pearson's Marksmen Death, had more men like Semmelweis right now . . . But let that pass. The truth was in him, burning him. He didn't even allow himself the alibi of saying he had been unknowingly responsible. And he was absolutely not academic. He didn't fiddle round philosophizing on just what this putrid poison death might be. Practical, he started right after a way to destroy it.

May, 1847—less than two months later—here's Semmelweis, after an autopsy. He washes his hands with soap, excessively. Then he plunges them into a basin—of chlorine water. He washes and rinses them round in that basin so long it seems idiotic. He washes them till they're all slippery. While he's washing them he holds them again and again to his nose, sniffing them. At last he nods. He is satisfied now there's not the faintest trace of cadaver aroma. The students round

him smile and maybe whisper wisecracks. It's a great moment that seems silly.

Then he stands over his students glaring at their chlorine
washing and scrubbing and now they don't smile, not with
Semmelweis looking. There's the first gleam of fanatical
light in his eyes—no monkey business.

Then they all go down the rows of mothers in the First
Maternity. As always the women are lying there with labor's
pain in their faces and all with the fear of fever in their eyes,
and why shouldn't they?

In April, eighteen out of every hundred had died there.
Semmelweis started the chlorine washing the end of May.
June . . . and the death rate had shot down to just a little
more than two per hundred. July . . . and only one in a
hundred died. This was actually less than the number of
deaths in the safe Second Division. So you see they were
silly to have smiled at Semmelweis. He'd washed the death
off.

In story books this would be the happy ending. And if
there'd only been those mothers to consider, Semmelweis
would have had smooth sailing because poor young wives
and abandoned girls could go happy-faced to the First Maternity Division now, not hearing that place called a murder den any longer. They and their husbands, and, if they
didn't have husbands, then their fathers and mothers, didn't
care a picayune how Semmelweis kept death from them. They
all would have voted him a raise in pay and a professorship.
But in real life—

In real life there are professors, and what is called the
organized body of knowledge, pure science, academicism.
Now in all the rows upon rows of fat-bellied books teaching doctors the art of helping women have their babies,
amid those reams upon reams of big-worded tosh about the
dread inevitability of the atmospheric-cosmic-telluric cause

of childbed fever, there wasn't a word about washing your hands in chlorine water.

And, what was worse, Semmelweis was not yet thirty, only an upstart assistant. True, he'd tracked down precisely—for the first time in history—just how blood-poisoning sneaks into healthy human beings from outside. But Semmelweis was wild, boyish, slangy, ungrammatical—lacking in academic decorum. The professors called him the Budapest Whippersnapper.

By common-sense thorough disinfection of his hands with lime you could buy for a couple of cents at a drugstore, Semmelweis had shown how to dodge this mother-murdering death. For the first time in all human record he'd proved it. But along with smashing this death, that bit of chloride of lime had reduced all the organized knowledge about the thirty unknown causes of childbed fever written in those fat books in jaw-cracker words during three hundred years . . . to rubbish. By his simple way of saving all those mothers in June and July he had proved that all professors of obstetrics who didn't chlorine-wash their hands were . . . responsible. The worst of it was that Semmelweis didn't mince words about it.

Is it any wonder Professor Klein and his learned colleagues now planned to put Semmelweis on the spot?

VI

Remembering today how often discoveries get rushed into print even before they're discovered, you'd have thought Semmelweis would have broadcast his great news in every medical journal in Europe. But no. He had, he said, "an inborn loathing for everything that is called writing."

There were three professors—none of them obstetricians—who stood up for him. There was the skin doctor, Hebra, the diagnostician, Skoda, and the famous pathologist, Rokitansky. They even read papers about his discovery, comparing him to Jenner.

He himself just went back to work in that First Maternity Division, driving the childbed fever death rate lower, lower, when suddenly there was a terrible accident. October, 1847 . . . and here were thirteen women lying in a row, ready to have their babies. They were absolutely guarded from the putrid poison, with Semmelweis seeing to it that everybody chlorine-washed his hands before coming in that room.

Suddenly, beginning with the woman in Bed No. 2, right down the row, twelve of them got childbed fever, eleven of them dying. In a moment he was onto the cause of it. . . .

That woman at the beginning of the row in Bed No. 1, had cancer. She had a purulent discharge from it—hardly different from the decomposed stuff Semmelweis and his boys had got onto their hands at those autopsies. They'd examined this woman first and then gone right down the row just washing their hands in soap and water. Blockhead he was!

But here was a new fact! Childbed fever comes not only from the bodies of the dead but from any purulent sickness of the living. They must chlorine-wash between *every* examination. . . .

Four hundred and fifty-nine mothers in the First Maternity Division died of childbed fever in 1846. It was the end of 1848 now. Out of 3,356 having their babies there that year, only 45 failed to leave there alive, happy.

Then old Klein got him. The annoyed old Professor got his friend Rosas—a lick-spittle of the higher-ups and a clever fixer—to bring it up with the Authorities that Semmelweis had worn the plumed hat of a revolutionary in the 1848 Rebellion. When Semmelweis applied for reappointment in 1849, Klein put in his place a fellow named Braun, who let it be known that he thought being so pernickety about clean hands was slightly ridiculous. Klein fired Semmelweis by giving him a job of teaching students in demonstrations on dummies, not on living women. . . . This for Semmelweis who'd first of all men shown how to save living mothers from death. Semmelweis moved back to his home town of Budapest, and, the month after he was fired, twenty women died of childbed fever in the First Maternity. Klein let it slide. Braun, the new assistant, yessed Klein, who thought washing your hands in chlorine water was rather silly.

VII

The day he went to his new job—honorary and unpaid—in St. Rochus Hospital, Budapest, out of six mothers who'd just had their babies in that barbaric hole, he found one dead, one dying, and four gravely ill of the fever. Naturally. . . . You see, their doctor was also Chief Surgeon. He came to them with hands foul from septic operations.

Such were his simple, terrible, fundamental observations. Sniffing out one source after another of blood-poisoning infection, he lost only eight mothers out of a thousand in that old St. Rochus pest-hole in the next six years. That was grand for the 998 surviving mothers and their men. It was annoying for almost everybody else, including and especially the doctors. Semmelweis was so idiotically clean that he bored them. He exhorted, he harangued, he nagged the nurses and orderlies, he badgered midwives, he stormed at students, even dignified doctors—insisting they disinfect not only their hands but instruments, syringes, bandages, even bed-pans. He was raw-nerved about women dying.

He got made professor in Budapest University. In the hospital lay women having their babies in tumble-down beds under raggedy linen with the stuffing sticking out of the mattresses in rooms stinking from the chimneys of the chemical laboratory and horrible with air coming through windows giving on a court into which opened the hospital water closets and the deadhouse. Even here, by making an everlasting, persistent, confounded nuisance of himself, he kept the death out of them. Being clean was his one simple trick. That was his one simple experiment. He had nobody to help him. He hadn't a dime for research. He hadn't an animal or a test-tube. Microbes were less than a myth to him.

Yet this fantastic Hungarian kept wiping the sweat off his bald, broad brow in these hot horrible maternity wards, and tracked down every single last source of the blood-poisoning that's killing our mothers today . . . with maybe two small exceptions. He couldn't have known that apparently healthy doctors and midwives can be carriers of hemolytic streptococcus and he made no mention of the danger of sexual intercourse just before labor.

In 1856 he made his last discovery. In the University Hospital he'd had marvelous results with no women dying. Then suddenly deaths flared up again. Here were women having babies on bed linen infected with purulent discharges from patients just dead. The hospital authorities were being efficient saving expenses by skimping the laundry bills. . . .

Semmelweis clamored. Nothing was done about it and you can't blame the authorities who after all didn't have to risk their lives having babies. Semmelweis roared. Then he took those dirty, dangerous sheets. He walked with them into the office of the high government official, von Tandler, and held those sheets right under the elegant nose of this dignitary. The refined man shuddered and the mothers stopped dying.

VIII

Now a strange storm began brewing inside him. In eleven years he'd made only two converts among all the professors of Europe, while all over mothers having their babies were paying with their lives in tens of thousands. Now and again the so-called epidemics of the fever became so frightful that they had to close the lying-in hospitals. Then they had to open them again because of waves of abortion, of child abandonment, of murder of children by their mothers. . . . Yet Semmelweis hadn't published a word, scientifically, but had only written naïve, slangy letters to those professors telling them his life-saving results. They ignored him.

In Vienna they laughed at him but now all at once he got tired of being called the Budapest Fool in Vienna, and tired of having that four-flusher, Braun, lying about the chlorine-washing, saying that more mothers than ever died, in spite of it. Now at last, in 1861, Semmelweis's masterpiece, the "Aetiology, Concept and Prophylaxis of Childbed Fever," exploded under the appalled noses of the obstetricians of Europe. No wilder, more repetitious, more jumbled, more wordy, yet no more exact, more classical, and surely no such heart-rending human scientific work has ever been written. The obstetrical excellencies read this terrific document in stunned silence. It was too devastating for any answer.

Semmelweis took their silence for insult. He singled out sundry professors—to demolish them with open letters.

"So I denounce you," he wrote to Professor Scanzoni of Wurzburg, "before God and the world as a murderer!"

Scanzoni didn't answer. Then Semmelweis committed an unpardonable breach, not only of good taste, but of medical ethics, and worst of all, published his blast in a scientific periodical, with the awful threat to go right over the heads of their doctors to the plain suffering people:

"You, father, do you know what it means to call to your wife's bedside a doctor or a midwife when in labor she needs their help? It means you are endangering her life. . . . If you don't want to become a widower . . . and if your children don't want to lose their mother, then for a few pennies buy yourself some bleaching powder, pour water on it, and don't let the doctors or midwives examine your wife before, in your presence, they have washed their hands in that bleach, and don't let them examine till you've convinced

yourself . . . that they have washed them long enough so
that they are slippery."

Through his writings there now went a dreadful refrain,
a slogan—"The murder must stop."

And now, just when the current began setting with him,
when the scared professors in Vienna and all over Germany
began getting on the band-wagon, he carried out that threat,
just when there was no longer need of it, really. He stopped
girls with their beaux, total strangers to him, on street corners, telling them to be sure about this chlorine-washing
business before they had their babies. His young wife Marie
noted a peculiar uncertainty in his walking. At polite dinner
parties he ate like a longshoreman and the least little bit
you crossed him he'd fly into a temper . . . with everybody
except his own little youngsters. It was pitiful the way he
kept complaining to his wife: "What's wrong with me?
There's something wrong with my head."

Summer, 1865 . . . Marie with their youngest baby still
at her breast helped take him to Vienna. What a triumphal
return it *might* have been. Professor Spaeth—whom he'd
blasted in his first open letter—had just come out like a man
admitting in print that cleanliness, absolutely clean hands
and instruments, was the one way to guard mothers from
childbed fever. It came too late to make Semmelweis happy.
They hurried him from the train to the house of his old
friend, Professor Hebra, who'd given him the first pat on
the back in those great days back in 1847, when Semmelweis
had first faced it that *he'd* been the killer.

In that house he'd delivered Mrs. Hebra's first baby—safely
—laughing in his wild gay way and holding the baby for
Mrs. Hebra to see, and shouting the Vienna slang for "It's
a boy!"

Those were the days. But now . . . Now Semmelweis
walked a little uncertainly into Hebra's house, looking like
an old man, though he was in his middle forties. His scraggly

beard was streaked with gray. His eyes . . . But where were those sharp observer's eyes now?

He looked up, saw Mrs. Hebra. For a moment the mysterious chemistry of those old memories seemed to clear his sick brain. He laughed the ghost of his old laugh, and said: "It's a boy! Do you remember when I first told you, 'It's a boy!' "

For a few minutes Semmelweis talked excitedly to Hebra, wanting to see Hebra's laboratory. Then the curtain lowered again and Hebra got him into a closed carriage and took him to the public insane asylum where they locked him in.

On the 12th of August, 1865, the famous Lister did his first antiseptic operation to keep death from sneaking into humans from outside. That was eighteen years after Semmelweis had proved how death can sneak in and had found —much more precisely than Lister—how death can be kept out. Who's forgotten Lister?

On the 17th of August, Semmelweis died. When he'd come to the asylum he'd had a sore finger from a knife-slip at a last operation he'd done in Budapest. So the blood-poisoning death he himself had discovered had sneaked into him, mercifully. So he only had to stay for two weeks in his living death in the asylum.

His biographers with one exception have tried to make a martyr of him. They've said it was the long neglect of his great discovery and the sneers of his professorial opponents that drove him crazy. I'm afraid they're being a little poetic about it. The cold unpoetic report of the pathologists after his autopsy showed chronic meningitis, atrophied brain, degeneration in his spinal cord. Those things are not the result of neglect or persecution. . . .

In the epilogue to his masterpiece, Semmelweis told how sure he was that childbed fever almost never came from "self-infection" of mothers.

He said he could only dispel his sadness at the deaths of

those thousands of mothers by looking into the happy future when no death would be brought in from outside to any woman having a baby.

"But if it is not granted to me to look upon that happy time with my own eyes," wrote Semmelweis, "from which misfortune may God preserve me . . .

"The conviction that such a time must inevitably come sooner or later will cheer my dying hour."

IX

God didn't preserve him from that misfortune. That is why it is now necessary, in this book, to write a bitter epilogue to the life of this tragic Hungarian. Isn't the failure of doctors to *use* these discoveries partly responsible for our too short lives?

It's seventy years now since Semmelweis wrote that wistful happy prophecy. Yet every year in our land seven thousand mothers are killed—there's no other word for it—by somebody's failure to practice this forgotten Hungarian's simple art of keeping out blood-poisoning death . . . by cleanliness.

It isn't because Semmelweis himself is forgotten, though he's forgotten all right. To save mothers he doesn't have to be remembered. His death-fighting tricks are so simple.

Even in our land, where childbed fever today is a medical scandal, in a period of years at the Lying-in Hospital in Chicago, 25,212 women have had their babies with just one dying from childbed fever caught in that hospital.

There's Semmelweis's prophecy come true with a vengeance—so you see it's simple, and entirely possible.

That marvelous record is thanks to De Lee. It's De Lee who has actually rediscovered—in all their simplicity—those facts Semmelweis found long ago. De Lee has more than a touch of the wild Hungarian's fanatical cleanliness. De Lee has lived most of the thirty-five years of his medical life in one or another of eight large hospitals and what he has seen has been plenty.

In all the general hospitals he's worked in he's seen child-bed fever. He comes out flat-footed telling present disasters in general hospitals. They're whispered about among doctors. They're never heard of by us plain folks. In this Class-A general hospital an outbreak of childbed fever with ten cases stricken, six gravely, three dying. In the next general hospital, twenty cases, six dying. And so on, all over. . . .

These secret happenings have stirred De Lee to say that a maternity ward of a general hospital is a dangerous place for a woman to have her baby. That's certainly ironical. Here you have all these general hospitals marvelously equipped with laboratories where microbe hunters are doing exact science, learning all the sneaking nasty deadliness of that rattlesnake microbe, the hemolytic streptococcus—that Semmelweis never saw, never even heard of. Yet here in these very hospitals you have billions of these very murderers lying in ambush. Many of these hospitals are armed camps of streptococci. . . .

Of course a general hospital can hardly help being infected with them. It would really be superhuman to keep them all from sneaking now and again from the medical and surgical wards, from the laboratories, from the deadhouse, over to the maternity ward. No, this isn't Semmelweis who's saying this. It's De Lee, 1927.

But, you'll say, look at our wonderful modern facilities! In place of the Hungarian's little old basin of chlorine water, we've got glittering autoclaves, all kinds of disinfecting gadgets, rubber gloves, masks, expensive colored alleged disinfectants that are right now making fortunes for their exploiters. . . .

Semmelweis, ignorant of the existence of the hemolytic streptococcus, called the childbed death "putrid animal matter." While we have tomes of complicated bacteriological data that would wrinkle the brow of that simple man. . . .

The curse of it is that, to run all these beautiful sterilizing gadgets and to use all these expensive gay-colored alleged disinfectants, we haven't got—Semmelweis. Instead we've got, well, let's call it "human frailty." De Lee explains it: If only high-pressure sterilizers always disinfected their contents. . . . If the laundry always washed and boiled the linen and blankets. . . . If the nurses always disinfected their hands between cases. . . .

In short, it boils down to this: If they all—like Semmelweis—only cared enough down deep about these mothers dying, then there'd be no excuses, no alibis. "When looking at the coffin of one of our clean cases we have little regard for excuses." No, it's not old Ignaz, it's De Lee who's saying it.

That's what brought De Lee to organize the Chicago Lying-in Hospital—simply living Semmelweis over again. It's his grim experience with human frailty and our highly developed American system of buck-passing that's made De Lee see the only way out of it:

To *isolate* mothers from this death.

x

But we've got to be practical. Of all the babies born every year, only a fraction of their mothers can lower their chances of dying from childbed fever by having their babies in super-clean hospitals, away from infection, like the Chicago Lying-in Hospital and others.

We have to be practical and can't wait for the day to come —the day De Lee and others are doing their almighty best to hurry on—when the maternity ward of every general hospital will be absolutely separate from the main building—so to keep out the blood-poisoning death.

Of course the mass of our mothers are lucky: They have to have their babies at home. . . .

The mass are lucky, too, having family doctors who are clean, who don't hurry from cases of boils, abscesses, infected wounds, sore throats, fevers—straight to the bedsides of women in labor. The general run of doctors don't do that, at least, without changing their clothes, and using absolutely sterile instruments and dressings. Many of them do make their examinations inside mothers—always—with sterile rubber gloves.

But we must be practical. There are still enough doctors not knowing Semmelweis, too busy to practice their Semmelweis, or not caring—so that childbed fever still kills one out of eighteen of all married women dying between the ages fifteen and forty-four. How are fathers and mothers going to know that their homes are going to be spared?

There's the idiotic old American panacea: There should be a law about it. Doctor De Normandie, of Boston, says every case of childbed fever should be made legally reportable, then we'd know who was responsible. You know how such laws work. Sixteen states already have such laws. How much have they lowered the threat of this flaming death?

But fathers and especially mothers can be practical. They can gossip. Through their women's clubs, bridge clubs, sewing circles, missionary societies—entirely offhand and unofficially, mind you—they can know which ones of their number went to what general hospital and didn't come back and why. In those chattering interludes between the official activities of cards, sewing, and saving the heathen, they can find out which one had what doctor attending her at home—only to leave a husband desolate, a baby motherless.

They could even check up on it, systematize it, be sure of it. Good doctors, clean hospitals, would have nothing to fear from it. All hospitals have got to have patients, all doctors are human. So with a boycott threatening their bread and butter . . .

And the doctors themselves have it in their power to backfire such a threat to their business. They have their County Medical Societies, where, in spite of all the peanut politics infesting these bodies, I've seen, here and there, the signs of a fine guild spirit growing. Dr. C. G. Thornton, of Lebanon, Kentucky, may be no death-fighting pioneer like Semmelweis, nor a brilliant rediscoverer like De Lee. But Thornton has a plan for it.

In the *Kentucky Medical Journal* he gives it. He's been listening to a report of how and why 308 Kentucky mothers died having their babies. He's a general practitioner and in twenty-seven years he's not had a death from childbed fever. He tells his fellow doctors he wishes there'd been just one more little thing in this learned report of how and why these 308 women died. . . .

When that report gave the deaths, if it had just given the names of the doctors who had attended those 308 cases . . . "Then we'd know where to begin work," said Thornton.

That may sound drastic, ruthless, but it's certainly the one way to abolish the buck-passing and that infernal system of getting out from under that's a blot on the profession we pay to keep death away from us. And it's nowhere near as drastic as Ignaz Semmelweis had to be with himself when he found he himself was the cause of mothers dying.

It's not nearly so drastic as our mild Oliver Wendell Holmes was. Even before Semmelweis, Holmes had got together some facts showing that this mother-killing fever was contagious. He'd studied the observations of the Englishman White and the Irishman Collins who knew it was good to be clean, but who'd never, like Semmelweis, worked out the precise science of it. That was certainly all thanks to Semmelweis. But Holmes was much more ruthless than our sensible Dr. G. C. Thornton. Holmes said:

"Whatever indulgence may be granted to those who have heretofore been the cause of so much misery, the time has come when the existence of this private pestilence in the sphere of a single doctor should be looked upon not as a misfortune, but a crime."

But let's be practical. You can't jail a doctor for killing a woman in childbirth. What mothers need now is not laws, nor highbrow science about the hemolytic streptococcus, but plain doctors like Thornton whose forthrightness comes somewhere near the blasting honesty of Semmelweis.

2. BANTING

WHO FOUND INSULIN

Isn't it folly for men against death to show the white feather in their fight against human suffering because they lack a million-dollar laboratory and for want of rich endowment to buy unlimited monkeys and guinea-pigs? Banting was only a young surgeon academically unrecognized and sweating in a room it was polite to call a laboratory and he made up for what he lacked in dogs by his country grit and stubbornness.

LIKE Semmelweis, the thing that strikes you first about Banting is his simple and devastating honesty. Like Semmelweis, too, Banting had no million-dollar laboratory nor any rich endowment to buy dogs to help him make his own deep discovery. Again like the Hungarian, this Canadian, Banting, never dreamed of showing the white feather in his fight against human suffering—in spite of the failure of eminent physiologists to find insulin, and in spite of the feeling of certain highbrows that such a discovery was impossible.

It is because my father so narrowly missed having his life saved by insulin that my awe of Banting and his strange remedy has never left me. I call insulin strange because it could have helped my father to live longer *with* diabetes than he was expected to live if he had never had diabetes at all. That certainly gives Banting a place in the front line of today's men against death.

My father died of diabetes in 1917, a starved shadow of the husky man he'd been in his prime. That was only four years before Banting began saving the lives of his diabetic dogs in the low-ceilinged room up under the roof of Toronto University Medical Building in the memorably hot summer of 1921. The sugar sickness struck my father in 1907 and it was terrible the way it suddenly changed him. I can see him now, as clearly as if it were yesterday, on the day I first realized something awful had got hold of him. It was a raw day in February with the sidewalks slippery. I met him shuffling down the middle of our village street. His face was gray and there was a droop to his shoulders that had always been so straight.

He tried everything. But those were the hopeless days when medical scientists were proving no such thing as insulin was possible. The highest authorities would have given you a laugh if you'd predicted that such a recently graduated plow-boy as Banting would right soon be finding something that would help to stretch out diabetics' lives by decades.

My father was only a small-town business man but he had respect for science. In those years while he was slowly dying, and I'd become a medical student, he was always asking me what researchers were discovering about this hole in him. So he described it. Dr. Foster at the University Hospital at Ann Arbor was giving him the very best modern diet treatment and that used to fix him up for a bit but then that acetone odor would come into his breath again. In his blue spells he seemed to hold it against me that all the best scientists could offer him was a slow starvation almost as cruel as death. . . .

All over were thousands like him, living by starving. In 1917 I watched my father die, at sixty. It seems weird now to think that, since that lovely June day only fourteen years ago, two discoveries have been made, both to be told of in this book of men against death, and both would have helped to make my father's life much longer. If it had then existed, Banting's insulin would have controlled my father's diabetes. But his diabetes, unchecked, sapped his power to fight invading microbes. So finally hemolytic streptococcus got into his throat and its then unknown poison finished him off by wrecking his kidneys. How he might have dodged that, you'll read at the end of the story of these death-fighters.

For many days before he died my father's sunken cheeks made him look, once more, like the faded daguerreotypes taken of him when he was a boy. He was out of his head most of the time those spring days. Once he looked at me, suddenly clear-eyed, asking, "Paul, what's death . . . ?"

If it had only been a few years later, I might have come to him long before he'd got to this sad extremity, telling him: "Dad, I've got great news for you. . . ."

This has made me hungry to dig to the bottom of those events that took place on certain hot nights in 1921 in Toronto. Who was Banting that he could work this magic?

II

Of course Banting had no business to discover insulin, let alone try it. Diabetes is a medical sickness and Banting never presumed to be anything but a surgeon in those hard-time days of his just after the war. An enormous amount of exact, complicated, big-worded knowledge had been piled up by physiologists and bio-chemists telling how the sugar sickness kills its victims. Of this knowledge Banting was innocent and it had never been his ambition to be a diabetes specialist. He wasn't brilliant—just stubborn. He'd come back from war with a very deep, very ugly scar on one of his forearms. "I'm going to keep that arm," Banting told the surgeons who'd said he'd die if they didn't amputate.

He served a term as resident at the Hospital for Sick Children in Toronto. Then he hung up his shingle to be a small-town surgeon in London, Ontario. After waiting for twenty-eight days in a row till his first patient came and having four dollars on his books at the end of his first month's practice, he landed a job as a part-time demonstrator in the Western Ontario Medical School, not because he was scientifically ambitious but to help himself eat.

He was conscientious at that teaching job and had plenty of time to be, and night after night he sat in his threadbare quarters plugging up the lecture he had to give the medical students next day. Till that strange night of October 30, 1920 . . .

That night in his farmerish, peculiarly stubborn way he was getting it soaked into his head how, if we didn't have pancreases, we'd all die of diabetes. Of course long before, in medical school, he'd learned how important this pancreas was for the digestion of food, how it's really a terrific and versatile little ferment factory, pouring through its duct leading to the small intestine a mysterious juice that chews up sugars, splits up fats, tears apart proteins for us to absorb and to use them.

Now Banting with his longish sort of inquisitive nose sat alone there this night hunched over his books, getting it through his head how Minkowski, the German, had cut the pancreas slick and clean out of a dog, sewed him up with every surgical precaution, then watched this poor beast—incredibly swiftly—get thin, get thirsty, get ravenously hungry, then lie down with just pep enough to raise his head to drink water that turned into urine loaded with sugar. . . . In less than ten days that dog died—of diabetes.

That ought to interest his students. Banting waded through a jungle of pancreas science to find out how the learned German, Langerhans, had spotted peculiar little islands in this remarkable gland—little bunches of cells strangely different from the ferment cells that made the digestive juices. These islands of Langerhans had never a duct leading from them. What could they be good for?

Banting got it down cold to tell his students that it was these insignificant Langerhans cells that really guarded us from diabetes. You could tie off the duct leading from a dog's pancreas so not a drop of digestive juice could flow out. That dog didn't get the sugar sickness. But just cut out the whole pancreas . . . !

Ho-hum, this particular night's drudgery was mighty near finished. But he'd tell them this, finally, next morning: The American searcher, Opie, had probed into the pancreases of folks dead of the sugar sickness, and found how those Langerhans island cells looked shot, looked sick . . .

Did they make a hormone, maybe? When they're healthy, don't these island cells pour into our blood an internal secretion, a mysterious something, some "X" that helps all the cells of our bodies burn the sugar they need for energy? Well —nobody'd ever found such a life-saving "X." . . .

Here's Banting this night in October, 1920, finding out how dozens of searchers had spent years looking for this mysterious "X"—all failing. Here's Banting at the end of another day. His lecture's ready. All over Europe and America are millions of folks with diabetes, thousands dying. Here are children suddenly struck with it, wasting away into emaciated dwarfs, always dying. Here are young men and women in their prime, thirsty, drinking and still always thirsty, and hungry, eating, yet hungry, going down hill more slowly than the children, but watching their bodies run away in dreadful rivers of sugar, and dying.

What could any of them hope from Banting? He himself would have laughed if you'd told him that within an hour . . .

He has it thoroughly through his head for his students that it's the island cells of the pancreases of all these doomed people that go mysteriously bad . . . but who can fix them? You can string out the lives of those poor kids for days, of

the young grown-ups for months, by the Guelpa-Allen under-
nutrition treatment that's a polite term for slow starvation.
That's that.

It's past bedtime. Idly he slits open a copy of the medical
journal *Surgery, Gynecology, and Obstetrics* that's arrived
today. He begins to wool-gather through it. Ho-hum. . . .
Wait . . . here's a new report on the pancreas and diabetes.
A funny coincidence, this. . . . By Moses Baron . . . and
who is this Moses? But wait . . .

Banting bends over the pages and now the drab lesson for
those students and his feeble, slowly growing surgical practice are as if they never existed. This Baron—here's something that's something! When people have gallstones that
block off their pancreatic duct, and they die, when you take
out their pancreas post mortem, you find the digestive-juice-
making cells have shriveled, degenerated, died. *But the Langerhans island cells have stayed perfectly healthy!*

Banting's lost in this dull scientific report now. By George!
Such people don't have a sign of diabetes. And wait. It's the
same with dogs, so writes Baron. Tie off their pancreas duct.
Then operate. They live all right. Then operate again. The
digestive-juice-making cells of their pancreas are degenerated.
But those island cells are okay—like those gallstone people.
And the dogs don't get diabetes. . . .

Banting's no longer a struggling doctor nor a miserably
paid half-time lecturer. He goes to bed but his brain's in a
buzz. He lies there . . . his brain is trying . . . that's the
word for it. His brain aches from what he later quaintly
called "trying to bridge a wide spark gap between two remote ideas." He can't sleep. His brain is strained the way it
strains trying to recall a name on the verge of your memory
or trying to get back an old tune you're on the edge of remembering.

Here's what gnawed him: Wasn't there some way to use

those healthy island cells from the degenerated pancreas of a dog with a tied-off duct to help keep alive a dying diabetic dog who'd had his pancreas cut out entirely?

At two that morning his hunch hit him. He got up, blinked at the light, scrawled three sentences in his notebook:

"Tie off pancreatic duct of dogs. Wait 6 to 8 weeks for degeneration. Remove residue and extract."

He went to sleep. Next morning he knew he wasn't made for a surgeon.

IV

Now Banting's in the office of the famous Professor Macleod in the Department of Physiology in the Medical School of the University of Toronto. He fishes for words. He's *got* to impress the Professor. But all he has is those three short sentences in his notebook, a fierce hunch, a plan of action, but words? Not Banting.

It's a contrast. Banting the farmerish up-country surgeon: Macleod as great as there is in all North America on the science of how our bodies burn sugar for energy. It's faintly ridiculous. Banting's like an inventor pleading his cause without even a model.

Macleod was a distinguished man and a busy one. What, exactly, was Dr. Banting driving at? What was his plan?

Banting fished for scientific expressions. . . . You see, if you tie off a dog's pancreatic duct, the digestive juice cells will go to pieces. . . . The island cells will stay healthy, and then . . .

Professor Macleod wanted to know had this degeneration after duct-tying been completely proved, confirmed, scientifically? Wouldn't it take Banting—after all he wasn't a scientist!—years to learn pancreas-anatomy, physiology, and did he know the chemistry of the blood sugar? And clinical diabetes?

Banting was now the way he'd been with the surgeons when he wouldn't let them amputate his mangled arm and . . . well, didn't Professor Macleod see? You take out such a duct-tied, degenerated pancreas. Its digestive juice is gone. There you've got the island cells—undigested, undamaged. *There'll be no juice to ruin them.* There you'll have your hormone, your "X"! There'll be the internal secretion needed for burning sugar. And then . . .

But how did Dr. Banting know there was an internal secretion in the pancreas, ever? Mightn't a healthy pancreas prevent diabetes some other way? Mightn't the pancreas change the blood running through it, remove poisons from the blood that prevented the body using sugar? There wouldn't have to be an "X" . . . Not necessarily!

Professor Macleod had gone on record suggesting this explanation in a learned treatise only a little while before and that reduced Banting's fine hunch—to nonsense.

Professor Macleod was a busy man but Banting fumbled and bent forward and stuttered but stuck to it.

But how did Banting know the digestive juices of the pancreas were bad for the island cells? If they weren't, then what good tying off the dog's ducts?

Banting felt it must be so. He repeated, he *felt,* it.

Surely Professor Macleod deserves much for his patience in listening to this fanatical scientific tyro. But at last Macleod asked Banting a question that was absolutely unanswerable. . . .

How could *Banting* hope to accomplish what the highest trained physiologists in the world had not succeeded in establishing or proving?

Well, Banting felt . . .

Well, what *did* Banting want, really?

"I would like ten dogs and an assistant for eight weeks," Banting said.

Professor Macleod will forever be famous for giving Banting exactly what he asked for, no less, no more.

V

Banting wanted to drop his practice, his teaching, burn all bridges behind him, so he told his old teacher, the great surgeon Starr. But Starr and his friends Gallie and Robertson and the generous, dark-eyed Professor V. E. Henderson all thought he was, to say the least, a mild lunatic for giving up his surgical career before barely starting it. They thought his wild idea would cool off if he went back and finished his year out at London, Ontario, and they all counseled him to go back. "Consequently I returned to London," Banting said.

But his idea instead of cooling, got hotter, burned in him all through that winter, heated him from the top of his sandy hair to his toes. He was utterly without animals, test-tubes, even any kind of a laboratory, so he read and read and read about diabetes and the pancreas and the utter failure of all distinguished searchers to do any good whatever to dying diabetics by feeding them pancreas or injecting them with it, and yet his hunch kept heating him. He cared nothing about building a practice and when his eyes got tired from reading he took up painting pictures, knowing absolutely nothing about it and with no one to tell him. He painted in oils with water-color brushes because he didn't know any better . . . but he painted.

May 16, 1921, and here he was at last, a scientist. Here he stood in a miserable, grimy little cubby-hole of a room in the Medical Building in Toronto, a self-appointed researcher, untitled, absolutely unpaid. He'd sold his office furniture and instruments. Oh, that would keep him alive, till . . .

It was comical. He stood before a bench never having made an experiment and insanely convinced that under his thatch he had the answer to the deep horrible riddle of the sugar disease. That bench was all his laboratory because the rest of this dreadful little room was used for routine chemistry by other workers. Here was Banting with everything Macleod had promised him, ten dogs, and eight weeks ahead of him in which to solve a most tangled medical mystery. And an assistant, too, not a doctor, mind you, but only a medical student, a boy just twenty-one. . . .

This assistant, Mr. Charles H. Best, was supposed to be skilled in the exact chemical determination of the amounts of sugar in the urine and the blood of his dogs who should become diabetic. Best did know more than Banting about blood and urine chemistry because Banting knew next to nothing about it. Best had blond hair and very wide-open blue eyes that were set in a pleasant face of high complexion —not a grim face like Banting's. Probably the best qualification of Best was that he understood, almost as little as Banting, the folly of this forlorn enterprise of eight weeks and ten dogs.

They began by failing.

Right off the bat they got busy to tie off the pancreas ducts of sundry of the ten dogs Macleod had allowed Banting. Here was Banting's first good break: he was a deft surgeon with four years of experience under the famous C. L. Starr and the very ticklish operations were apparently great successes and the dogs recovered beautifully and here it was the 6th of July, beastly hot, and seven of the eight weeks were gone. . . .

Now the pancreases of these dogs should be degenerated. The pancreatic juice-producing cells should be dead. The island of Langerhans cells should be healthy, and now to inject them into pancreasless dogs dying with diabetes. Such doomed beasts were ready. . . .

Alas! Here were two dogs they'd just chloroformed, and both of them with perfectly full-sized pancreases. A miserable fizzle! And one week left. . . .

It was when the going got tough that Banting got good. Now the flash of his knife in his nimble hands, with him peering, head bent over the opened bodies of those dogs, eyes close to the slash, slash, slash of his knife delicately cutting all around those ducts he thought he'd tied off so tightly . . .

Blockhead he'd been. He'd tied them *too tight!* Then gangrene. Then oozing of serum. Then nature growing a new duct round the wall of the old one. . . . And only one week left . . .

Up and up the stairs from their work-bench went Banting and Best, round and round a narrow long winding stairs to a tiny room where they operated their dogs. It had no windows. Its grimy skylight let through more heat rays than light rays. Here in the strong smell of ether with the sweat running down their faces they operated the rest of their dogs all over again—

Here was good news: in some of these beasts with bellies slit open, the pancreas was mighty hard to find—was really degenerated. Now to make double sure, triple sure, Banting tied off even these ducts in two and three places, with different tightnesses of his ligatures. Then they sewed those dogs up again. Then they waited again in the heat.

VI

Now at last the chance to test the hunch. Ten in the morning of July 27 and of course the eight-week limit Banting had asked for long since past. No money to pay Charlie Best for his time now, so Best borrowed money from Banting. A giant tractor couldn't have pulled Banting away from his little black bench now. Weeks ago, when work had just started, Macleod had left for Europe. It's again to the credit of Professor Macleod that he didn't write to stop Banting now that the eight weeks were up, and that he let Banting struggle on, but how he went on God knows.

This steamy hot day a poor dog, miserably thin, lies on their table. Nine days before Banting had slit out his pancreas and with the dog going down hill like a shot, day after day, Banting had drawn samples of dark blood from the beast's veins with a syringe while Best sat before his colorimeter, watching the sugar in the dog's blood go higher, higher. It got harder for the dog to stand up. He could hardly wag his tail when they came for him. He was horribly thirsty and hungry as a wolf and it was precisely like a bad case of human diabetes. Pancreasless, this beast's body simply couldn't burn sugar.

The day before they'd given him sugar-water but not a bit of this glucose stayed in him to help his starving tissues but all kept running out of him in rivers of urine.

This morning of July 27 he was dying. His eyes were glazed over as he lay there hardly able to lift his head and right here by him was another dog, frisky, healthy. Weeks before, this one had recovered from Banting's operation to tie off his pancreas duct, and now . . .

The sickening smell of chloroform and swiftly Banting is into the belly of this healthy animal, finding, exposing, neatly slitting out what's left of the pancreas. Yes!

Okay . . . degenerated, hardly the size of your thumb. Now all you hear is the sick dog's breathing and Banting and Best growling monosyllables and the click of steel on steel and now here lies that shriveled morsel of what used to be pancreas in a mortar, chilled, ice-cold.

Best cuts it, mashes it, with a little cold salt water makes a brew of it, filters this soup through paper, warms it gently to body heat, sucks it into a syringe. Now . . .

There's a quick gleam of metal and glass with Banting bending over the neck of the doomed diabetic creature and now the soup made of the degenerated remains of the pancreas from the dog with the tied-off duct has gone into his dying diabetic brother's jugular vein. . . .

An hour goes by as if it were a minute. Best straightens up from his hunch-backed squinting into the colorimeter where he's measuring the dying dog's blood sugar. "Fred," Best says, "his sugar's down! Way down to zero-point-one." That was hardly more than the sugar in the blood of a perfectly healthy animal. . . .

Upstairs there in the dog room Fred Banting didn't need Best's blood sugar tests to tell him the fantastic thing that now was happening. This dog who hasn't even been able to lift his head for water to wet his poor parched mouth, raises his head now. He looks at Banting. Banting stares at him as he sits up. In an hour he's standing up and that hour's a blank, is no time at all to Banting who stands there in a daze of wild happiness. The dog looks at Banting and wags his tail when he should by rights be dead, but here he is, walking round, wobbly, but walking. . . .

Up and down and up and down that narrow spiral staircase, never realizing how he's sweating, runs Best carrying urine from this miraculous dog down to his chemical bench. The day before their doses of sugar-water had run right through him. Now his body can use sugar again. It's unbelievable. In the next five hours his urine's sugar free, nearly . . . with seventy-five times less sugar than it held in the same five hours the day before. Upstairs alone in the heat, Banting watches that dog who with bright eyes looks back at Banting and wags his tail for a thank-you.

The next day the dog is dead.

VII

How could they have expected this miracle to have lasted? What they'd shot into this pancreasless doomed creature was only a wee bit of borrowed pancreas, slit out of that dog whose duct had been tied. Well? Banting looked across at Best, hating to say it. But how many dogs would they have to sacrifice to keep one diabetic dog living, for a little? It was utterly impracticable!

Anyway, hadn't this first marvelous recovery been, maybe,

accidental? Was it true? Banting looked at Best, and back they went in the heat up those spiral stairs—visionaries, crazy pioneers. Nothing could stop them. No, it wasn't an accident, and here it was the 4th of August and here was another absolutely doomed diabetic dog raised from the dead, like Lazarus, no less. But alas . . .

Here was the deuce of it, the hopelessness of it, the sheer lunacy of going on with it. First: the magic didn't last. When you brought your dying dogs back to life it was only a ghastly foolery, a matter of hours. Again: you'd have to keep on injecting pancreas soup made of other dogs' degenerated pancreases, and here was the impossibility of it . . .

To keep this second dog alive for just three days they'd had to kill two healthy dogs, use all the degenerated pancreas from both of them. It was nonsense.

Those three terrible days Banting hadn't slept. He'd tried everything, injecting liver prepared exactly like pancreas. Then he'd tried spleen and it had done no more good than liver which had done nothing whatever. No, it was beautiful how Banting's hunch that October night, 1920, had turned out to be absolutely right. Now all these three days it had been an outlandish see-saw of hope and despair for the dying diabetic creature. The second day, with their little supply of miraculous pancreas extract dwindling, Banting and Best had run from their black bench to that hellish attic and back to their bench again till midnight, when the dog was sinking. Then they really began working. It was marvelous. At midnight, at one, at two, at three, they shot dose after dose into the dying dog's jugular vein. He got stronger and stronger. At four in the morning at dawn as the robins were waking they gave him his last five ounces—all they had left. Seven in the morning, Best and Banting looked through red-rimmed eyes at Best's chemical test showing their good beast was excreting not a trace of sugar in his urine . . .

Noon the next day the dog was dead.

Long ago they'd run out of the ten dogs Banting thought he'd need to prove his hunch was true. Macleod was away in Europe without the faintest notion of what Banting was up to. He never dreamed that right now, in his own department, there was boiling one of the most exciting adventures in the whole record of science, with an ex-farmer boy-ex-surgeon, and a fourth year medical student the pioneers in it. Banting couldn't ask Macleod for dogs. "But we got plenty of dogs, all right," Banting said.

Three in the morning of August 19, and Banting sits alone in that attic. "I was sitting watching the terminal symptoms of Dog 92," Banting said. Dog 92 was their pet, had the run of the laboratory, and now she was dying. Pancreasless, for eight days they'd kept her alive, healthy, her blood sugar low, hardly any sugar in her urine, with her frolicking as if no sure doom hung over her. Now she was dying.

"I loved that dog," Banting said.

It had taken the degenerated pancreases of no less than five dogs to keep her alive eight days . . . five they'd had to kill to keep this one living What could be more senseless, even ghoulish? But she'd been a wonderful help to them. She'd hop up onto the table and lie quiet on her side while Banting drew blood from her for Best's blood sugar tests. Risking her life proved for them it was no use injecting pancreas that wasn't degenerated. Coming back from the grave she'd shown them that their pancreas extracts were much more life-saving, sugar-burning, when you extracted with acid than with alkali.

With one foot in the grave she'd come back miraculously so many times in succession after those doses of degenerated pancreas extract, that Banting was absolutely sure now he'd found his life-saving "X." He was so sure that he gave this mysterious stuff from the Langerhans islands of those degenerated pancreases a name . . . "isletin."

That's the name it should have kept, but didn't.

But now Dog 92 was dying, with not a drop of this extract left. He sat there mulling it, bitterly. Why fight this cruel game longer? Isletin existed, was no longer his crazy fantasy. It did make diabetic doomed animals burn sugar, and live. But it was a nearly unattainable jewel, rarer than any precious stone, and in the world there were millions of sick diabetic folks needing it, hundreds of thousands dying for lack of it . . .

"Suddenly it occurred to me . . ." Banting said.

So, next morning, here was Best putting a perfectly normal dog whose pancreas duct had never been tied, under ether. Swift slashing by Banting. Brewing of extract from this dog's small intestine by Best. They were looking for *secretin*— which is made in animals' intestinal membranes, which is then absorbed and, going through the blood to the pancreas, sets it to secreting its digestive juice. One way or another Banting must get rid of this digestive juice that knocked out the life-saving isletin. So, for four whole hours that morning this dog breathed gently under the anaesthetic while Banting bent over her injecting her own secretin back into her. . . . Till Best finds there's not a drop more of digestive juice leaking from the duct of that dog's exhausted pancreas. Then quick they take the pancreas out, chilling it, mincing it . . .

Up above in the attic Dog 92 lies in her cage, just breathing . . .

Now it's seven in the evening. It's a go again. Her glazed eyes are clearing, and now, when Banting opens the door of her cage, she jumps out, frisks around, puts her paws against this grim kind master who's so often doomed her, then saved her.

"I'll never forget my joy as I opened the door of her cage . . ." Banting said.

But again . . . idiotic, impractical. You couldn't go on exhausting the pancreases of living dogs, or cattle, or pigs, by this delicate operation to provide isletin for millions of sick folks all over whose lives were running away in rivers of sugar. It was only . . . scientific, beautiful, but useless. Banting slogged ahead, hoping.

And why not? It was lovely the way Dog 92 was living. It was a record! Twenty days she'd lived now without any pancreas in her. Then she died finally, with Banting furious about it. There was absolutely nothing of your piddling purely academic scientist about him. Not with his brain alone but with all of his body he invented, cooked up idiotic schemes, devised impossible experiments to keep this beast's life spark glowing. Every now and again as now at three that morning, a sudden "here's-the-way-to-get-around-*this*-corner" would come to him. Then he'd tear into it as if God's hand had given him a great push from behind. Who could stop him?

VIII

November now . . . and at last Banting had it. The leaves were gone from all except the white oaks and the beech trees and it was bleak Ontario winter not yet lovely with its blanket of snow and now never a doubt of it Banting and Best had the trick to get unlimited supplies of their life-saving pancreas extract—isletin.

Macleod had come back from Europe but Macleod was busy with his own experiments on anoxaemia which had nothing to do with diabetes. Banting was broke and so was Best and now they were at the end of their tether with the goal almost touched but with it looking as if everything they'd sweat for had gone for nothing. Till Professor V. E. Henderson came to their rescue, gave Banting a job in his own Department of Pharmacology as lecturer, only Banting didn't have to lecture at all, but did have money to eat to keep him alive to experiment. . . .

How complicated, how silly their last summer's experiments looked now in November! Now they were keeping profoundly diabetic, pancreasless dogs alive, beautifully healthy, indefinitely, with pancreas from unborn calves.

It turned out to be so simple—why hadn't Banting thought of it in the first place? One night, with things at low ebb, he'd thumbed through an old scientific work by the searcher, Laguesse, on the pancreases of newborn babies. Those pancreases are rich in islet cells of Langerhans, but with digestive juice cells feebly developed.

Banting the nighthawk alone that night mulled over it; for Banting there was something mystically good about notions you doped out alone in the night. Sure . . .

If that's so for newborn babies, it's true for newborn animals; if it's true for newborn animals, it's more true for embryo animals long before they're born . . . their pancreases should be almost pure islet tissue! Banting went to Professor Henderson next morning with this new hunch. "But how're you going to get unborn puppies, Banting?" Henderson asked. It was impractical again. They'd have to breed dogs, and wait.

No, not this time. Banting'd been a farm boy, knew cattle. Banting knew cows are often bred to fatten them prior to slaughtering. . . . By noon next day Banting and Best were back from the slaughter house with the pancreases of nine calves—three to four months embryo. It was superb, precisely as he'd hunched it. This stuff sent the poisonously high blood sugar of the very first diabetic dog they tried it on, down like a shot. Now their worries seemed over. Now it was as if he'd stumbled on a gold-mine of life-saving isletin and ideas swarmed in his head.

Now they didn't have to depend on embryo calf pancreas any longer, finding they could get big pancreas out of just slaughtered full-grown cattle and from it extract this precious isletin if only they used the little simple trick of extracting with acidified alcohol instead of salt water! Acidified alcohol checked the action of the digestive juice that ruined the isletin and dissolved out, ready for use, the magic isletin. It was too simple! Why do searchers seem always to have to go into the jungle of the unknown, blindfolded, and backwards? But as Boss Kettering says: "All problems are simple . . . after they're solved."

Here it was January, 1922, and the female, black-and-white, somewhat collie dog, No. 33, had lived seventy days though her pancreas had been cut clean out of her. . . . Sixty days ago she should have been dead. . . .

Why hadn't Banting thought in the very first place of the obvious trick of holding the digestive-juice cells of the pancreas in check with acidified alcohol? Again as Boss Kettering says: "Nothing is so obscure as the obvious."

Here it was January. That somewhat collie female dog, *completely diabetic*, had lived seven times as long as she had any scientific right to.

IX

Joe Gilchrist had graduated in the same class with Banting in medical school, and even before that, when they were kids in knee-pants in Northern Ontario, the Bantings and the Gilchrists used to have dinner together on Canadian Thanksgiving Day. Joe had crocked up suddenly with the sugar sickness during the war. For five years, now, he'd been getting thinner and thinner, with sugar almost constantly showing in his urine, with the dreaded acetone odor stronger and stronger on his breath. . . .

Gilchrist the doctor knew what it meant to have diabetes at his time of life. He'd had a sunny disposition but now the acid-poisoning was driving him into morose hopelessness. He dragged himself about on the rounds of his little medical practice in Toronto trying to support his mother. He dragged himself out on shuffling walks trying to make his sick body burn sugar and so keep down the acid poisons. He stuck to the terrible starvation diet of Dr. Allen that was the one slim, almost hopeless hope for young diabetics. It was hardly food enough for a baby. It kept him alive but didn't let him live. Then that fall of 1921 he bumped into Banting.

"Maybe I'll have something for you pretty soon, Joe," Banting said.

Then came October, and the flu got Gilchrist, one of those infections that's the dread of every diabetic. It wrecked him so he couldn't eat three ounces of carbohydrate a day without showing sugar and he was hanging on by his eyebrows and couldn't work any more and knew that if he let down for just one meal, maybe, or at most two meals, the coma would get him. If he would just satisfy the hunger that gnawed and gnawed him, just that little bit, the coma would get him and almost surely finish him. . . .

Wouldn't it be better so? Wasn't it easier just to pass out —unconscious, never knowing it at the end?

Gilchrist hung on, though you couldn't have blamed him if he'd let go. Who'd have blamed him for not pinning too much hope on Fred Banting? He knew Banting for the stubborn plodder that he was, never brilliant. And, for Gilchrist, who was Banting? Only his friend since their marbles and football days. You see Gilchrist was too close to him. . . .

Already Banting had taken his jump from dogs to humans, had first of all shot himself with this isletin, then shot his pal, Charlie Best, to prove that this stuff so life-saving to dogs, wouldn't harm humans. Then, too, there were a few very bad diabetics who'd been shot with the new "X" at the Toronto General Hospital and there were fantastic rumors. Then again Banting had gone to New Haven, Connecticut, and read a paper about this strange stuff and the wonderful things it would do for diabetic dogs, before a learned medical Congress at Yale University. It was said he'd stuttered, that they'd let him have not too much time to tell of it—what with all the important scientific papers to be read that day— but rumors were certainly floating around throughout the medical profession and even among plain folks. . . .

Finally here it's February 11, 1922, with Gilchrist in the laboratory with Fred Banting and Charlie Best. He's their experimental animal now, very little better off than one of their dogs they'd made pancreasless. Will this new isletin make Joe's body burn sugar? They feed him an ounce of pure glucose. They make him breathe as deep a breath as his feeble life spark will let him breathe, into the Douglas bag. . . .

Will his body burn any of the sugar they've just fed him? Instead of devouring itself, burning its own fat and protein? "Nothing doing," Best says, taking the reading.

"R.Q. . . . zero point seven," Best tells Banting.

Gilchrist has this on the dogs: he knows what those grim figures mean as well as Banting and Best. . . .

Now they shoot in the isletin with a quick jab of the syringe needle. . . .

They all sat there waiting. Now and again Gilchrist blew into the Douglas bag for Best to test the amount of carbon dioxide he breathed out compared to the amount of oxygen he breathed in. . . . An hour, two hours, and nothing doing. The carbon dioxide proportion climbed no higher: Joe's body wasn't burning the glucose they'd fed him. . . .

Banting was down in the dumps about it. Hardly daring to look at Joe, Banting left to catch a train to go north to his folks. It was a washout. It was the old grim story: what worked for dogs might do nothing for humans. . . .

Banting left just too soon. Best urged Joe to stay. "Let's have another go at it, Joe," Best said. Now when Joe breathed into the Douglas bag, it was funny, but he found he could breathe much better. He felt as if he had lungs again and he wanted to breathe harder like a fellow testing his lungs on one of those machines you blow up at a fair. Then he said: "Charlie, what's your shot done to me?"

Suddenly for the first time in months his head felt clear as a bell again and his legs lost their infernal heaviness.

He hurried home, called Banting's folks long distance to tell them to tell Banting what had happened, the moment he got in from the train. He ate supper, for the first time in years, a real supper. After supper he took two little cousins of his out for a walk. "And I'll never forget it," Gilchrist said, "never . . .

"Everybody stared at me. There I was walking along grinning from ear to ear. I walked along dragging my cousins after me and grinning," Joe said.

"Everybody we passed turned round staring at me. It was as if I was walking on air. I hadn't felt like this in five years," Gilchrist said.

Next morning his legs began dragging again. Never mind, he'd go back, get another shot of isletin—

He couldn't get another. Banting and Best had no more of it.

x

Those were tough days for Banting, though you'd think by now things would have begun breaking right for him. By now Professor Macleod realized that his young man with his hare-brained scheme had pulled off what the greatest physiologists had failed at, utterly. Of course Macleod was proud that he'd given Banting those first ten dogs and the assistant for eight weeks. Now Macleod dropped his own work on anoxaemia. Together with all his assistants Macleod went to work on this life-saving isletin of Banting and Best, and first of all Macleod insisted its name be changed to *insulin*—that was maybe better Latin, or something, I don't know. Macleod and his assistants set to work with terrific energy, now, dotting i's and crossing the t's of the discovery that Banting and Best had roughed out in its simple outlines. Macleod began making real *science* of it—

But Banting was through with such details. What bothered him now was trying to save desperately sick folks now pouring into Toronto, on stretchers, *in extremis,* begging for his isletin. Starting from his stammering little speech in New Haven before the highbrows, rumors now brought them flocking. It was tough to have to tell a mother begging, pointing to her emaciated, languid, dry-skinned, thin-haired little girl . . . "We're sorry, but . . ."

It was a hurly-burly now. Everybody wanted to work on insulin. Dr. Collip, on leave of absence from Alberta University, had come and Banting had shown him how they were getting their life-saving stuff out of pancreases with weak alcohol, then purifying it with alcohol very concentrated. Collip shut himself up privately and thought he'd got a way to get insulin so pure it wouldn't be dangerous to humans. Lord knows they needed plenty of it now, with all these dying folks coming, hoping, then finding they were only grabbing at another straw. . . .

Macleod put Collip to work to make insulin on a large scale. Banting and Best were at this moment sort of lost in the shuffle. Alas for Collip—what worked well in his test-tubes failed in commercial manufacture. As for Banting, these were not nice days for him. He had no job. He was broke and owed money. Sick folks were leaving Toronto bowed down in the bitterest of all disappointments. Poor Joe Gilchrist was hanging to life by less than his eyebrows. . . .

Professor Macleod now appeared before the Association of American Physicians, the most scientific body of American physicians—so scientific that, without irreverence, it may be called somewhat snooty. Professor Macleod gave them great news. It was what sports would call a natural.

"I move that the Association tender to Dr. Macleod *and his associates*[1] a rising vote expressing its appreciation of his achievement," said Woodyatt of Chicago.

"We are all agreed in congratulating Dr. Macleod *and his collaborators*[1] on their miraculous achievement," said Allen,

[1] These italics are, in both cases, this writer's.

most famous of diabetes experts. It was Allen who'd perfected Dr. Guelpa's starvation treatment. . . .

Allen at the Rockefeller Institute, on dogs, had proved scientifically that Guelpa was right. With unlimited dogs in the world's finest laboratory where it doesn't matter much if you break as much glassware in a week as Banting and Best had used for their whole discovery, Allen had proved starvation keeps diabetics alive a little longer. . . .

It was manly of Allen to congratulate Macleod. Allen himself had lowered blood sugar in diabetes with pancreas extracts. "But the obvious reason why such experiments proved nothing, is found in the great toxicity of such extracts, so that the animals receiving them were injured instead of benefited," Allen admitted. . . .

"I wish to thank the Association very much in the name of my associates and myself," Macleod answered.

Meanwhile Banting and Best were at their wits' end for insulin. Joe Gilchrist didn't know how much longer his eyebrows would hold him. Suffering folks were dragging themselves back home to die. It was now that Best showed Banting the true helper he was. Authorities at Connaught Laboratories gave Banting and Best money for dogs, rabbits, chemicals to buy unlimited pancreas. Back they went with their old-time fury, to start where Collip had run on the rocks—

"I was Fred and Charlie's human rabbit; I was the chief rabbit," Joe Gilchrist said. Now every single batch of insulin, slowly getting less poisonous, stronger, was tried out first on Joe. Best at the Connaught Laboratories was getting the hang of it. . . .

It was ticklish business. In January Collip had found how insulin was a two-edged sword and he'd invented a quick clever way to measure its dangerous power. He shot it into healthy rabbits and it was remarkable how it burned the sugar out of these beasts' blood. And when their blood sugar got down just so low, they'd go into a coma, throw terrific convulsions, then die. There was an exact arithmetic to it, and this test turned out to be the standard way to find out the strength of any batch of insulin. Gilchrist was the human rabbit for such tests. . . .

Now Banting and Gilchrist at the Christie Street Hospital for Returned Soldiers in Toronto showed the real miracle of insulin. They gave it to none but most desperately sick diabetic Canadian veterans and these boys now fought a desperate battle with death hanging over them and they called Joe Gilchrist not Doctor, but Captain.

One day, after a shot into himself of a new batch, Joe began sweating though the room was cool. His knees wobbled. He couldn't remember what he was doing. His brain couldn't find the words he hunted for. He was scared. He said he felt like one of those poor rabbits with an overdose who go dashing round frightened, insanely bumping into benches and tables. . . .

Joe saved his own life, thanks to Professor Henderson's simple trick of taking a quick dose of glucose. Henderson had taught Banting that a little shot of sugar raises the too low blood sugar of rabbits, literally bringing them back from the grave.

Joe and his boys were a grand bunch of rabbits, all of them, those first days in May and June, 1922, when insulin was still crude and dangerous. From abscesses from its injection their arms, their legs, their thighs got crosshatched with scars so you'd swear there was no place left to inject them. But they lived. They weren't starving any longer. Strength flowed back into these boys who'd become miserable objects of Government charity. . . .

"We're feeling great this morning, Captain," they'd tell Joe.

Jobs, the chance to earn their own livings, to be men again—this was possible now. And they only laughed and never minded the terrible burning and pain of those early shots of insulin, while Best fixed and fixed at making it painless and safer.

"We weren't martyrs or heroes, absolutely not," Gilchrist said. "We all knew we were dying. When you're that way you'll try—anything."

Of that scarred crew of human rabbits of the year 1922 at the Christie Street Hospital in Toronto, to this day—though a few have passed on from other causes—*not a single one has died of diabetes.*

It was weird for me not long ago when I sat, late at night, talking to healthy Joe Gilchrist. Nine years ago in Banting's tough summer of 1921, Joe was a bag of bones, starving. 1922—and he should have been dead. Now here he sat, an energetic medical consultant, successful, laughing, sure he has as good a chance for long life as the next man . . . all from two tiny shots of Banting's "X" that go into him every day. . . . It was like talking to a man come back from the grave.

XI

May, 1922, and hardly a year had passed since those first fumbling experiments of Banting and Best on their black bench and in their little hot attic. Now Banting, Gilchrist, Campbell, Fletcher, and other Toronto doctors began almost resurrecting folks with powerful insulin that Charlie Best slaved day and night to make for them. Up till now, better than sixty diabetics out of every hundred had died from coma. Practically all diabetic children perished from this unconsciousness, stealing over them from the accumulation in their blood of acid-poison from the faulty burning of fat lacking the good fire of carbohydrate to burn it.

Now with such children it was the way it had been with that famous Dog 92—unbelievable. . . .

Folks came who were losing two thousand calories or more in their urine as sugar and acid. They came hungry for air, gasping. Hungry for food, when they ate, they could only vomit. Thirsty, they couldn't retain even the liquid that was given them. They were cold. Their wrecked pancreases could no longer change their food into glycogen, the animal starch, for their liver and muscles to then turn into sugar their bodies could burn—for energy. Failing so, the bodies of these poor people turned on their own tissues in a horrible auto-cannibalism. Their eyes became soft as jelly-fish. Their skin was parchment dry. Their muscles seemed to melt away. Now at last coma—the merciful end for them. From this coma, up till these May days of 1922, almost no diabetic had ever returned to tell the story. . . .

Till insulin, with Banting and his helpers bending over these dying ones. Now a flutter of the eyelids, a muttered "Where-am-I. . . ." Banting and his helpers returned eight of their first twelve cases of coma, not only to life but to strong life and health again.

What remedy in all death-fighting history could be as fantastic as this one, that made the last desperate end of a sickness almost as easy to treat as its very beginning?

Today there's absolutely no need for any diabetic dying in coma. In 1927 Dr. Joslin of Boston had 1,241 diabetics and 43 of them died, but not one of coma.

In another way Banting's insulin has turned the cruel course of the sugar sickness topsy-turvy. In the old days before Banting, children were the doomed ones. The older the diabetic the better his chances. Now this law is reversed to the natural law of life. Now there's no limit—within the limits of human life—to the years a diabetic child may live, Joslin says.

All over our country diabetics do die in coma but that's not the fault of Fred Banting. It's the fault of incompetent doctors. "I believe more deaths are chargeable to this deficiency than to any other single factor," Joslin says.

With good doctors people don't die of diabetes any longer

at all. It's the enemy of old people, arteriosclerosis, that kills them. Joslin believes that diabetes—through Banting—has been actually turned into a good sickness that may help to clear up this mystery of the hardening of arteries in all people.

With an excess of fat diabetes begins, and from an excess of fat diabetics may die—because too much fat taken in food piles up in the blood and gets into the arteries. That's Joslin's hunch about it.

If Joslin can prevent his diabetics dying from hardening of their arteries by diets with not too much fat, then what will be the lesson for those of us, not sufferers from the sugar disease, but faced with this greatest of all threats of old age?

That's what those forlorn experiments of Fred Banting may finally lead to. Diabetics, kept healthy by insulin *and just the right diet,* may teach us all another way to stretch out our lives. Banting would certainly have smiled his slow farmerish smile in those tough days if he'd been told that this "X" he was chasing would bring the average age at death of Joslin's patients to ten years above the average age at death of all citizens of Massachusetts. . . .

Of course insulin isn't a cure, because bad diabetics have to go on taking it, balancing it against the right amount of food. But many have to take less and less of it and it looks as if, taking the load off the sick pancreas, that organ actually gradually may repair itself. . . .

"Injections of insulin annoy a baby less than the average child, and the average child less than the adult," Joslin says. You should see the smile on the face of one of Joslin's ten-year-old girl patients as she slips the syringe needle under her own skin. . . .

Memories carry me back to my father in his last days, dying while the ovenbirds sang their cheerful "teacher!—teacher!—teacher!" just as they're doing this May morning as I write. He would never have minded two daily shots of insulin. . . .

So I sit, before this honest, simple Fred Banting, who looks much more like a farmer than a highbrow scientist. As Joslin puts it, Banting has answered the terrible question of the Lord to Ezekiel . . .

"Thus saith the Lord God unto these bones; Behold I will cause breath to enter into you, and ye shall live:

"And I will lay sinews upon you, and will bring up flesh upon you, and cover you with skin, and bring breath into you, and ye shall live;

". . . and breath came into them, and they lived, and stood upon their feet, an exceeding great army."

The hundreds of thousands Fred Banting has saved ease my heartache that comes from his being born a little too late to bring back breath and life to my father.

A little while ago it was my honor to sit one evening in the company of a gathering of extremely scientific searchers, who were relaxed and gossiping scientifically.

Two of them smiled just a wee bit sniffishly at the mention of Fred Banting . . . full of his discovery I'd maybe bubbled over a little about him.

They said it hadn't been Banting particularly, and when giving them the facts I pushed them back to the wall, they said well, if it *had* been Banting he'd been lucky and would never make another discovery like it.

But who will?

3. MINOT

AGAINST DEATH

~~~~~~

Isn't a man's real laboratory in his head and aren't his best tools his horse sense and his eyes and hands? Minot was a practicing doctor who found the life-saving answer to the mystery of one of the most inexorably deadly of all human ills—not in a laboratory—but in his private practice.

~~~~~~

WITHOUT Banting's insulin to keep him alive, Minot could hardly have lived long enough to try his stunt of feeding liver to people absolutely doomed with pernicious anaemia. In 1925 there was no disease more surely deadly than this weird thinning of the blood. Being told you had pernicious anaemia meant the undertaker for you more surely than if the governor had signed your death warrant for first degree murder.

In 1926, George R. Minot and William P. Murphy made the statement that they had kept on feeding lots of liver every day to forty-five folks in a row. With the marrow of their bones mysteriously refusing to make red blood these folks all had one foot as good as in the grave. Liver—and not one of these people had died. All had up and got their blood back and got better.

This news was certainly as staggering as any in the history of modern death fighting. These days when the practice of medicine has grown so scientific, you'd expect it would take some extremely complicated deep science out of a white-tile-and-glass-door-knob laboratory and cooked by some abstruse highbrow investigator . . . to get people better from a sickness all doctors everywhere knew was fatal and no help for it. But here were a couple of plain doctors claiming it. Here, for an ill too mortal for a quack to claim to cure it, was new hope, by a trick so simple that a scientist would be confused and flabbergasted by it, yet so rudimentary a child could understand it.

Is it any wonder that, for a time after Minot made his discovery, people went on dying from pernicious anaemia when they wouldn't have had to at all? And even now. . . .

His find lacked the almost indispensable element of complexity that is the window dressing of science. Not only doctors but their patients—all human—need the mystery of scientific hocus-pocus to convince them that here's really hope against a scourge so deadly. . . .

But here was something so a-b-c that it must be fishy. True enough, Minot was a Harvard University Medical School professor . . . but this liver-eating business! It smacked of nothing you'd expect from such a nabob of knowledge but much more of what some pipe-smoking crone would brew on the night of Walpurgis. It was grotesque coming from such a conservative physician as George R. Minot of the sedate New England Minots from the Back Bay of the city of Boston where it's supposed the arts are effete and the sciences moribund. But this was primitive.

Minot's discovery was really as weird and subtle at bottom as it seemed drab and simple on its surface. He didn't have the luck of being able to look on at a grim experiment of the kind that nature made for Semmelweis with those mothers dying in the two Maternity Divisions in Vienna. He didn't find himself shoved forward by a clear-cut, logical hunch of the kind that drove Fred Banting through his attic experiments willy-nilly. Minot did have this in common with those two plain doctors Banting and Semmelweis: he loathed human suffering with a hatred never letting him realize that here was a misery entirely inexorable. He was a true man against death.

II

You'd have thought, knowing Minot when he was a medical youngster, that his life wasn't going to be upstream enough to toughen him for such a crude, bold discovery. He didn't have to work his way through Harvard Medical School nor even to hock his watch to buy books and there was in his family a tradition of science and doctoring—enough to put him into a groove that you'd bet would kill any chance of his doing anything profoundly original. His father, James Jackson Minot, is a retired excellent Boston Back Bay doctor, formerly an active member of the staff of the Massachusetts General Hospital. His grandfather, James Jackson, one of the finest doctors America ever boasted, had been the very first physician to Massachusetts General. His great-uncle Francis Minot had held this same position, and his cousin, Charles Sedgwick Minot, was a most distinguished biologist, a shark on why we die, the author of a deep book called "Age, Growth, and Death." So George R. Minot of the present story was really too successful before he ever got started.

He had one hurdle to cross: he was never very healthy. He was the delicate, mentally precocious type you'd say might be doomed for a certain serious sickness. His fragility might have allowed him to make a mildly eminent name for himself without doing anything really outstanding. Only he was always working. He was a terrible worker.

Right from the start for no good reason he was eager to the point of fanaticism about every kind of disease of the blood, not of cats or monkeys, but blood of sick human beings. Dig into the records of the Massachusetts General Hospital where he was an interne in 1912, and you'll find in his queer handwriting his mulling and stewing over the hopeless case of a certain poor woman now dead.

Making his rounds every day, he saw her day after day always the same, her face more ghastly than just plain white because of its tinge of faint lemon yellow—waxy. There was no question of what she had nor any doubt of her doom. She was known in the records as No. 190182 and on her record is scrawled, by young Minot:

"Though sitting up & enjoying being out of doors she remains weak and her blood chart doesn't vary. . . . It seems diet with HCL must be the proper treatment for we are dealing with a stomach with lack of HCL . . . to be sure what we need to know is the treatment of pernicious anaemia."

That was to be sure what all doctors needed to know, but didn't, but from all these Minot was naïvely and even ridiculously different: he had no notion it was impossible to know it. He couldn't get it through his head, as the great Sir William Osler has so touchingly explained, that there are ills you just can't cure, and won't ever . . .

Minot had maybe not quite enough respect for the mature judgment of great medical whales like Osler or old Thomas Addison. Sixty-three years before this year 1912, Addison had announced his discovery of this peculiar thinning of the blood—which was precisely as mysterious and every bit as deadly as the day that square-faced, grumpy, old man had first told his Guy's Hospital students about it.

"Its approach is slow and insidious," Addison had said. "The patient can hardly fix a date to his earliest feeling of that languor which is shortly to become so extreme."

Addison's hawk eye for telling one disease apart from another was as marvelous as his conviction that most remedies were useless, even quackish. Here was something dreadful . . .

"The countenance gets pale," Addison said. "The whites

of the eyes become pearly, the general frame flabby rather than wasted. There is increasing indisposition to exertion with an uncomfortable feeling of faintness and breathlessness on attempting it."

Addison was a haughty and terrifically conscientious old physician who was altogether too interested in *observing* fatal illness to take the time to make much money, and now and again he would get up out of bed and scare the nurses by popping into Guy's Hospital wards at midnight to look for some symptom of a patient he'd forgot to spot during the day. He was swell with his patients and hoped they'd get better. It was said he often forgot to prescribe for them. What good . . .

"The whole surface of the body presents a blanched, smooth, and waxy appearance; the lips, gums, and tongue seem bloodless . . . appetite fails," Addison said.

"Extreme languor and faintness supervene, breathlessness being produced by the most trifling exertion or emotion. . . . The patient can no longer rise from his bed, the mind occasionally wanders, he falls into a prostrate and half torpid state, and at length expires," Addison ended it.

That was that, and had stayed that for sixty years. From Addison down to Sir William Osler, who was marvelous at being sunshiny at bedsides, doctors had sat sympathetically by many thousands of poor people whose blood had faded away till the sheet at last had been drawn—reverently—over their faces. There was only one thing to cheer doctors about this malady . . .

"There is no disease in which clinical diagnosis by competent observers is so often confirmed at autopsy," said Dr. Richard C. Cabot. In short, doctors could be sure ahead of time that they'd guessed right about what it was their patients were going to die of. . . .

III

There was one thing everybody working with Minot, those early days at Massachusetts General, noted about him: he went into such infernally elaborate details working at every patient that you'd have thought each one was the only patient in the hospital that he had to take care of. And he acted about pernicious anaemia as if there was nothing known about it at all. It was scientifically correct to believe that these stricken folks' blood thinned because there was some mysterious poison in their bodies dissolving their red blood corpuscles. Minot looked at it left-handed. "Isn't it possible that this patient's blood thins because her bone marrow can't make new red corpuscles?" Minot asked himself.

It was not original with him but it was also not scientifically popular to think it. Minot was continually poking into the arms of pernicious anaemia patients and taking tubes of their blood to the laboratory, smearing thin films of such blood on thin flat pieces of extremely clean glass. . . . Through his microscope he'd squint and squint at their disc-shaped red blood corpuscles, looking like little poker chips faintly green-red against a gray-white background under his lens. . . . This was curious! Every once in a while one of these pernicious anaemia folks would get strangely better for a little while. . . . Now here were red blood corpuscles that were different. . . .

Staining them with a dye called brilliant cresyl blue here were many of these little poker chips with the bright blue network inside them. . . . Often there were a lot of them at the beginning of this mysterious, cruelly temporary period of their getting better. . . . These were called *reticulocytes*. They were baby red blood cells supposed to have just been poured into the blood from that blood-factory, the bone marrow. . . .

They looked sort of hopeful to Minot. Then, a week, a month, a half year later, these folks would start going down hill again, and now under the microscope these baby hopeful cells would grow less and less. Again they might appear while pseudo-hope flowed all through the bodies of these people, and then fade away again and then usually the people would die. They usually lived about two or three years in all after the anaemia first began showing itself. A few lived ten years. They all died. Why *couldn't* their bone marrow make new blood?

There were maybe some sophisticates in Boston smiling at Minot for going on digging at a sickness so perfectly . . . settled. Then Minot went to Johns Hopkins University, always working at blood, blood, blood. There was a smack of the one-track fanatic about the way he was always disappearing carrying blood from sick folks into his laboratory.

IV

"Dammit, Minot, can't you see it's the *bone marrow* that's sick?" Wright asked.

Minot was now back in Boston in Dr. James Homer Wright's laboratory deviling Wright to look through the microscope at the bone marrow of some unfortunate somebody who'd just died from pernicious anaemia. It took nerve to ask Wright anything. He was a pathologist who was always getting furious, exploding into devastating damns and goddams.

"But, Doctor Wright, what are these cells down here toward eight o'clock in the field? Are those megaloblasts?" Minot asked.

"I don't care a damn what you call them! *Call* them megaloblasts! Call them just blasts if you've got to have blast in it. But can't you see they're *young?*" Wright said.

It was obvious Minot was foolishly bothering him and Minot kept bothering him.

"But what do they mean—here in this pernicious anaemia patient?" Minot asked him.

"What ails you? Can't you see this fellow's bone marrow is chock-full of young cells that can't grow up, that can't grow into full-fledged red blood corpuscles? Why . . ."

And Wright burst into epic cussing at the shame of Minot's blindness.

"But how . . ." Minot was at him again.

"Yes, how!" Wright roared. "How! How! How! If we only knew how the hell this happens . . ."

So Wright, getting sorer and sorer, kept showing Minot the exact look of this weird blood sickness through the microscope, kept making it real, salty, bitter, vivid for Minot. "Who the hell knows how or why?" Wright asked him. "Why can't these baby bone marrow cells turn into good full-grown red cells?"

Minot soaked it in, looking, squinting, dreaming.

"You know what these blasts mean?" Wright asked. "They mean this whole bone marrow's like a tumor . . . embryo kind of stuff, undeveloped stuff . . . overgrowing the marrow fat, overgrowing everything, but not developing. It's just the marrow trying to make blood but it can't go through with it. But get out! What the devil do you bother me for?"

Wright loathed interruptions. He spent that whole morning with Minot, in fact, many mornings. Wright was a marvelous teacher. He is now to some extent forgotten because he stayed working and cussing in his little laboratory, was seen little in print, and hardly at all at back-slapping scientific soirées. Being a pathologist, he had this limitation: he was concerned entirely with the way sickness killed humans, not about how to keep humans from dying.

Minot soaked it into himself how hopeless the whole business was . . . pernicious anaemia really a tumor of the bone marrow . . . but what's more dreadful than a tumor, a cancer deep in you, especially when it's tucked away deep inside the marrow of your bones, shin bones, arm bones, back-bone, even?

By now Minot had started a little practice in Boston and he actually thought you could be as thorough in your every-day practice as you were in a university laboratory. He was irritatingly elaborate, with every kind of patient, rich or poor, who came to him—just as scientifically pernickety as he was at Massachusetts General or at the Harvard Medical School where he now held some kind of small position. He was a great friend to his patients, but they were all experi-mental animals to him; only first of all they were always human beings. "May I take walks, Doctor?" a fellow would ask him.

"You may walk as far as the river, but no farther. You may walk two blocks along the river. Then you must come back home by the shortest way," Minot said. Then he'd sit down and figure out exactly the shortest way. Then he'd re-peat, "By the shortest way, remember!" Then his blue eyes blazed, showing the patient he didn't mean maybe. He had a prodigious memory for everything that happened to all sick folks, knew how they slept, their poor little joys, their family troubles, what they ate—down to the last crumb of it. . . .

And all the time he was literally a bug on every kind of blood trouble, became a shark telling the fine shades of dif-ference between secondary anaemias that result from hem-orrhages, or from fish tapeworms, or cancers, syphilis, ma-laria, pregnancy . . .

Between all these and that colossal disaster, that one hope-less one—pernicious anaemia.

"Is there anything you could do, Doctor, anything?" pa-tients would come, asking him, when he was working with the experienced doctor, Roger I. Lee. Many were too weak to put one foot ahead of the other and some could hardly talk what with their tongues so sore and raw and beefy red.

So long as they stayed still they were reasonably comfortable but gradually they felt themselves getting weaker and weaker and weaker.

"You might have an operation if you're in shape to stand it," Minot would answer them. "We can't promise anything" —there was a fierce honesty in Minot's eyes—"you understand, we can't promise . . ."

So surgeons took the spleens out of nineteen of Lee and Minot's doomed ones—1914 to 1917. It was strange how some pernicious anaemia folks had what are called remissions of their trouble, their blood getting thicker with them feeling much stronger for maybe nine months or a year. Now Minot watched these folks—spleenless. He studied their blood prodigiously, looking and looking for those blue-networked baby blood cells, the reticulocytes. Often he did see more of these hopeful little cells right after the operation. . . . Then they'd relapse again. The devil of it was there was only one spleen to take out of them. . . . They'd start downhill again. Then they'd die. They all died, all nineteen of them.

It was bitter for Minot. He'd learned all the tricks of the bedside manner from so great a doctor as Thayer of Baltimore who'd learned it from no less than Sir William Osler himself and there was no doubt you can wonderfully benefit sick folks by always being cheerful and even quietly gay in their sickrooms. It's *personality*. The deuce of it was that personality didn't make these folks' blood any thicker. Minot was hell bent on getting their blood to get thicker and stay thick and he deplorably lacked that fatalistic resignation which was one of the charms of physicians like Osler. Minot tried everything.

He tried—with Roger I. Lee—transfusing blood into pernicious anaemia people, just as many others were then trying it. 1914-1917—they gave forty-six such people seventy transfusions of good thick blood.

"Inside a few weeks there was definite improvement . . . in about 50 percent—" Minot said.

They all died finally.

It was a personal dishonor, it was a rock of offense to Minot that they should die. He was really extraordinary about it because who can blame any doctor for *finally* becoming a little nonchalant about folks dying?

Even when those transfusions didn't seem to help these people to make new blood of their own at all, even then Minot was all for keeping on putting other people's blood into them. . . . Even then . . .

"Patients in some instances can be kept alive by repeatedly filling them up with blood," Minot said. "Sometimes in the very sick it is temporarily life-saving," he wrote.

God knows how he kept at it with it so farcical, almost, you might say, idiotic, useless. He knew they had to die.

All authorities everywhere knew these people couldn't live. Minot was too sensitive. He should have taken counsel from Osler who is so eminent that he's actually called the modern Hippocrates. Then Minot would have stopped being raw-nerved about it. Osler said:

"To accept a great group of maladies, against which we have never had and *can scarcely ever hope to have curative measures* [1] makes some men as sensitive as though we ourselves were responsible for their existence."

Osler said this in his great speech on the treatment of disease at Toronto in 1909 in June.

"We work with wit and not by witchcraft," Osler went on. "And while these patients have our tenderest care, and we must do what is best for the relief of their suffering . . ."

Of course Minot didn't believe in witchcraft, was not superstitious, was scientific. But he was sensitive.

"We should not bring the art of medicine into disrepute by quacklike promises to heal, or by wiredrawn attempts at

[1] The italics are this writer's.

cure in what old Burton calls 'the continuate and inexorable maladies,' " Osler said.

Nobody knew better than Minot that pernicious anaemia was *the* most continuate and inexorable malady. He was no quack. He never promised to cure it. He couldn't get over being sensitive about people dying from it.

v

Now he was promoted at Harvard Medical School, put in charge of a medical service at the Collis P. Huntington Memorial Hospital, where folks with cancer were studied, and where he probed the riddle of people whose blood-forming tissues were out of whack with terrible ills like leukemia. He was Associate in Medicine at the Peter Bent Brigham Hospital, too, and was consultant in diseases of the blood at the old Massachusetts General besides. Chinked in between these jobs were hours for his private practice and in all these places, researching as he then was on cancer, he saw much pernicious anaemia. He was always mulling over the riddle of cell growth. Why would some cells in some people fail to grow up, why did they remain dangerous baby-cells . . . as James Homer Wright had explained. . . .

In 1921 Minot began to feel rocky. He was tall and had always been thin as a slat but now he came back from his Cape Cod vacation even thinner. He caught himself buying bananas in mid-afternoon. He ate like a grave-digger but it put no flesh on him. He couldn't stop working, he never stopped even for one day, but his back hurt him and he was all the time thirsty and felt rocky. So now he shut himself up alone in his own little lab and faced it. He stood there alone one evening holding a test-tube over a sputtering Bunsen flame watching what was in that tube boil and bubble from blue to green to yellow and now to ominous, sinister red. "It was as strong a sugar test as you'd find in any urine," Minot said.

He was only thirty-four. When you got sugar disease that early you were nearly as good as a goner. He was married and had young children. He put himself in care of a diabetes expert and if you hadn't known he was fighting to keep from dying you'd have called it comical the way Minot followed every direction of his starvation diet—precisely. Every morsel he ate he weighed out on scales. He only went out to dinner to homes of folks he knew so well that he could take those little scales along with him.

Every moment hunger gnawed him with him knowing that giving in to it would kill him. He was hardly half a man now. Going down and down hill in spite of that diet yet he never stopped working and it was only a savage will to live that kept him hanging by a thread to life and the way that diet kept the spark glowing in him made him slightly cracked about the marvelousness of dieting and its possible good for all kinds of sicknesses.

VI

Then Banting found insulin and that saved Minot's life. He came back strong, swiftly, magically, the way folks do whose lives have been saved by insulin. His stronger and stronger enthusiasm for diet, diet, diet unquestionably led him toward his day of days, toward the bizarre discovery that loomed in the future—with him not knowing it. 1922— and Minot living again, with not the glimmer of a notion his find was around the corner for him. But then as Bill Castle puts it: "How the hell can you call it a discovery if you know what it is that you're going to discover?"

Even as far back as 1916 Minot had begun quizzing not only pernicious anaemia patients but all kinds of sick people about their habits of eating. Young internes put their hands over their faces and said out of the corners of their mouths: "Dr. Minot has just discovered that old Mrs. Blank never ate spinach till she was ten years old!" Then they'd giggle.

Already Minot believed he was on the trail of something very peculiar about pernicious anaemia people, finding many of them were strange eaters, fussy, finical, eating with irregularity, choosing food peculiarly. He kept asking them uncommon questions that hardly any doctor takes the time or patience to ask his customers. He kept harping at them and wasn't content when they told him they had meat every day but kept asking them whether they really ate it and what kind and how much and he noted that many didn't care for it though they had it on their tables and then too some had a strange liking for fats and butter. . . .

Behind their hands the young internes said: "Dr. Minot has discovered that this patient has always eaten two or more pats of butter with her meals!" They snickered.

So Minot, while he watched pernicious anaemia doomed ones get paler, waxier-looking, while he watched some get paralyzed, and all go downhill, kept badgering them with questions. He kept edging toward a certain diet for them. . . .

He started way off from nowhere, with a logic that made two plus two equal five, with science that even those whippersnapper internes laughed at. . . .

It's in northern countries that most pernicious anaemia is found, Minot read.

It's in northern countries there's the greatest production of dairy products, Minot mulled it.

But what of it? Plenty of people in these dairy regions ate a lot of other things besides cream and butter and surely there are millions of cream and butter eaters who show never a sign of pernicious anaemia. . . .

Now, maybe a diet with very little fat in it . . . Minot pondered.

Wait! Pernicious anaemia is a lot like pellagra—sore mouth, upset digestion, nervous troubles.

Well, Goldberger had proved that not eating enough meat, not enough protein, was at the bottom of pellagra.

He remembered that a diet rich in liver was reported "to be useful," as doctors say vaguely, in sprue. Well, didn't sprue people have anaemia?

For these musings any professor of logic would certainly have marked him zero! Was pellagra really so much like pernicious anaemia? Wasn't pellagra curable by just eating meat and milk? But hadn't Minot tried feeding lots of meat, of protein, to pernicious anaemia people? Hadn't they died anyway?

In a formidable book "Newer Knowledge of Nutrition" Minot had come across certain obscure virtues of proteins in—liver. Liver whooped up the growth rate of young white rats. Liver of white rats fed to guinea-pigs with the scurvy raised the amount of hemoglobin in those guinea-pigs' blood . . .

But what of it? Pernicious anaemia wasn't merely lack of hemoglobin, no. Minot remembered old Wright cussing. "It's the bone marrow that's sick. It's the *blasts* in the sick bone marrow not being able to grow into red blood corpuscles . . ."

Grow . . . Minot pondered. Liver . . .

In that fat book Minot kept running across the word liver. But what had sick bone marrow to do with liver making baby rats grow? But then there was this stuff about the baby lions. . . .

Unhappy zoo-keepers tried to raise lion cubs on lean meat and lost their little lions, who got miserably rickety, with no good bones. Bones . . . Minot thought. Then the book went on: "But when cubs are fed upon liver, fat, and bones . . . they grow to be strong and beautiful animals."

There it was again. Bones bad when no liver. Lions eat liver and get fine bones. Marrow of bones sick in pernicious anaemia. . . .

It was far-fetched. It was all in Minot's head, walking to and from work, at bedsides watching sick folks getting better, in the night watching people dying, in the morning while he shaved. . . .

It was no finely planned research. Nobody gave Minot ten million dollars for an institute to discover the cure of pernicious anaemia or to prove the virtues of liver. It was all in his own private practice and how can you do science in private practice? It was all vague, cloudy, bobbing up now and again in his head in a swirl of other thoughts and a thousand other preoccupations. It was Minot . . .

Here was another piece of science that should have stopped Minot rather than encourage him. Dr. Whipple and Dr. Hooper and Dr. Robscheit who later became Dr. Robscheit-Robbins had bled healthy dogs, bled them and bled them till they got very thin-blooded. They had then fed those dogs liver. Their blood came back.

But it wasn't pernicious anaemia but only *secondary* anaemia those dogs got from bleeding. And it was a-b-c of medical science that secondary anaemia has absolutely nothing to do with pernicious anaemia! You can't give dogs pernicious anaemia . . .

And Whipple didn't claim liver feeding could have any effect on pernicious anaemia. And anyway it didn't look as if liver could be anything special. Whipple had stated that beef heart and beef muscle could cure that dog anaemia too. "Cooked liver ranks with cooked muscle," was all Whipple said.

And Minot knew that all the beef muscle in the world wouldn't help his pernicious anaemia folks, fundamentally. In spite of beef eating they all had died. Muscle meat was as good as liver for dogs who only had secondary but not pernicious anaemia, so why try liver on humans?

So Minot began feeding liver.

VII

He didn't have the nerve to suggest feeding it to his hospital patients . . . his colleagues might well have given him the horse laugh. So he began feeding liver to one of his private patients and there was a lucky angle to it, because this man was one of those pernicious anaemia people who was taking a long time to die. He still had a pretty fair appetite and the great thing about him was that he was extraordinarily conscientious . . . like Minot.

"Please try eating liver a couple of times a week," said Minot to this fellow. Minot advised this man to eat a lot of meat, lean, and very little butter, and told him to drink very little cream. Minot told him lots of green vegetables and fruit might help him but to go easy on starches and sugars. So it wasn't just liver; it was no experiment. . . .

It was sort of aiming all over the tree to bring down the squirrel. It was maybe good doctoring but would you call it science? Of course it was science but not standard science. "Be sure and eat liver twice a week," Minot said.

This man went home and ate exactly what Minot told him—and then some. Maybe he had a hankering for liver. Anyway it's recorded that he ate more liver than was expected. Meanwhile this patient sank below the surface of Minot's thoughts. Minot had other patients nearer death and had a thousand other things to think about. He was a new man from insulin and was going full steam ahead again but at last this fellow came back to see Minot. "Like all of them, I suppose," Minot said.

Minot gave him a casual look, then looked harder. "Hello!" Minot said.

"Yes," the man said, "I certainly feel much better."

"Yes, I know you're better," Minot answered.

But Minot had seen more than a hundred others, like this man, get better, then worse, then maybe a little better again, then die. He tested this man's blood and it was some thicker. "Keep on with your diet," Minot said. "Don't forget about the liver."

That same fall of 1923 there was another pernicious anaemia patient, a woman, much worse than the first one, and Minot gave her the same directions, exactly. He admits he had no faith in it. He knew they were finished. What a lousy disease! It didn't fool Minot but certainly fooled the poor devils who had it, the way they'd come back to him hopeful, smiling. It was grim the way nature let you down. Of course nature lets us all down finally but with this melting away of the blood it was terrible the way it let its victims down after giving them hope. Downhill this woman's blood would go, her blood getting thinner and thinner till it would hardly flow when Minot would next jab her finger for the blood film. Downhill all these doomed ones would go, their illness sometimes starving them, other times paralyzing them, making them all weaker and weaker till at last it let them off from their terror and worry at their weakness by a merciful torpor, killing them, killing all of them.

Again these two liver-diet people left the top of Minot's thoughts with him busy at his cancer researches at the Huntington. Cancer . . . that was surely a hopeless game too, yet you could save lots of cancer sufferers if you got them early. . . .

Now these two people came back to him again, one after another . . .

Hel-*lo!* By Jingo! Here were *both* of them feeling better . . .

"Yes, Doctor, I feel better than for a long time," the very sick woman said.

Both these folks' blood was certainly on the up for red blood corpuscles and wasn't it funny the way those patients said they could *feel* themselves upping before ever you could

count significantly more corpuscles in their blood? But they'd
be relapsing again, sure . . .

"Will you please try eating liver every day?" Minot asked
them. "Please *weigh it out*. Weigh it out and be sure to eat
one hundred and twenty-five grams of it—that's around a
quarter of a pound—every day," Minot said.

Wasn't it too bad that most pernicious anaemia folks were
so finical about eating? If they'd only eat, then he really
could try dieting them. And liver! Liver was no kind of
grub. "I myself don't like liver," Minot said.

Now again these two patients, a week or two apart, came
walking back to Minot's office and they came in with a
strange new pep in their step and the tips of their ears were
a little pink now and there was just the beginning of a pink-
ish flush in their faces that had been for such a long time so
waxy. . . .

"It's wonderful how my appetite's coming back," one said.
"I can eat now, Doctor," the other said. "My tongue's quit
being sore."

So it went all during 1924, Minot, as he told me long
after, "not thinking much about it," but pretty soon here
were ten pernicious anaemia patients Minot was telling to
eat so many grams of red meat, just so much fruit, such and
such quantity of green vegetables, very little food rich in
fat . . .

"And at least a quarter of a pound of liver every day,"
Minot insisted.

It was all peculiarly illogical. He admitted he hadn't then
really sold himself on it. Yet when these ten folks, some of
them, didn't like liver, he kept kidding them into eating it.
With their appetites finicky, their insides upset, their tongues
raw and sore, Minot cajoled them. He looked in cook books
to find tasty ways to prepare liver and wrote out appalling
directions for them with his everlasting exactness and when
they bucked at it there was a strange blaze in his eyes, a

quick darting turn of his head with Minot glaring at them. "Be sure to take that liver," Minot said. And they took it.

"And yet I was still lukewarm about it . . ." Minot admitted.

Late winter of 1925 . . . the bunch were all alive. Some should have been dying and some should have been down very low with blood thinning and thinning. Some had already been down to as low as one and a half million red corpuscles to the cubic millimeter of their blood—which should have five million, when healthy. But look at them now. Here they were, two million eight hundred thousand; three million two hundred thousand; three million eight hundred thousand . . .

Here was one, by Jingo, with better than four million red cells to the cubic millimeter and that was beginning to get close to what any healthy man had! And here they were, feeling better, and looking not so deadly waxy, and Minot— not yet realizing what it meant in the top of his thoughts but only way down maybe in the sub-cellar—kept insisting more liver, keep eating liver, be sure you don't forget your liver, eat your liver every day . . .

That was maybe the one absolute difference between George R. Minot and any other doctor in the world. Other doctors might have said, "A little liver now and then might be good for you. . . ."

VIII

Also any other doctor, especially a really scientific one, might have said about all these people feeling so much better: "Ah . . . a most peculiar coincidence. . . . Oh . . . a most instructive coincidence."

Against each one of these ten he could put some other poor devil out of his past vast experience with pernicious anaemia, who'd come back smiling with his blood getting thicker, and then . . . But wait—here were *ten* of them, all at once, all mending. . . . But Minot was too cagy to trust

such embryo statistics, knew the ill always had its ups and
downs before killing its victims. . . . But didn't he know
deep in him below mere logical thinking that *this* was different—so many all at the same time all on the up, all more
peppy? All with color and hope in their faces, all going
strong with thicker blood, all together? . . . But against
this loomed a thousand facts saved up in the storehouse of .
his head by the bitterness of twelve years of watching people
die. . . . There was only the stark fact of these ten now
living, now better . . .

"I did not talk about it at that time because I didn't
think it was anything to talk about. I hadn't become en-
thused . . ." Minot said.

So he just fed them more liver.

IX

Minot said it was Murphy who gave him the first real enthusiasm. William P. Murphy was not today's notion of a
medical scientist but just a young doctor five years out who
wasn't from Boston's Back Bay like Minot but who, like
Minot, had a yen to study blood sicknesses. Murphy was just
a Congregational clergyman's son born in New York State
who had got to Boston via Wisconsin and Oregon—which
made it no easier. Minot now hinted to Murphy about things
happening to these ten patients, sort of offhand asking him
to try a special diet on pernicious anaemia patients who
were then in a very bad way in the Peter Bent Brigham
Hospital. It was tough for Murphy at first.

He couldn't get nice liver. It was hard to get anything
from the hospital commissary but beef liver that was too
tough to be tasty even for well people, let alone those desperately sick. You understand the hospital generally served
its patients excellent food but buying liver for these folks
every day was, well—it was just downright poppycock. It was
dietetically ridiculous!

Here was a great break for Minot: Murphy was what you'd call a liver-fiend, ate liver for the fun of it. That made him a fine liver salesman and what his goods lacked in tastiness he made up by his enthusiasm. "I certainly had to sell those folks liver-eating . . ." Murphy admitted. It was all a business of Murphy liking liver and absolutely obeying Minot— it was that *against* the academic knowledge, the science of the very scientific Peter Bent Brigham Hospital. For eight months, from May till autumn, 1925, it wasn't easy . . .

But right off Murphy began getting as excited as such a slow-talking, phlegmatic young man can get. People he knew should have been dying, should have been actually dead, began to get hungry, began to get up and walk, began actually to beg for more liver because they themselves felt it was liver. It was fantastic.

It was marvelous the way Minot kept it under his hat— it was hardly human. He belonged to a dinner club of the best medical brains of Boston—very able highbrow men— and here it was February, 1926, and here they all were at Minot's house, with after dinner Minot telling them the scientific work he was right then doing. He didn't even then peep a word about liver. He talked about lympho-blastoma. He did show them a chart showing the extremely peculiar fact that the red blood corpuscles of pernicious anaemia people got back to normal size when their red blood count rose to five million.

Not one man there asked him how in the world pernicious anaemia people ever got blood counts of five million. . . .

This was at a time when many people who should have been dead were up working and walking. . . .

Now rumors began to be whispered. Minot's close friend James Howard Means of Massachusetts General Hospital came to Minot asking him: "Have you heard of the remarkable work some one is doing with liver-feeding for pernicious anaemia at the Brigham?"

Absolute, unbiased respect for hard facts—that was Minot's scientific religion, and now he had a perfect check on his own first astonishing results. Murphy hadn't known Minot's own astounding observations. . . .

It took guts and shrewdness for Minot to check himself that way but now he was ready for any skeptical friend who might come arguing. "But, George," one friend asked, "why *liver?*"

Pernicious anaemia couldn't be a disease like rickets or scurvy that you get from lack of vitamins. Nobody eats much liver regularly so it can't come from *lack* of liver, so how can just eating liver fix it?

By now Minot and Murphy had jumped the quarter of a pound they'd been feeding their patients up to half a pound of liver a day; all of their patients were every day eating more liver than ever . . .

"But, George," friends admonished him, "it can't be just liver. It can't be so simple!" And many cautioned him to go easy about publishing it.

Now Minot and Murphy fed more and more liver up to all that their suffering patients could stand. It wasn't enough for Minot that they should merely feel better. He jammed liver into them until they really felt grand. It tasted awful to a lot of them. But Murphy asked them what matter— when they all felt new strength, new life surging through them again? Murphy was the boy to point that out to the finicky ones. For a science so crude it was wonderful how exact it was. It worked on every pernicious anaemia patient except those wretches so far gone they couldn't eat anything at all. In the first two years four died that way and it was hell to lose them.

Then a woman patient came along. She asked Murphy

was it absolutely necessary for liver to be cooked? Couldn't they mash liver into a pulp, fresh, and feed it, semi-liquid, in orange juice? Minot and Murphy didn't mind it that this woman wasn't a medical professor. . . .

Now sick people came to the Peter Bent Brigham Hospital *in extremis,* absolutely at the end of their tether. They came with their blood ten times thinner than it should be. They came in with next to no blood at all. They were brought in on stretchers, unconscious. Now Minot and Murphy sat by their beds. They poured fresh pulped liver down them through stomach tubes. They kept pouring it down that way for two, three, four, five days. They didn't give up though this fellow's breathing was so faint you could hardly detect it. They kept pouring liver down the stomach tube so long as there was still faint beating of that woman's heart. They didn't stop so long as there was still the tiny flick of these folks' eyelids. They stuck at it till all these doomed ones' eyes opened with them so near dead they could hardly move their heads. They stayed by those bedsides feeding liver and liver and more liver and saw life come back into those lost ones whose eyes opened, whose lips began moving, at last, to whisper that they felt a little bit better. . . .

In a week they were sitting up clamoring for something to eat. In less than two weeks they were wanting to walk.

x

Now finally in 1926 Minot's discovery came out of the obscure fogs of the primitive into the spotlight of the eminently respectable. Before that same gravely scientific body at frivolous Atlantic City, where Macleod had set fire to the shirt-tails of medical dignitaries by his description of Banting's discovery, Minot now told about how he and Murphy had saved folks with liver. He wanted to call his report "Treatment of Pernicious Anaemia with Liver." His advisors—with that caginess inseparable from modern science—

got him to tone down his title so that he called it "treatment by a special diet."

At the end of his speech a rustle of decorous excitement ran through the assembly. What, weren't any of these people dead?

After the meeting Minot slipped back upstairs in a hurry to his hotel room to his wife. "I grabbed my figures and charts. I went all over them," Minot said. "I could hardly believe, myself, that all I had told them was true."

Now Minot had refined his discovery from its original stark crudeness into a science that had an exact arithmetic, a lovely precision about it. You remember how, back in those sad days when pernicious anaemia was so inexorably fatal, there were times when, for no reason, the victims felt better. During these remissions of sickness you remember how Minot had peered through his microscope to see the hopeful, blue-networked young blood cells—*reticulocytes*—begin to swarm in the blood of the doomed ones who for a short time felt better. . . .

But now it was marvelous. Now he fed folks liver. Now before ever their blood began to get thicker, at the very moment they felt strangely better, Minot could count these same hopeful reticulocytes that poured from their bone marrow into the blood of these sick people. It was mathematical. It was too regular to be medical! It was exact, like physical chemistry. The more desperately low in blood cells the blood of his patients, the higher the curve of the count of these reticulocytes would go—*within five days after Minot began stuffing them with liver.* . . .

This test proved scientifically that these people were right when they thought they felt better. It was the first sign that a sufferer's sick bone marrow was back at its old job of making new blood. It was a super-accurate yard stick to measure the possible life-saving power of this or that substitute for liver—and to measure it quickly, in a few days, so you'd not risk very sick patients' lives. It was desperately necessary to find such a substitute, because many folks' stomachs got absolutely fed up with liver, liver, liver—no matter how tender or tasty.

Unable to stick with it they'd begin sliding downhill again. . . .

It was fundamental that there was some mysterious lack in the machinery of all pernicious anaemia people, that to make up for it they had to eat liver and keep on eating it and eat lots of it.

XI

Now Minot's test for reticulocytes made this hunt for liver substitutes easier. In a few days you could tell whether this or that food, or such and such a shot in the arm, had a blood-building wallop in it. Now real scientists became excited about Minot's discovery. Now Professor Edwin J. Cohn—of the department of physiology of Harvard University Medical School—began digging into liver to try to find out what this mysterious life-saving "X" in liver might be. . . . He found you could get rid of a lot of the liver but have an extract left that was really life-saving. . . .

Minot and Murphy fed extract after extract that came from Cohn's purely scientific investigation, to patient after patient with pernicious anaemia. They peered through their microscopes day after day at the thin blood of these people to see if this or that extract would set their sick bone marrow to working. They peered, looking for those hopeful reticulocytes. . . .

What were folks going to do who got so fed up with liver that finally they'd die rather than go on eating it? It was tantalizing, and more than a little bit ghastly.

Cohn did give them extracts that weren't too hard to take, that were loaded with enough life-saving "X" so that you had to take mighty little each day to keep you alive. But these extracts cost plenty of money and already it was plain that, in our country, there wasn't a chicken for every dinner bucket. . . .

What could folks do who hadn't money enough a day to spend for extract to keep them from dying?

These grim questions—though not purely scientific—gripped Minot and Murphy. . . .

Murphy with a young medical student assistant, named Bowie, began cooking soups from liver, simmering down soup extracts to try to get a lot of liver into a little bit of soup very easy to swallow. Then Bowie went over to help Dr. William B. Castle who worked with Minot at the Thorndike Memorial Laboratory and now for the comfort and the lives of poverty-plagued pernicious anaemia people Bill Castle and Bowie cooked up a simple home brew.

Castle who is really a fantastic combination of simple horse sense, plain doctor, and deeply original searcher, now put his head to work on the liver extract science of Professor Edwin J. Cohn—of the department of physical chemistry in the laboratory of physiology in Harvard University Medical School. Bill Castle, in whose long lanky body there's no scintilla of scientific snootiness, admitted it was one of his woman patients who gave him his hunch. Now out of the complicated science of Cohn's "X" hunt, Castle cooked up a liver broth that tasted like beef broth. . . .

You could make it tasty out of liver so tough, so cheap, you'd think it fit for no better than dogs. . . .

Even the poorest folks could boast a meat grinder, fruit jar, a couple of sauce pans, some cloth of the kind you use to strain jelly, and a tumbler. . . .

Castle's home brew had a blood-building, life-saving kick that was as powerful as the fanciest calves' liver. . . .

Even the poorest people, hanging onto life as it's the right of even poor people to do, could rake up twenty cents a day for tough beef liver, to live, to work again.

XII

That's what is finest about this gang of Boston doctors—
the way they didn't stay piddling in their laboratories re-
fining Minot's crude discovery into a thing of sterile, infernal
academicism. They got it down as fast as they could to the
roots of humanity, down to the lower five, to the sad needs
of the humblest women and men.

The end of their adventures is by a long shot not yet, and
can't be told in this book of men against death, because it's
going on right now. Minot's simple little test of counting
those hopeful blue-networked young red blood cells now
started searchers all over to deeper, stranger discoveries, so
that the end of Minot's story grows surer, happier. Of these
new adventures the discoveries of Bill Castle are the most
bizarre and the deepest. Bill wondered and wondered what
was at the bottom of the strange failure of sick bone marrow
to make blood. . . .

He had a hunch that it's the stomach—of all things!—that's
responsible. Old copper-gizzard drunks often develop pernicious anaemia. . . . Folks whose stomachs had been completely taken out for cancer, and who by some miracle live,
then die of pernicious anaemia. . . . Do *normal* stomachs
make something out of food, some "X" that then goes
through the blood to start the bone marrow making new
blood?

Castle had no laboratory animals to try it on. Laboratory
animals don't get pernicious anaemia. Only human animals
get it. But Bill Castle was in a most peculiar sense not one
of your kept scientists—so he turned himself into his own
experimental animal. . . .

In an awful experiment torturing himself and laughing
about it he lent his own healthy stomach to pernicious anaemia sufferers. Every day, day after day, week after week, on
an empty stomach in the morning Bill Castle ate rare ham-

burger steak, then a little later put his finger down his throat until . . .

Presto! Yes—he had it, no doubt of it! Out of this chopped meat his stomach did make the mysterious "X." . . . Because, fed to sufferers with their blood terribly thin from pernicious anaemia, the result of the experiment Castle had carried on in his own body brought the reticulocytes swarming again into those people's arteries . . . just as liver itself would bring them.

Now Dr. Sharpe of Parke, Davis & Co., and Dr. Sturgis and Dr. Isaacs, who have a really elegant pernicious anaemia laboratory at the University of Michigan, turned Castle's self-torture to human use. They invented ventriculin, dried powdered pig stomach, that's as powerful against pernicious anaemia as liver is, and tastier. . . .

And Castle's gone on, and found that, if you shoot a certain one of those scientific liver extracts of Professor Cohn's into the blood of people with pernicious anaemia, its blood-building effect is enormously more powerful than when they just eat it. . . .

And now Castle, and Sturgis and Isaacs, have proved how pernicious anaemia people can come once a month or once every six weeks to a hospital or a doctor's office. A little shot of extract into their arm veins—and now they don't have to eat liver, or ventriculin, or cook up a daily home brew of liver at all, to stay healthy, and working. . . .

So far as I know, this is the first utterly incurable ill in all history for which men against death have found something really life-saving. It is what is called a colossal advance in medical science but when you boil it all down it was just pure Minot.

DOG NO. 33—"*The female, black and white, somewhat collie dog had lived seventy days . . . sixty days ago she should have been dead.*"

MINOT—*"He was a true man against death."*

BOOK II

RED BRICK BUILDING
ON THE HILL

4. SPENCER

IN THE HAPPY VALLEY

"*To the memory of our fellow laboratory workers who, while engaged in the study of Rocky Mountain spotted fever, have contracted the disease and died.*"
Hygienic Laboratory Bulletin No. 154

ON a hill in Washington, D. C., overlooking the Potomac River, there is a long, low, red brick building with a ramshackle charm that makes it unique among today's elegant laboratories.

From other laboratories have come maybe more "far-reaching" discoveries. In no other have I met searchers who so fetch me by the don't-give-a-damn way they face their most dangerous enterprises. The laboratory is odoriferously untidy. The workers are really just plain scientific firemen ready at the drop of a hat to snuff out this death or that.

The deaths they fight are often little ones that are not spectacular, not threatening any great part of our people. The folks they save are often *unimportant*. Yet among the comrades in this red brick building there's an understanding —never openly expressed nor advertised—that it's not only necessary but actually desirable to risk your skin on trivial pestilences not affecting the national death rate.

Spring, 1922. . . . Spencer of the U. S. Public Health Service was ordered to proceed from this Hygienic Laboratory to the Bitter Root Valley in western Montana. There, each Spring while life was awakening, a particular ghastly death came to certain hunters, ranchers. But why should

119

anybody be ordered to waste time with the riddle of Rocky Mountain spotted fever? It killed each year but a few—and those mainly hill-billies—of that happy valley.

Fewer (so wrote an indignant Bitter Root doctor) than died of measles in one month in the city of Butte. Solid Bitter Root citizens derided the thought of this malady endangering the prosperity of their valley which was a garden spot for cows and strawberries.

True enough, you'd find spots in the foothills on the western slope where little log ranch houses stood empty with doors hanging open. The creak and whine of the hinges of these doors—if you had imagination—sang dirges for forgotten ranchers who'd gone suddenly black and died from the spotted fever. But their number was negligible and their importance in the Bitter Root body politic debatable. So why bother?

Spring, '22. . . . Spencer packed up his microbe-hunting tools and his wife and two babies in Washington. It's true the spotted fever was in its localized way pretty nasty. Some years it killed every man who caught it. In 1912 it had sneaked into McClintic of Spencer's own service, got McClintic while he hunted it near Sweathouse Creek. Every year it took at least eight out of every ten, yet there were few years when more than ten in all came down with it. So what of it?

The Montana doctor, McCray, had tried to find a serum to guard his fellow citizens and one morning woke up with bloodshot eyes and an ache in his bones. In ten days McCray had gone West to join McClintic. Yet (so thought serious Bitter Root citizens) it was nothing to get het up about. Talking about it hurt business. You were safe so long as you didn't have to go up certain west slope canyons. That was science enough.

Now here getting off the train was Passed Assistant Surgeon R. R. Spencer (Spenny in the Service) with his wife, two babies. There were certainly no brass bands blaring a welcome at the railroad station in Hamilton. He was only a not eminent cub microbe hunter out here to dabble—as usual—at an ill that sneaked into sometimes as few as five folks in one year. People who had to, or who idiotically wanted, you understand, to go into those canyons.

They would come back and then pretty soon break out with red-purple blotches all over them. In a few days their delirious screams would gurgle into silence with them dying as if an invisible hand had choked them.

But lately the brother and sister-in-law of Montana's governor had gone up into those lovely foothills in the Spring, with white water foaming over the banks of the little rivers, with the sap stirring the cottonwoods into Spring's first promise. They came down and in ten days they were dead.

So here was Spencer, hardly more than a scientific greenhorn and death-fighting tenderfoot, hunting for a hole for an emergency laboratory in Hamilton.

II

He was met by R. R. Parker, who was not a doctor of medicine at all but a doctor of bug-hunting, of large bugs, mind you, not of microbes. This fever killed so mighty few folks there was nothing to get hysterical about, yet (so decided the solid people of Hamilton) you never could tell. So Spencer and Parker set up their laboratory in an abandoned schoolhouse a mile and a half outside the town. It was too far for the fiercest microbe to jump.

Our tyros had one good fact for a take-off: you only get the spotted death if you're bit by wood ticks. Parker had worked for seven years as an entomologist in Montana. Outside his routine humdrum, bug-mapping activities, Parker had got sucked into a fanatic yen to unravel the spotted fever riddle.

In their bare schoolhouse lab Parker and Spencer now

fumbled at plans. Why was it nobody ever caught spotted death from wood ticks in the hills on the *eastern* slopes of the Bitter Root? The ticks were no different!

This business of the ticks being the criminals had first been discovered by two plain practicing doctors of Boise, Idaho, where there was spotted fever, too, only not so deadly as the fever in the Bitter Root. The Idaho fever killed only five out of every hundred it hit. This (probably) justified the strange human experiment by which these doctors, Mc-Calla and Brereton, now proceeded to slake their curiosity. . . .

They pulled a tick off the chest of a man bad with Idaho spotted fever and stuck it onto the arm of a fellow in the hospital with both feet amputated following frost-bite gangrene. They then took that tick—already fat and well-fed—and stuck it onto the leg of the fellow's wife. ". . . With full knowledge and consent of the patients," explained McCalla and Brereton.

It was the good luck of their two now absolutely forgotten human experimental animals to be in the ninety-five percent bracket of people who didn't die. . . .

Such was the outlandish beginning of spotted fever tick science. Now, in Hamilton, Parker asked Spencer how come that only the *west* side of the Bitter Root was dangerous? Why, on the west side, were only certain canyons deadly, with others perfectly safe?

It was an excellent scientific question. Long ago the famous microbe hunter, Ricketts of Chicago, had given them the tools to try to answer it. Because he'd overworked himself microbe hunting, Ricketts had come out for a rest to Missoula, and promptly had gone to working the moment his eyes lit on the mystery of certain unfortunates—gasping and black with spotted death. In two weeks Ricketts had this savage doom multiplying in guinea-pigs . . . then in monkeys.

Now Parker had a hunch. Was it maybe that, in the deadly canyons, there was one special kind of wild animal, one kind of rodent in which the fever virus smoldered? Now in their schoolhouse Parker unfolded vast plans to Spencer. . . .

Ricketts had done a lot for them. He'd gone (for his health, mind you) up into those lovely canyons for ticks. He'd found how, via those ticks, he could keep the death going from guinea-pig to guinea-pig *ad infinitum*. He'd plunged (for his vacation) into vast dangerous fooling with guinea-pigs, ticks, and monkeys. He'd gone into nasty little valleys avoided by your most hard-bitten cowman, combing the horses, cows, bulls, steers, rabbits, bushes, and sage-brush, looking for ticks *that might be infected in nature*. . . .

He'd found them. So he proved it. But that had done nothing to keep these people from dying.

III

Why were only certain of these west side canyons dangerous? Was it maybe some peculiarity of the country? Parker, who was an extremely systematic and energetic man, now cooked up vast plans to photograph every nook and corner of these canyons from airplanes, to get ticks off every kind of bird and beast of those hills and valleys, to find out just what particular kind of rodent secretly harbored the fatal virus—and so gave it to ticks. It was really a fantastic project!

It was all like looking for one needle in endless haystacks. It was hardly more practical than the sad project on which McClintic (of the red brick building on the hill) had years before met his doom. To wipe out the spotted death you had to get rid of all ticks, argued McClintic. Young ticks, just hatched, could only keep alive, grow, by sucking the blood of the small wild animals that lived in the hills—so McClintic reasoned. With three or four crack shots easy to find in the valley, McClintic had shot, trapped, and poisoned pine squirrels, rock squirrels, and gophers. He'd hunted down yellow-bellied chipmunks, cotton-tail, and jack rabbits. He'd poured carbon bisulphide down prairie dog holes, in this wild country that was a bottomless zoo for every kind of big and small wild rodent you could think of. At last one morning he'd woke up shivering with pains shooting up and down his bones. He'd looked at his wrists. Then he'd hopped a train East, got back to Washington in time to see his wife—on the day he died of the Rocky Mountain spotted fever. . . .

For a disease so negligible as this spotted fever undoubtedly was, the State of Montana spent a great deal of money. They tried to get the ranchers of the Bitter Root to dip all their horses and cattle to destroy full-grown ticks, while the crack shots and poisoners kept trying to rid the whole valley of rodents to exterminate the little seed ticks. They'd given Dr. McCray money to try to work out a serum. He'd got a little scratch on one of his hands. He'd died of the spotted death before he faced how fantastic it was to think of finding a serum for a death so inexorable.

And all the time the ticks of the Bitter Root crawled, grew, multiplied, made meals of blood off the inexhaustible thousands of gophers, squirrels, rabbits, that kept pouring out of Montana, Idaho, Wyoming, into Bitter Root Valley. And every spring hill men went into those west side hills in the line of their duty and you know what happened to them. And in New York in the safe Rockefeller Institute the now forgotten Japanese helper working with Noguchi to find a vaccine passed out quietly (but horribly) and was buried (so far as I know) without honors paid to soldiers. All efforts seemed silly. Get the ticks out of the country? It was like carrying sand in a sieve. . . .

And now here was Parker with his project of spotting the real fever reservoir, the special fever-carrying rodent.

While Spencer fumbled at fixing up the schoolhouse laboratory, Parker the bug hunter started up into the hills. He had big Henry Cowan to help him. Cowan was scared of nothing and looked more like a grizzly bear than a man, and to help Cowan there was Salsbury, who was a Christian Scientist, and didn't believe in death. Now the three of them climbed up into the deadly Blodgett Canyon.

Slowly through the brush and the brambles they slogged their way. Ahead of them they waved white outing flannel flags. Slowly they went, brushing with those flags the bushes ahead of them, up the Blodgett Canyon, and further up. On the branches of the bushes all round them the ticks were waiting. The ticks were stirred from their winter's sleep by the March sun and were hungry for blood. The ticks held onto the branches by their middle legs. They waved their fore and hind legs grotesquely, ready to grab onto anything moving. Parker, Cowan, and Salsbury covered their white flags with these eight-legged varmints. . . .

Every now and then they took off their shirts (even Salsbury who didn't believe in death) and peered all over each other's naked skins. Every evening they carried writhing masses of these blood-hungry ticks in pill boxes back to Spencer. Every night going to bed they looked at themselves naked, searched themselves all over.

Now here sat Spencer among boxes full of this sinister crawling harvest that Parker and his men had been gathering. Were all of these ticks deadly . . . or any?

Now they bumped into a new fact that blew Parker's tick-survey project to smithereens, or at least chased it from their heads for years, and set the whole pack of them off on a hot scent, a microbe hunt as fantastic as any you could imagine. It all started from a certain laziness inherent in Spencer, or, maybe, you'd call it his knack for experimental short-cuts. Spencer's job, you see, was to test out—for Rocky Mountain spotted fever—all the ticks his bug-hunting pals flagged out of Blodgett Canyon. It was the devil of a nuisance. . . .

It was an infernal bother to shave so many guinea-pigs.

shake each lot of ticks into a sticky, writhing ball of bug life, plank each lot onto a separate guinea-pig's shaved belly, fasten them down under brass gauze held in place by a big band of adhesive tape. . . .

Then you had to wait days, weeks, watching for your guinea-pigs to show signs of fever. . . .

Why not mash up each lot Parker brought him, in a mortar, and shoot this tick soup into guinea-pigs, simply, with a syringe? So argued Spencer. It wouldn't take half the time, said Spencer (making no remark about its being also much less labor). Already he'd dabbled at a little experiment that made it look as if shooting this stuff in was, maybe, surer. . . .

In addition to a dreamy indolence, there was about this drawly Virginian (Spenny in the Service) a contrariness, a going at things in a not standardized way; he was a sort of mental southpaw. Now he tried just shooting these mashed-up ticks into guinea-pigs—though this was, God knew, not the way ticks gave man or beast the spotted death in nature. Spencer now set himself down to the dull job of shooting one hundred and one batches of wood ticks that Parker had brought down (carefully labeled) from one hundred and one meticulously marked more or less deadly spots in that canyon into one hundred and one guinea-pigs. . . .

It was a magnificent failure.

Not one of these creatures so much as batted an eye. Mind you, under the skins of these animals had gone great masses of ticks from those very places where men had gone, a few from year to year, to come back and a few days later begin to shiver with the first hint that the spotted murderer had got inside them.

There was something peculiar about it, too, and never before heard of. When they tried to kill those guinea-pigs with a red-hot deadly virus of spotted fever—which they kept running through guinea-pigs in their laboratory—those tick-tested pigs were immune! What could be at the bottom of it? Why should the ticks from the deadly Blodgett guard beasts instead of kill them?

Here was the short-cut, a washout, thought Spencer, and Spencer's the first to admit that the whole business might have fallen into a limbo of scientific failure right there—but for Parker. That bugologist was a most systematic man. He was a precise, saving man, and so it came about that certain ones of each of those one hundred and one batches of ticks were put back, each lot neatly and precisely labeled, into the ice-box by Parker. He knew the experiment was a fizzle and there is no reason for his having saved those ticks—excepting that he just naturally didn't like to throw anything away.

IV

Now big Henry Cowan's famous mountain goat turned Spencer's experiment from a flop into a find utterly new and fantastic. Henry Cowan and Elmer Greenup were in Blodgett Canyon tick-hunting and it is not recorded whether Parker had asked Henry to try to bring back a mountain goat or whether Henry popped him off for the fun of it. Anyway, here came Henry in the laboratory with that momentous goat slung across his enormous shoulders. Parker was a fiend for ticks from all over. . . .

Here sit Henry and Elmer Greenup, at the monkeyish job of picking wood ticks out of that dead goat's hair. These ticks were exactly the same as the ticks they'd flagged off the bushes—excepting this: *that these goat ticks were fat with fine meals of blood while the bush ticks were flat, dry, bloodless.*

It seemed silly to test these goat ticks: no mountain goat ever gets Rocky Mountain spotted fever, nor was there any record of anybody ever discovering this fever sleeping in the blood of a goat, *carried* by a goat. But Parker was all for testing every conceivable tick from every bush, bird or beast. . . .

Here's Spencer, now, bending over a mortar, mashing the goat ticks Henry and Elmer give him, into a nice tasty-looking soup. . . . There seemed no special reason to be careful. Now into the bellies of guinea-pigs goes the goat tick soup.

In three days the fever of all those guinea-pigs is registering 105 and goes on up to 106 and they all die . . . all of them.

That snaps Spencer out of his dreaminess. Now the school-house laboratory begins to buzz with plans for curious, never-before-heard-of experiments. The flat bloodless ticks from the bushes never hurt a guinea-pig when you inject them. The blood-filled ticks from the goat are terrifically deadly. Both ticks come from the same dangerous spot in the Blodgett Canyon. How come the difference?

Does the fever sleep in the ticks in the wilds while they lie frozen in Montana winter? Does their first thirsty drink of blood in the spring air stir this fever virus from something harmless (and even sometimes protective) into something horrible, deadly? It was because they were only gropers, naïve, scientifically *ignorant*, that they could hazard such a silly theory.

Now, from one of those batches of ticks that Parker had flagged off the bushes, that Spencer had found harmless and wanted to throw away, that Parker had put back in the ice-box for no reason but his inherent savingness—

Now Spencer went back to one of those carefully labeled pill-boxes. From this pill-box he and Gettinger shook out a mass of those harmless varmints. They dumped them onto the shaved belly of a guinea-pig, and imprisoned them under brass gauze held down with a big wide adhesive tape, and it was droll the way the head and behind of this guinea-pig, sticking out, made him look like a ridiculous little animated dumbbell. For three days those ticks (hidden under the wire gauze) went on a jag of hot healthy guinea-pig blood till they were swollen to near coffee-bean size. . . .

Now Spencer putters over this guinea-pig that he and Bill Gettinger have turned into a tick cafeteria. Spenny and Bill work bare-handed and why not? . . . those ticks are absolutely not dangerous. Together they pick the blood-glutted ticks off their experimental rodent who squeaks absurdly. Bare-handed they drop those ticks fat with blood into a mortar to grind them up in a little salt water. Now big Bill keeps new healthy guinea-pigs from kicking and writhing. Spencer (looking like his nickname of Spenny) sends his syringe needle jab-jab-jabbing shots of this tick soup into them.

Together they smile a little maybe at the annoyed squeak of these guinea-pigs. . . .

But in three days the sleek coats of these beasts have roughened with them hot with high fever and getting thin so fast they seem melting away, literally, and in a few more days they die. They all die unheard-of rapidly.

They've turned their wild guess into a new fact. . . . By one meal of healthy guinea-pig blood a harmless tick turns —suddenly—into something not too gentle. But what of it?

v

The first fumblings of March were a memory now and here it was July with all of them veteran searchers and with it hot in their schoolhouse (walled off as it was from the breeze by the mountains). They were all of them taut. They were going like a house afire proving again and again this fact of the blood-meal turning those ticks suddenly nasty.

For conquering the spotted death this fact had no discernible importance. To them this didn't matter. They were all of them tasting the salty tang of finding out that what they'd bumped into by accident the first time, worked like clockwork every time, again, again . . . that it was true.

Bill Gettinger was not the least excited of the lot. He was only a lab swipe. He was saving up every cent he could scrimp from the support of his mother to bring true his dream of becoming a doctor. He was crazy to be a full-fledged searcher, like Parker, Spencer. What luck now for Bill to be up to his elbows (bare-handed) in ticks and guinea-pigs. In his bones he felt he was helping these great men (great to Bill Gettinger) make scientific history. That chance came to few pre-medic boys. Didn't Bill know it? And wasn't he making the most of it!

Now it was one of those hot days that are in Montana but Bill was shivering. This hot day Bill was slow on the pick-up, and heavy in the arms and weary in the legs. Spencer thought it a bit funny. "Bill was a hog for work, a great helper," Spencer said.

Bill didn't like to tell Spencer about those new little shivers. Just a few days before with Spencer he'd been pulling those blood-glutted ticks off a guinea-pig. Spencer'd caught Bill picking at a no-account pimple on his neck. . . .

"Be careful. Remember what we've had our hands into," Spencer'd warned him. But ticks were only dangerous when they settled down to make a meal off you. . . .

Bill had looked at his hands. "Oh, hell, that's all right, Doctor, I've washed 'em," Bill said. Bill was powerful, a miniature edition of Henry Cowan.

But now today in the heat Bill's teeth were chattering with him feeling seedier and his arms hanging and his thoughts going clotted and thicker. . . .

"Bones hurt you, Bill?" asked Spencer. He asked it off-handed. Bill laughed and said he'd be okay tomorrow. That night Spencer had a hard time sleeping.

Next morning Bill dragged himself out to the lab with his face a dull red and his eyes not liking the July sunlight. The laboratory wasn't buzzing. It was still.

The lot of them crowded round Bill and he stood there

with them telling him to keep his mouth shut and with him trying to laugh while they took his temperature.

"Let's have a look at your wrists, Bill," Spencer told him. Then they took him to the little hospital in Hamilton over the drugstore.

They had the devil of a time keeping Bill in bed up there. That night Spencer didn't sleep at all. "God-damn it! I'll fight it! I'll lick it!" Bill roared at them.

It now took much more than Spenny to hold him. Folks stopped each other on the street in Hamilton jerking their thumbs at the drugstore. Oughtn't to of brought that boy into town. . . .

"Give me that God-damned rabbit, there!" roared Bill Gettinger. His fever was up to 105 now and over. Bill blasted and damned imaginary ticks and guinea-pigs. . . .

He had an awful time, living his experiments over, chasing infected ticks that kept getting away from him and it seemed, sick though he was, that he was stronger than ever. . . .

Solid citizens of Hamilton stopped, hearing the struggling and roaring up there in the drugstore. Bad business . . . setting up a pest-house right here in the city. . . .

Six nights now Spencer'd had next to no sleep. It was tough to look at Bill's face and see Bill fighting to keep fear out of his face, and then go off raving again.

"Bill kept right on experimenting in his delirium, right up to the last day," said Spencer.

So Bill Gettinger didn't get to be a doctor after all. He'd had great luck, though, to taste the salt of working with Parker and Spencer.

According to the letter of its compensation law, the United States Government remembered Bill Gettinger's mother with a pension of fifteen—or is it thirty?—dollars a month. It was mighty fair of the Government. It was what Bill was contributing to his mother's support the day he absent-mindedly picked at the little sore on his neck.

Spencer and Parker weren't what you'd call popular. The Government ought to shut down the laboratory. Why—it was murder to ask anybody to work there.

Parker and Spencer tacked a plain sign up over their schoolhouse:

PERSONS ENTERING THESE PREMISES
DO SO AT THEIR OWN RISK!

They hired a helper in place of Bill Gettinger. They didn't laugh as much as they used to. They all settled down to multiply death around them.

VI

Mind you, they didn't then any of them dream how their deadly experiment was going to help them but they kept getting it down patter and patter doing it over illogically knowing it was important. Parker still stuck to his dream of the tick survey. Spencer didn't think much of that. But both of them grabbed at this or that silly straw, hoping. . . . Of course long ago Ricketts (a little while before he'd gone off to Mexico to meet his own death fighting the Mexican typhus —tabardillo) had turned on a faint ray of hope. He'd found if creatures once do pull through the spotted fever, they're *immune*.

He'd got a couple of monkeys who'd had one foot in the grave with it, and a few miserable guinea-pigs God had let get over it. Then he'd shot them with more deadly blood than you'd think their hides would hold. They'd none of them turned so much as a hair.

Of course Spencer knew it was idiotic to even dream of trying to immunize anybody by giving them a sickness they had eight chances out of ten of dying from. But here they had a little gleam of hope of their own. Here were those

COWAN—"—*more like a grizzly bear than a man.*"

FRANCIS—". . . *it's damned clumsy to work with rubber gloves.*"

unfed, flat ticks Parker and Henry Cowan had flagged off the bushes of the Blodgett, harmless. Those ticks Parker had saved in their pill-boxes—when shot into the hides of those one hundred and one guinea-pigs *before* their blood-meal— had mysteriously made twenty-nine of those one hundred and one guinea-pigs immune. How come?

But not even Spencer was bold enough to try shooting live ticks (even though unfed with blood) from dangerous places into ranchers and sheep-herders as a preventive.

Now Summer was gone and this Autumn Spencer and Parker turned their stove-heated four schoolhouse rooms into a zoo of every kind of baby, young, and adult tick. Those rooms held millions of wood ticks—some harmless, some with enough of the spotted death in them to lay low a hundred men. They launched into an immense experiment. . . .

Was it only a meal of healthy guinea-pig blood that had the power of turning an infected tick from something harmless into a being suddenly murderous? Would horse, cow, goat, ground-squirrel do the same? Or would it make the ticks gentler, maybe life-guarding?

In a sinister room lined with tiers of big cages swathed in shrouds of white cloth tied tight at the top they now raised thousands of baby "seed" ticks, little devils so tiny you could hardly see them. Now they infected these tick babies by tying them up in muslin bags to suck meals of blood from rabbits whose blood swarmed with the virus of the spotted death.

Then they'd untie the tops of the shrouds surrounding these cages. They'd reach into the canvas bottoms with their bare hands gathering up myriads of these crawling mites that (swollen with their deadly meals of blood) had dropped off the rabbits. They were never sure they'd collected every last one of these tiny varmints. . . . Always a few kept getting away from them. . . .

Those baby ticks were hardly bigger than pin-heads and

as fast as the wind. Spencer found it hard to keep up that nonchalant spirit traditional among his pals of the red brick building on the hill in Washington. Nights he dreamt of spilling boxes of blood-glutted infected ticks on his lab table. He'd scurry round (in his dream) trying to recover them. He couldn't get quite all of them. Then he'd wake up, sweating.

The hell of it was that the next morning he had to go back to reality that was nearly as bad as his dream.

Parker was an absolute tick wizard. Now for months they nursed those ticks they'd infected as babies on the rabbits, watching these seed ticks shed their strange white skins and molt into eight-legged nymphs, watching those nymphs drowse off into a mysterious sleep, then feed again on rabbits, and molt to full-fledged adults. Through all those months they'd watched the fever sleeping and waking to horrible deadliness after a blood-meal through all these stages of the tick's life cycle.

Parker was now a tick *maestro*. "Nights I kept dreaming there were ticks crawling all over me," Spencer said. Mornings he'd go to the laboratory and they'd all get into a sweat because here were certain dozens of dangerous insects not accounted for. Evenings they'd go home and find ticks (blood-filled) sticking to their clothes. One evening Spencer picked one of those ticks off one of his own babies at home.

I must explain that both Parker and Spencer were paid handsomely by our Government—four thousand dollars a year. It was enough to let them live pretty well in the happy valley where living is really cheap and with good practical sense they used what was over to take out a lot more life insurance. It is not on record whether they went into detail on their application blanks regarding the exact nature of their occupations.

All the time they were going great guns with their experiments. No doubt now: the blood of any kind of animal changed infected ticks with the fever sleeping in them into worse than big sticks of dynamite. It was the devil and all to keep track of all the ticks they put (under wire gauze covers) onto cows, goats, horses. The goats (being inherently the hungriest and least pernickety of mammals) were wonderful at getting the gauze tick houses off themselves, trying to eat adhesive tape, wire gauze, ticks and all—all the ticks that didn't get away from them. It was comical.

They finally fooled the goats by wiring the ticks on top their heads between their horns but not before the laboratory was a pest-hole outside as well as in. One Sunday afternoon the lab janitor's little boy came there. The old man had been told not to let the boy play in the lab so he made him play in the yard . . .

In a week the child lay burning with fever. He lay there all spotted. He was delirious and his breath came in gasps, then stopped, then came in feeble gasps again. "I don't understand how that kid pulled through," Spencer said. "I've never seen anybody come so near to dying. . . ."

This winter in the schoolhouse they all turned into a gang of experimenting gnomes, tick-obsessed and tick-haunted. The result of their insane enterprise to this date may be summed up by stating that they had succeeded in surrounding themselves with as vast a lot of crawling death as had been got together in any one laboratory—ever.

VII

Late in the Autumn of 1923 Spencer went back to the red brick building on the hill in Washington, carrying with him sundry sinister families of *Dermacentor andersoni* (highbrow name for wood tick) in pill-boxes. You may be sure he told no tall stories of the weird happenings in Hamilton to McCoy the director, to hard-boiled Eddie Francis, to that scientific Moses, Goldberger. To all of these veterans, danger of death was commonplace. None of them were worried in the least by Spencer's Rocky Mountain spotted fever ticks, not even by the ticks in certain momentous pill-boxes marked "Lot 2351B."

Parker held the fort in the schoolhouse in the deep snow in Hamilton and now in Washington and Hamilton they doubled their experiments. Parker could tell you the exact pedigree of any tick in any one of their array of pill-boxes. He'd become cunning at the tricky business of making a tick do in a laboratory what God had created him to do out-doors in nature. Now here was Spencer in a more or less smelly room in the red brick building on the hill. Gingerly he unpacked Lot 2351B—a devilish brood nursed all the way from innocent unhatched eggs to adult tickhood—infected.

For one hundred and twelve days Spencer had left these flat, bloodless ticks of Lot 2351B in the ice-box, hibernating, sleeping as they would have slept in the Blodgett snows in Montana in winter. Now it was January and out they came from their ice-box sleep. There they lay on his lab bench, flat, withered, curled up as if dead, not a leg stirring. It was six months since they'd sucked the deadly spotted fever blood from a rabbit in one of those cloth-shrouded cages. . . .

Spencer ground up a couple of these no-account-looking bugs in salt water and injected them into a couple of guinea-pigs. Of course—the fever was sleeping. The pigs squeaked, chittered, frisked, stayed perfectly happy.

January . . . but now he'd make an artificial Spring for them. He took two more withered bugs of Lot 2351B and stuck them in an incubator at human body temperature and at the end of a day saw them wiggle their eight legs in a strange awakening. Into two more guinea-pigs went these ticks mashed up in salt solution. Wait! What was this?

These two unlucky rodents began showing spotted fever. Just warming those ticks had begun to stir the sleeping death into action. . . .

Now Spencer incubating them set the legs of some more of these nasty little brothers and sisters of Lot 2351B to waving. Then he clamped them down on the shaved bellies of four healthy guinea-pigs. . . .

In three days Spencer pulled those now fat, blood-gorged bugs off the animals (who had already begun to look seedy). Each tick he held in a pair of forceps. He slashed each blood-swollen tick open with a slender knife. Each slash there was a spurt of blood. "Yes—I did get a spurt of that blood in my face, once," said Spencer.

Now Spencer ground the bodies of these ticks into an evil-looking paste. . . .

Five days later he came to the little room in the red brick building on the hill to see something astounding. Already the guinea-pigs he'd shot with these blood-filled ticks were on their sides, gasping, dying. It was twice as fast as it usually takes the spotted death to make away with an animal! Never had any man seen such devastating power in the living poison of spotted fever.

In one measly tick there was enough living poison to kill three thousand guinea-pigs. It took one hundred ticks to make up one gram weight. . . . One gram of the blood virus of spotted fever (kept going in guinea-pigs) never could kill more than a thousand animals. . . . One gram of these mashed-up ticks of Lot 2351B could do three hundred thousand to death. . . .

We may permit Spencer some small chills shooting up and down his spine at the thought of the stuff they'd been nursing (not realizing) this last year in the laboratory at Hamilton. It was not till he'd made these dilutions, these injections of exact amounts of less and less blood-glutted infected tick that he came face to face with the extraordinary death they'd all been hatching. Even now he didn't realize another fact yet more sinister:

The fever you multiply in ticks by giving them a blood

meal is far more savage than the fever you just keep going in guinea-pigs' bodies. The virus in the blood-drunk ticks can go through unbroken skin. . . .

Happy in his ignorance Spencer now sat wool-gathering over the scrawled record of the guinea-pig holocaust these Lot 2351B ticks had set going. Now suddenly a hunch flashed through him. . . .

A vaccine! Why not? What matter that nobody had ever been able to see the spotted fever microbes? What matter they'd never been able to culture this death in test-tubes? Why, of course. *These ticks were their test-tubes.* They'd multiplied the death—enormously—in ticks. . . .

Spring, 1924 . . . and now Spencer said good-by to the veterans of the red brick building on the hill and hurried back out to Montana to Parker in the schoolhouse near Hamilton. He knew that their danger (crudely multiplying this super-hot virus) was enormously greater than the danger from tick bites you got in nature. He knew now why many who went into those dangerous canyons came back unharmed—though tick-bitten. . . . The ticks had to stay on you, hours, days—your own healthy blood waking their virus to deadliness. . . .

This was not now what obsessed him. Now Spencer rushed to Parker with a hunch that really sounded ridiculous. They'd turn these ticks (super-deadly) into a life-guarding vaccine. Look at the enormous lot of hot virus he'd grown in those Lot 2351B ticks by that simple three-day meal of guinea-pig blood. . . . Well, why not pour a little weak carbolic acid on these mashed-up ticks, and then . . .

Well, maybe, but . . .

Spencer had some small scientific ground for his harebrained hunch. Breinl, the Austrian, this very year had guarded guinea-pigs from typhus fever by shooting them with typhus-infected lice that he'd dipped in carbolic acid. . . .

But of course you'd never get enough lice to turn them into a vaccine for full-grown people. The experiment was absolutely academic, not practical. Long ago, Ricketts (just before he'd gone to Mexico to die fighting tabardillo) had guarded a guinea-pig from spotted fever by shooting the beast with a blood-filled infected tick he had dipped in chloroform. But Ricketts hadn't lived long enough to find out whether this lone experiment was anything more than a happenstance.

Here was Spencer back in the schoolhouse absolutely mad to try his own scheme. There was good science to show that his carbolic vaccine idea was nonsense. Both Spencer and Parker knew when you killed the Rocky Mountain spotted virus in a *guinea-pig's* blood by germicides or by heating it, that the virus was absolutely no good for making animals immune.

But wait, expostulated the no longer dreamy or lazy Spencer. The virus when it grows in the ticks may be *different!* Wasn't it a fact that those unfed flat ticks off the bushes (before their blood-meal) once in a while guarded guinea-pigs against fatal virus?

Yet it was all preposterous. You'd never get people to let themselves be shot with this horrible brew of carbolic acid and ticks. . . . And, anyway, how'd you ever raise enough ticks to vaccinate all the threatened ranchers, hunters, sheepherders of the Bitter Root and the rest of the Northwest—whose duty or fancy took them to dangerous places?

In a week Spencer and all of them were up to their ears in Spencer's bizarre experiment.

VIII

"We all wanted to jump up and crack our heels together," Spencer said.

Here it was less than a month after he'd got back to Hamilton. There was a hectic week with all of them helping Spencer as he bent over his bench concocting dreadful stews of infected wood ticks, blood-gorged. Each little tick had the power to lay low five thousand guinea-pigs with spotted fever. Now Spencer adds carbolic acid up to one-half of one per-cent with that strange gang watching him and presto! This dangerous brew no longer looks so ugly. Next morning the gory mess of mashed-up ticks has settled out under the action of the carbolic. Over the sediment you see a clear wine-red fluid—looking innocent enough. Then there's Parker and Spencer and big Henry Cowan and the rest of them bending over a bunch of guinea-pigs kicking and squealing and there's a clink of steel on glass and a gleam of glass of a syringe in the hands of Spencer . . .

Two weeks of waiting, and then . . .

"We certainly wanted to jump up and crack our heels to-gether," said Spencer.

And sure enough this half-mad band of experimenting gnomes had a right to. Here were ten guinea-pigs—vac-cinated—who'd got each one of them a thousand fatal doses of the spotted fever hot out of a dying animal. . . . All ten, all safe. . . . Two not vaccinated had got the same dose of the same fatal stuff at the same time—and were now down with the spotted death.

IX

Here for the first time in the history of this spotted death (so obscure and so terrible) was something you could give a beast to make him immune with no risk of dying in order to gain that immunity. No risk for guinea-pigs, no. But for men? Wouldn't it be the sane thing, the shrewd and cagy thing, to try it next on monkeys?

Spencer couldn't wait. And besides, they had no monkeys. And also, the harsh climate of the Bitter Root would kill off monkeys if they did have them. But who knew whether those ticks brewed with weak carbolic acid were really safe—for men?

Spencer was all for trying it. Had the carbolic acid (weak as it was) killed off the spotted fever virus? There was sound science saying no. Other spotted fever searchers, and profoundly learned death fighters who'd delved into typhus fever, infantile paralysis, rabies—all were agreed that for a virus to guard men *it's got to be living*. Their carbolic ticks guarded guinea-pigs, yes, was harmless to guinea-pigs, sure enough. But who knew (if the carbolic acid hadn't killed it) that though harmless for guinea-pigs it might yet lay humans low?

Nobody knew.

So Spencer tried it. On the morning of May 19, 1924, he rolled up a shirt sleeve over an arm. It wasn't the arm of some no-account ranch hand, nor of Henry Cowan, nor of Parker nor any assistant in the schoolhouse. Into Spencer's own arm went enough brew of those spotted fever ticks to bring down five thousand guinea-pigs with spotted death. That's to say, to have brought them down before the weak carbolic acid was added. . . .

Spencer (who is a most mild dreamy man) gets indignant at any hint that there might be anything of the heroic about this self-experimentation. "Why, it would make me feel silly if anybody tried to make out there was anything really risky about it," Spencer said.

What didn't harm a measly guinea-pig couldn't hurt a full-grown man, at least Spencer was certain of it.

"Then again, you see, I was scared of this spotted fever," Spencer said. "Look at all that hot virus we were breeding, with all those ticks around here. Why shouldn't I have grabbed at *any* way to protect myself?"

It is fair to ask, finally, what Goldberger, Eddie Francis, George McCoy—all of the red brick building on the hill— would have thought if Spenny had slid that first shot of spotted fever tick soup into the arm of anybody but himself?

So it came about on this 19th day of May in 1924 that, for the first time in human record, a vaccine made from the death-laden carcass of an insect was used to try to guard a human being from death. Spencer felt very well after it. He took a double dose (enough before the carbolic to have killed ten thousand guinea-pigs) four days later.

Now this Summer of 1924, two years after the hot Summer that saw Bill Gettinger still imagining experiments—profanely—as he died in the Hamilton Hospital—new white-shrouded cages crowded the tick-rearing room of the schoolhouse. More cages swathed in white, holding rabbits aswarm with spotted death in order to give blood-meals and infection to more thousands of ticks, now jammed that room. Ticks were under rugs. Ticks crawled into cracks. Ticks were on lab benches. Ticks were where they ought and ought not to be. Ticks were everywhere. . . .

They found ticks in their clothes nights when they got home and I've no explanation why all of them—except Spencer who'd guarded himself by vaccine—didn't now come down with spots on their wrists and aches in their bones. When you think of the orgy of large scale standardized production of vaccine from blood-filled deadly wood ticks that they now indulged in . . .

Why didn't all of them take the vaccine then? Is it possible they thought Spencer was just . . . lucky? For their reasons there's no record.

There is record that, this Autumn, Henry Cowan one morning felt pains in the marrow of his bones. Henry—more like a grizzly bear than a man—had played with Rocky Mountain spotted fever for years, now. He'd laughed at folks scared of going up into those canyons. Countless times he'd de-ticked himself, laughing. Now his eyes hurt him—something awful—and all I can say is that probably big Henry hadn't got it through his head how Spencer's science had bred a spotted death a thousand times stronger than any found in the canyons. . . .

Anyway, burly-shouldered hill man Henry ten days later went to join Bill Gettinger. Let us hope that Bill and Henry are happy along with McClintic and McCray—and that Jap lab helper from the Rockefeller Institute—that all these five are happy at wassail in that part of Valhalla set aside for microbe hunters who weren't maybe quite careful.

Of course Henry's death settled it and now under the skins of all our searchers went Spencer's carbolic tick brew.

Maybe Spencer after all wasn't crazy. . . .

X

From 1902 till 1930 a gang of seventy-five searchers (counting in lab swipes and bottle washers) have groped and puzzled at this no-account fever. In that time six—*not vaccinated*—have caught the ill. And six died.

Since Spencer's self-inoculation that May day in 1924, eight workers guarded by Spencer's tick brew have come down with aches in their bones and spots on their bodies. Only one—microbe hunter Kerlee—went to join Bill, Henry, and the rest of them.

It was certainly funny the way the vaccine turned this sickness so horribly and almost surely deadly into a mild illness hardly worse than measles. Before Spencer no man past sixty ever lived to tell the story once the spotted fever began to swarm in his blood. . . .

But right after Henry Cowan's death had kicked all of them into taking the shots of carbolic tick brew, old Chafin the laboratory janitor came down. He only had a little dose of the fever, with the spots not turning black, with no worry on his face. It was like a kid suffering from chicken-pox.

When you remember how the solid citizens of Hamilton and the rest of the Bitter Root (a splendid valley with 15,000 contented happy people) were sure the spotted fever was no-account, it's funny how the ranchers and hill-billies who had to go up the canyons yelled for the vaccine. . . .

In four years eighteen folks, *who weren't vaccinated* because they were foolish or because they didn't know about it, caught the Bitter Root Rocky Mountain spotted fever. Fifteen of them died.

Aside from the lab men who were so terribly exposed to it, only three of the *vaccinated* hill men came down in the Bitter Root with this sickness. Of these three not a single one died.

Near Thermopolis (which I suppose means "hot city") in Wyoming there's a particularly nasty little spot near Kirby Creek where the spotted fever is just as dangerous as it is in the Bitter Root. . . .

Before Spencer not a single rancher who got the fever in that horrid spot had ever lived to tell the story and in two years—from one camp—four men had died. In three years only two men recovered out of seven cases in all. . . .

Both those fellows had good shots of carbolized spotted fever ticks under their skins.

In southern Idaho between the Snake River and the Sawtooth Mountains where they have the nice mild form of the spotted fever that kills only five out of every hundred, Spencer and Parker have vaccinated thousands of unhappily tick-pestered men. . . .

Of those thousands only one lone hill-billy came down with a gentle case of the sickness—and he'd got only a single shot of the vaccine. Plenty not guarded got it.

So Spencer and Parker turned that miserable wood tick—*Dermacentor andersoni*—from a killer into a saver of men.

In the Bitter Root Valley there's now a tremendous demand for Spencer's safe stew of ex-deadly wood ticks—enough of a demand so our Congress has actually appropriated a big sum of money for a swell lab to take the place of that tick-infested little schoolhouse.

So their adventure has changed from crazy and forlorn to respectable. So far as I know, there's been no reward voted to Spencer or Parker or any of the rest of that gang of experimenting gnomes. Why should there be?

Why indeed, when you think of the relatively few lives of almost completely unimportant people they risked their own lives to save?

Nor is there any provision (in case!) for their wives or their children. And why should there be? First, they've got their vaccine to guard them, now. Next, they've invented a much safer way—starting out from full-grown ticks and not from those swift sneaky seed ticks—to manufacture the vaccine.

Finally—unless I'm mistaken—they're still both carrying lots of insurance.

Of course that costs them money. But who wouldn't *pay* for the fun of such a bizarre tempestuous tick fight as this one that's earned them their places in the Valhalla of men against death?

5. EVANS

DEATH IN MILK

~~~~~~

*"It seems as if those bugs had a special animosity to-
ward me, since I made that discovery," Evans said.*

~~~~~~

IT'S true that Evans found the Bang and the Bruce bugs
to be brothers before she came to hunt microbes in the
red brick building on the hill. She made that momentous
discovery—muffed deplorably by the top cut of the world's
microbe hunters—when she was only a cow bacteriologist
buried away in the U. S. Department of Agriculture.

Yet her discovery might easily have stayed academic,
useless, if McCoy hadn't had the shrewdness to give her a
job in his house of danger in Washington looking down the
Potomac. It was here, after all, that Evans proved that the
Bang bug—despised cause of abortion in cows—might bring
suffering, even death, to humans exactly the same as its
brother, the Bruce bug, could bring it.

In the red brick building (where facts are first and hang
the consequences) Evans had her real chance to track down
this sickness lurking unsuspected in the milk supply of
America and Europe. It was ticklish business. Powerful eco-
nomic toes in the shoes of pseudo-science had to be stamped
on. These Bang bugs, torturing you with shooting pains,
weakening you with drenching sweats, wasting you with
months-long fever . . . were trailed into elegant dairy herds,
even *certified* dairy herds. It was a major scandal. . . .

And if these bugs of Bang were hiding in such high-toned
cattle it was obvious they were rampant in the cow-proleta-

riat of our country and Europe. There's no doubt she needed the backing of the tradition of honesty, of terrific accuracy (almost unique) in our red brick building. That set searchers all over finding out how this *undulant fever* was hooked up to one simple lack in a great part of our milk supply.

In the best don't-give-a-damn tradition of the red brick building Evans nailed down her proofs when she was so sick she should long before have stopped working. Her curious adventure hasn't by a long shot chased the nefarious bug of Doctor B. Bang out of the American milk supply. But enough is now known (thanks to Evans primarily) so that before taking the risk of drinking a glass of milk I can guard myself by asking a simple question . . .

There's no cure for undulant fever, but there doesn't have to be now. By asking that question I'll be able to guard myself simply.

II

This fever had hardly been heard of in our country when Evans began those fumblings that ended finally in her proving that the Danish cow bug of Doctor Bang and the Maltese microbe of Doctor Bruce were twin brothers. Even so the ill had undoubtedly long been at its malignant work, turning kids into invalids, taking mothers from their housework, fathers from their bread-winning. There were thousands—Walt Simpson has estimated several thousand—sick with it. All over, grave pill-men were miscalling it typhoid, or flu, or malaria, or even tuberculosis. Such were the diagnoses of the most elegant and expensive physicians. Others covered up their ignorance of what ailed these people by looking owlish and muttering "nervous breakdown" or "rundown condition. . . ."

In 1917 Evans was nothing more than a pleasant-looking girl bacteriologist, anonymous among insignificant boy and girl microbe hunters in the Dairy Division at Washington. It meant nothing to her then that thirty years before David

Bruce of the British Army on his honeymoon in the Island of Malta had probed into the spleens of sundry British Tommies dead of Malta fever.

Evans was then only a mote among drab-seeming thousands swarming out between four and five every afternoon from those tax-eating enormous buildings in Washington. She hadn't then heard of how Mary Bruce (thirty years before) had been called in off the tennis court to hold monkeys for her Hindenburg-mustached husband, David. Those were the forgotten days when Bruce and his bride had got themselves amateurishly sticky making culture medium to feed problematical microbes. From the deadhouse Bruce had brought bits of the spleens of perished Tommies and in culture bottles these two honeymooners now trapped the Malta fever criminals, of a shape somewhat spherical, and, therefore, rejoicing in the scientific name of "coccus."

That was before Evans (baptized Alice) had first seen the light of day among Welsh farmers in Northern Pennsylvania, in a hilly triangle whose corners were, roughly, the towns of Tunkhannock, Hop Bottom, and Mehoopany. The harsh lay of this land and these barbaric names might lead you to think that the folks here were hill-billies. But Evans even now will belie her apparent gentleness with such a violent defense of their culture that there's little doubt her birthplace must have been a veritable (if bucolic) Athens. . . .

But while Alice Evans was learning to toddle in the rough North Pennsylvania country, the Bruces had nailed it down that their new coccus gave the folks of Malta pains in their shins, their joints, that it weakened them and even doomed them—not too seldom—with wasting fevers. . . .

Medically the whole business remained (till Evans) merely a Maltese, or at best Mediterranean, curiosity, having nothing to do with Evans, as she sat, in 1917, in a big Government building in Washington messing with the milk drawn under sterile conditions from the udders of sundry immaculate cows. Outside there was martial music and patriotic huzzahings and the city was brilliant with wine-faced generals, gay with foreign uniforms, idiotic with all kinds of bemedaled magnificoes making the world safe for democracy. Evans was a cog.

Executive dairy gentlemen for no discernible reason had ordered her to see what microbes might linger in the milk of cows you'd say were too aristocratic to harbor any really nasty bacillus. . . .

Routinely she plated endless samples of milk. Till her eyes were tired she squinted at unending series of gay-painted smears of microbes not harmful enough to be interesting. In a state of fundamental hopelessness she plodded, like all girl bacteriologists. She was destined to no famous end. The best she could hope for was to get to hew wood and carry water (technically) for some microbe hunter whose man's brain was fit to exploit the drudgery of her hands . . . and maybe have a low-voltage thrill at seeing "by So-and-so and Alice C. Evans" under the title of one of those possibly futile thousands of scientific papers ground out by the Government printing presses. . . .

So Evans counted the harmless bugs in the milk of these cow grand-duchesses. Not the most be-whiskered medical eminence so much as dreamed that this could have anything at all to do with Malta or any other fever. It is true that the captain of a vessel of forgotten name in 1905 had shoved off from the coast of the Mediterranean island. Guzzling the fresh milk of nanny-goats that were their cargo they'd come down with the shattering shin-bone pains of Malta fever. It was by this unscientific happenstance that the eminent and baffled British Commission for the Study of Malta fever finally got it through its collective head that this is the one way you catch the ill—only by guzzling goat's milk.

But Evans hadn't heard of that. And anyway these high-toned cows with whose milk Evans now puttered, weren't goats, nor were they from the Island of Malta. This fever that comes in waves, these ups and downs of pain, those exhausting baths of sweat . . . were of no interest to Americans. Aside from a few cases found down in Texas and New Mexico among shiftless Mexicans—who liked goat's milk—not a case had been seen on the North American continent.

III

In less than a year Evans had bumped bang into a fact that was incredible, totally unlooked-for, impossible by all rules of microbe hunting, violating the canons of cow science—a fact that was medical blasphemy. She was plodding through a grind of nursing, staining, peering at the staphylococci—spherical microbes growing in bunches like clusters of grapes—in one hundred and ninety-two samples of milk from one hundred and sixty-one cows from five elaborately chaperoned herds of dairy cattle.

Her specialization was Ford-factoryish. Her job was staphylococci, and somebody else down the lab bench was detailed to dig out the *streptococci*—from the same milk samples, mind you! These, too, were spherical bugs, and more romantic because possibly dangerous. But after all nobody had told Evans she mightn't dabble (on the side) with microbes that were rod-shaped. So it came about that, outside the strict definition of her duties, Evans bumped into the nefarious rod-shaped bug of Doctor B. Bang, of Denmark.

With her staphylococci she'd been painstaking and accurate, finding some of these ball-shaped bugs pour out pigments of ivory yellow that distinguish them from their cousins who paint themselves ocherous orange and are distinctly different from other bug relatives whose colonies are pretty marguerite yellow. . . . It didn't even fall within her duties to find out if these colored pets might be fatal to rabbits. . . .

"The writer wishes to express her thanks to Dr. George M. Potter . . . for making the animal inoculations and post-mortem examinations," Evans wrote at the end of one of her not too fascinating scientific reports. She said, at this moment, only one microbe hunter's consolation: some of her gay-colored micrococci did actually bring death, to rabbits. From this fact Evans drew a strange conclusion . . . when you remember how aseptically those herds were kept and tended.

"The data here recorded add evidence to the growing conviction that all milk is safer for consumption after it is pasteurized."

This was certainly jumping at conclusions, absolutely not justified by the deaths of a few rabbits from large injections of her gay-colored staphylococci. . . . You could kill a rabbit with anything if you injected enough of it. . . .

Then Evans bumped into the bacillus of Bang—hiding in the milk of one of those high-toned herds. She went to Eichhorn, the Chief of the Pathological Division of the Bureau, to get the low-down on this extremely annoying bacillus. It was well known that this Bang bacillus wasn't in the least harmful to humans but it was nefarious the way it was making cows lose their calves—all over. It was on a long, smoldering, uncontrollable (?) rampage through American dairy herds, the worst menace to the American dairy industry. It was no respecter of bovine aristocracy. It made even registered cows abort their babies and even some certified herds were known to be riddled with it. . . .

"Have you ever compared the Malta fever coccus with the Bang bacillus?" Eichhorn asked Evans.

"Eichhorn didn't say *why* he asked me that question," Evans explained, long after. After all Eichhorn couldn't have thought this comparison enormously important or he would long ago have made it himself. Who indeed, among all the great whales of microbe hunting, had dreamed of going on the scientific wild goose chase of comparing the Maltese coccus that caused grief in the shins and fevers in the bodies of Maltese goat-milk drinkers, with the bug of Bang at the bottom of cow abortion?

The distinguished cow scientist, old Doctor Bang himself, hadn't so much as dreamed of it. If you'd suggested it to fierce old David Bruce, he'd probably have glared at you, and bubbled and grumbled: "My *dear-r-r-r* man . . . !"

Even Theobald Smith, who was incontestably the dean of American microbe hunters, who'd been one of the first to find this Bang bacillus of cow abortion in fresh milk, had shown no alarm about it. Nor had he seen any possible connection between this Bang bug and Malta fever. That alone should have stopped Evans—the famous Theobald seeing no need of it. . . .

In fact, this question of Eichhorn was most random. Didn't every microbe hunter know the Bang bug was shaped like a rod? Didn't even tyro bacteriologists realize the Bruce bug (of Malta fever) was shaped like a ball, was spherical, was a *coccus?* It is true there were pedantic taxonomists who'd raised the quibble that the Bruce bug could sometimes look like a very short rod and other times seem to be a very long sphere.

IV

So Evans went at it. She sent to the American Museum of Natural History for a culture of the Malta fever microbe of David Bruce and got back a tube full of no-account bugs that had been twenty-one years out of the body of a human who'd been tortured by Malta fever. She borrowed five more families of this alleged micrococcus from the laboratories of the Bureau of Animal Industry, where for long they'd led useless lives merely eating beef broth jelly at Government expense in an endless series of test-tubes, through which for years (to no known purpose) they'd been transplanted. They were all thoroughly domesticated microbes who'd forgotten that their ancestors had once invaded, tortured, very likely killed this or that obscure native of Malta.

But wait . . . these Malta fever microbes and the celebrated cow bacillus of Dr. B. Bang did look alike. Grotesquely . . . when you painted the two species of them side by side with the same colored chemical and looked at them one after another you'd get completely mixed up and you couldn't tell the difference. . . . Not if you were honest. Not if you marked one sample A and the other B. Wait . . .

Evans's blood was up now, though it's an exaggeration so to describe the emotions of a young woman obviously not a *hunter,* and definitely so gentle . . . that's the word for her. Now she planted sundry families, strains they're called in microbe-hunting jargon, of this bug of Bang that murdered calves in their mothers' wombs, on every kind of microbe pabulum.

Side by side on the same kind of microbe food she raised families of that sapper of human vigor—the Maltese microbe of Bruce.

To look at the growth of them, who could tell them apart? Day after day (a subdued excitement was growing in her now) Evans took racks of tubes from the incubator, peered at them, growing in milk, growing on potato, swarming on the surface of nutrient jelly of agar-agar. . . .

Who could tell the difference?

She screwed up her courage and went to see Dr. John M. Buck of the Pathological Division of the Bureau of Animal Industry—unlike Evans this Dr. Buck was not only permitted but accustomed to make animal experiments with microbes. She didn't dare to come out flat-footed, since nobody had even dreamed of it, but just the same Evans now advanced it to Buck (giggling apologetically maybe) that the cow-aborting bug of Bang and the Maltese microbe of Bruce . . . were the same!

But they couldn't be. They were. But were they?

Of Buck she now made a strange request. She would like female guinea-pigs, pregnant guinea-pigs, and now here was Evans with eight of them, squealing and amusingly barrel-shaped full of unborn guinea-pig babies. Now—with concealed anxiety mixed with ghoulish hope—Evans stood by while the able Buck injected the Maltese microbes into four of the expectant guinea-pig mothers. Into another four of these exasperated guinea-pig matrons went the cow-aborting bacillus of Bang. . . .

"Within a few days three of the animals of each group aborted. Five days after the inoculations were made, one animal of each group was killed, and agar-slope cultures were made from the organs. In three or four days the characteristic 'dewdrop' colonies made their appearance on both sets of slopes. No distinction could be found between the growths of the two organisms until the slopes had been incubated for several weeks. . . ."

This was Evans's drab report of an event that shook her to the soles of her shoes. They were the same, no doubt of it—these microbes that the whole bug-hunting world had never dreamed were identical. Now Evans began to be haunted by the portentousness of this fact. . . . American dairy herds were shot with this Bang bacillus infection. . . . But were they the same? They couldn't be. But were they?

She was hesitant, tentative and groping in her thoughts just as she was unsure, shy, bashful in her talking, and now this unsureness shoved her into long thorough experiments. She was still alone with her secret. Did cow authorities, did public health departments, did the American dairy industry realize what it meant if these bugs *were* the same? Back she went to her lab bench.

Now for the final test, the blood test, the real, decisive ultimate way to say yes or no about these microbes being brothers. Into a row of tiny glass tubes in a rack Evans pours exact equal amounts of fluid with a grayish turbidity, whirl-

ing and silky with millions of Malta fever microbes suspended in salt water. Close by there's another rack with the
same number of tiny tubes cloudy with millions of the abortion bacilli of Doctor B. Bang. . . .

Into *all* the tubes Evans now pours from a long pipette
exact amounts of the blood serum of a cow . . . into successive tubes, by dilution with water, goes less and less serum.
The cow-donor of this blood serum has been inoculated
many times with the abortion bacillus Bang. So her serum
has gained the strange power of clumping, of throwing down
out of the salt water in which they're suspended—Bang bugs,
but no others. Mix them with the serum of a Bang-immune
cow and they'll settle to the bottom of their tubes like flakes
of snow. It is pretty, and specific, and ultimate. . . .

Late that afternoon long after the big building had poured
out its Government hirelings and with her laboratory silent,
Evans walked to the incubator where she'd put those two
racks of tiny tubes. Now she sat before them, not quite believing what her eyes showed her. . . .

"I'm sure that sight was the thrill of my life," Evans said,
long after. "I was alone there and every one else had gone
home. . . ."

It was final. In *both* racks of tubes a strange change had
happened. They weren't turbid with suspended microbes
now. The water in both rows of tubes was crystal clear. In
the bottoms of all the tubes—even those containing less than
one part in a thousand of the serum of that immune cow—
there was a white sediment of microbes. . . . In *both* rows
—in the tubes with the Bang bugs and the tubes with the
Maltese microbes of Bruce—

The dark-eyed woman tapped tube after tube. Upward
into the clear water rose a whorl of the agglutinated clumps
—like snowflakes.

It was her trail's end.

V

The Bang and the Bruce bugs were twin brothers. It was
. . . settled!

"Sort of vaguely I knew what it meant," said Evans years
later. "I knew the abortion bacillus was infecting dairy herds
all over America. I knew most American milk wasn't pasteurized. I'd just proved there was no practical difference
between the abortion germ and the Malta fever microbe. So
I realized . . ."

But alas, Evans was completely unknown, and her name
(scientifically) carried no weight, so she only reported,
cagily:

"Considering the close relationship between the two organisms, and the reported frequency of virulent strains of
Bacterium abortus in cow's milk, it would seem remarkable
that we do not have a disease closely resembling Malta fever
in this country."

It was part of the silliness of life that, for six years, Evans's
discovery went completely without general notice in American medical circles. Nothing could have been more remarkable than this sudden merging of a sickness of the men of
Malta with an ill of American cows. Yet nobody—save for
a few searchers you could count on the fingers of one hand—
got steamed up about it.

Of course, wise old Ludvig Hektoen gave Evans's scientific papers a prominent place in his *Journal of Infectious
Diseases*. On the Pacific Coast the stubbly-mustachioed,
mountain-climbing ex-Swiss, K. F. Meyer, found that her
facts were exact:

"*Bacterium abortus* is, for all practical purposes, always
present in the certified milk produced in the San Francisco
Bay region . . ." wrote Meyer, ominously.

"But aside from Meyer, almost nobody would believe me,"
Evans said. And there's no doubt that certain popes of Amer-

ican microbe hunting (let's forgive them) pooh-poohed her. It was understandable. If Evans were right, somebody much more outstanding than Evans would have run onto it long before. Such is the silliness of scientists, and if science were more human, scientific periodicals would run funny columns for the amusement (and instruction) of scientists.

VI

Of course there was a seeming logic of events against her. If the bugs were twins, why wasn't Malta fever rampant in America? Millions of Americans were drinking raw milk of infected cows. Our medical profession is the world's alertest, and why hadn't a single one of these up-to-date doctors found a single human being sick with the cow microbe of Doctor Bang? Up in Minnesota there were a couple of fellows, Larson and Sedgwick, who'd got positive blood tests for the Bang bacillus in the blood of women who'd prematurely lost their babies . . . and the same test from the blood of babies who'd drunk raw milk contaminated with that nefarious germ. But they hadn't found the microbe in these women or babies—and that was the end of it.

Evans wasn't an M.D.; not even a Ph.D.—but only plain Miss Evans, so it's no wonder at all that her modest claims were ignored. None of our expensive foundations, manned by super-microbe hunters, equipped with every kind of apparatus from the electrocardiograph to delicate forceps for removing beans from little girls' noses and splinters from little boys' toes, none of these, with their deans, directors, and scientific dignitaries, had ever detected one case of Malta fever due to the cow bacillus of Doctor Bang. Why shouldn't that have stopped Evans? She did hesitate, for four years.

She began to doubt her own facts. She actually probed into the milk of abortion-infected cows, trying to prove how few of the Bang bugs left a cow by the milk route. That might account for there being none of this ill where your eyes were bright and you were feverish without feeling it, where your shins were painful, and where drenching sweats weakened you at night. . . .

And yet, and yet? She wrote another scientific report explaining why there shouldn't be this fever in spite of the bugs being twin brothers. Yet there was about her a halting stubbornness. . . . "On the other hand [she wrote] are we sure that cases of glandular disease, or cases of abortion, or possibly diseases of the respiratory tract, may not sometimes occur in human subjects as a result of drinking raw cow's milk?"

Now you find her anonymous still, along with many another technician, doing war bacteriology. By a stroke of good luck Evans came under the eye of George McCoy, that most remarkable director—who doesn't believe in directing. Lean, pompadour-haired McCoy was as shrewd a judge as you'll find of microbe hunters—male or female. Evans had gone through the training mill and was off for duty in an army cantonment. . . .

"Stay here with us, Miss Evans," McCoy said. "You can do as much good here, working at meningitis, as you could in any army camp. . . ."

Now Evans was permitted to bleed, cut up, inject animals dead of assorted sicknesses. In her excitement about the meningococcus that was killing the boys in the camps before they had a chance to get shot to make the world safe for democracy, her pets, the twin-brother bugs of Bang and Bruce, grew dusty in her memory.

Now suddenly—such is another queerness of science—she found she was internationally famous. In a babel of tongues from the laboratories of a polyglot assortment of microbe hunters with jaw-cracker names from Holland, Austria, Italy, Germany, and Tunisia . . . came unanimous reports: Evans is right about the Bang and the Bruce bugs.

From her own country there came, silence. She had no M.D. and so couldn't become an officer in the U. S. Public Health Service and even if she'd had the M.D. she couldn't have . . . because she was only a woman. So she stayed an "associate bacteriologist" plugging away at meningitis . . .

Until suddenly in 1922 many things began to happen together, confusingly, irritating her, because, in the midst of her duties, she'd begun to feel seedy, nobody knew from what cause. Nobody up in the red brick building (except Evans herself) seemed concerned about it. Evans didn't want to squawk, in this hard-boiled gang of death fighters of the Hygienic Laboratory. They had a tradition that it didn't much matter if they caught the plagues they were studying and they even—like Goldberger and a whole gang of them— tried inoculating themselves with those plagues . . . just for the sport of proving their scientific opponents were wrong.

It was disgusting she was sick—with all this work piling up on her. Folks had been drinking goat's milk out in Arizona. Gleason Lake of the Service had been sent out there and now here was Evans, with her reputation as an expert in blood-testing for Malta fever microbes, sitting—feeling seedy—before a bunch of blood samples sent in by the industrious Lake. . . .

She felt pretty good each morning, but every evening she'd drag herself home, shivering, dog-tired, meaning to take her temperature and then confusedly forgetting to . . .

Till one day there came to her lab bench a mailing case and lackadaisically Evans opened it taking out two little tubes, and a letter in the same mail wanted to know were the microbes in these tubes *Bacterium abortus* or *Micrococcus melitensis?* The tubes and the question came from microbe hunter Amoss and his interne assistant Keefer of the famous Johns Hopkins Hospital in Baltimore. You'd have thought that, in such a scientific institution, they'd have found out for themselves. . . . She certainly was feeling seedy today. But wait . . .

Amoss had actually read her old papers on the twin brotherhood of the Bruce and Bang bugs!

The bugs in these tubes had come from the blood of a man sick for weeks in the Johns Hopkins Hospital.

His blood tested positive for the bugs of both Bang and Bruce.

His sickness had been mysterious . . . and they'd made that blood test as a last resort. If this had been Malta, any Maltese doctor would have called it Malta fever!

But this was America, and the patient swore he'd never drunk goat's milk nor been near any sort of goat. . . .

And he admitted he'd been a great drinker of fresh cow's milk . . . raw.

As she read her excitement grew and her tiredness chased itself and, clear-brained, she set up rows of tubes for the complicated tests that she believed (erroneously) might tell the two bugs apart. Two days went by, with her tiredness coming back in waves so she could hardly drag herself from her bench to the incubator or the centrifuge. Now at last she felt she was sure of it. . . . Luckily she didn't then know that these Bang and Bruce bugs were such sort of Siamese twin brothers that even her delicate tests weren't reliable. . . . But she was sure the microbe criminal from the very sick man in the Johns Hopkins—was the cow bug of Bang.

VII

Evans herself was mighty sick but still was what is called, in doctor's jargon, ambulatory . . . which is to say she could stay on her legs without falling over. So she dragged herself up the hill to the red brick building, stuck to her microscope just as any of them up there would do, long after they should no longer be doing it. Of course not being a doctor she couldn't go out hunting for undulant fever patients. But there was more than one way to skin this cat. . . .

She got hold of bits of blood from hundreds of samples of blood that came (routinely) to the red brick building for the Wassermann test. Out of five hundred—five of these samples tested YES for the fever. Of these five, there were two (happily she didn't know her complicated tests couldn't show it) that tested for Bang and not for Bruce.

Well, if the cow bug could sicken humans, then the human Malta bug . . . must sicken cows! She went back to her old friends of the Department of Agriculture, gave them a Bruce microbe culture that had come from the blood of a fellow out in Arizona who'd foolishly drunk the milk of a goat. That bug made a pregnant heifer lose her baby, exactly as if she'd been infected with the bug of Bang. . . . *For all practical purposes,* they were the same. She was done up. She had high fever now, with shooting pains all over her body. She gave up, and went to the hospital.

And, before the World's Dairy Congress held at Syracuse in October, 1923, her first really bold scientific paper was read . . . by somebody else, Evans being no longer ambulatory. The distinguished international cowmen in solemn assembly had to listen to it. . . .

"The question arises with increasing emphasis why no disease resembling Malta fever results from drinking raw cow's milk. . . ."

Of course the intelligent dairymen present pricked up their ears.

"It would appear . . . worthy of investigation to determine whether *abortus* infection might not be responsible for mild disabilities in our own localities . . . for the cause is never determined, of many cases of low fever . . ."

Bolder still came the words of this up till now enormously ignored young woman . . .

"If there is no other reason for milk pasteurization, it

would appear to be folly to drink raw milk containing *abortus* organisms. . . ."

Of course they all knew the herds not only of America but of the world were shot with the Bang bugs.

Shortly after this, when, for a little while, she felt well enough to put one foot ahead of another to get to the red brick building, Evans found Pooler, her lab helper, feeling seedy. He'd been monkeying round with the Bang and Bruce germs. . . . Maybe? She tested his blood: no . . . nothing doing. But in making the test, Evans used her own blood, supposedly normal, as a blank, a check test.

Evans's own blood tested positive for undulant fever.

So by accident she found what had been ailing her.

VIII

She had ups and downs of feeling worse or better. Being a woman among those hard-boiled men of the Hygienic, she hated to let on how seedy she felt. Only another *woman* making a fuss over nothing . . . that's what she thought they'd think of her. Now her dark hair began graying, and now she began to fade from the fight just as the first hints of a sensation, a scandal about undulant fever began brewing. It had a really ironical angle to it that Evans (fundamentally just a lab girl) not an eminent mender of men nor yet a doctor of cows, had now caused the beginning of a marriage of efforts of cow and human doctors in a new fight against sickness and death. . . .

I don't doubt she herself saw the irony of it . . . and that she appreciated, too, the triviality of her discovery. "It is (only) as if twin brothers had been adopted by different families (vets and medicoes!) and been given different surnames," Evans wrote, "and for twenty years no one recognized the similarities between the boys because they were seen at different times and in different places. . . ."

That was really all there was to it, and now those bugs

(feeling as she said a special animosity toward her) didn't leave her much fire of life and anyway wasn't this getting to be a man's job now?

Now matters were coming to a head and at Ithaca at Cornell University there was a young doctor, not of medicine, but of cows *and* philosophy—Charles M. Carpenter. He looked the young professor, yet you'd not consider him out of place driving into town on a wagon-load of turnips. He was an excellent pathologist and knew the ins and outs of the havoc the Bang bug works on pregnant cows, but best of all the kick of a good hard fact could get him out of the comfortable groove he was working in. It chanced that a Danish boy (working his way through college) lived at Carpenter's and this boy was now sick.

He'd been diagnosed typhoid fever by Ithaca doctors but the blood tests said no; he'd then been diagnosed miliary tuberculosis and given up to die. Carpenter, only a cow (and philosophy) doctor, shouldn't by rights have messed into it. But he knew Evans's work. He took blood from the sick boy's arm to his own lab and sure enough . . . it tested YES for Bang infection. What Carpenter got for his pains was the horse laugh from Ithaca doctors (excepting one). No such serious sickness could come to humans from cows. . . .

But now another student came down sick, getting worse, very bad indeed, supposedly—said the doctors—with streptococcus blood-poisoning, only they couldn't find streptococci. Again Carpenter messed in; again YES . . . for Bang bugs. This was only the blood test, so far. . . .

With a thoroughness strictly Carpenterian, this young cow scientist poked his needles into the arm veins of the boys. He planted their blood on a variety of succulent microbe foods. He nursed his cultures with the skill of a cook and the tenderness of a brooding mother. . . . It's awful how feeble Bang bugs are when you first get them out of an animal's body . . . in fact that's one of the ways to be sure you've got them. Well, he had them. With uniquely Carpenterian persistency and to the probable annoyance of those two boys (though they may have been too sick to mind it) Carpenter repeated those blood cultures seven times in succession. No doubt of it: they were sick with the bacillus *that belonged in cows.*

Carpenter didn't mind it that Evans was no doctor but only plain Miss Evans and he hurried to Washington. She was in the whole world the last word on it. Then with a clatter and bang (there's something a bit ungainly about his energy) he was back at Ithaca. Not caring a damn where the chips fell he hewed to the line and proceeded to stick his nose into just where those two extremely sick boys had got their infection.

They'd got it from one of the finest registered herds round Ithaca. They hadn't tended those cows, mind you. They hadn't butchered them. They'd just drunk great quantities of their high-toned milk . . . raw. Now for thirty days in a row (he seems to me to have been too anxious to prove he was right) Carpenter shot samples of the mixed milk of this herd into guinea-pigs. Yes: every day of those thirty days that milk was highly infectious with bugs of Bang. Well . . .

Evans, you see, when no doctors turned up cases of Malta fever for her, had explained it by guessing that Bang bugs must get gentle by living a long time in cows. But here Carpenter was *killing* guinea-pigs in a month, and some even in two weeks, with Bang infection from these cows' milk. And killing guinea-pigs (who aren't very susceptible) is something neither a Bang nor its twin brother the Bruce bug accomplishes very often or easily. . . . And of course, the two boys, both of them (which was more important) had nearly died. . . .

Carpenter is outwardly diffident, even timid maybe. Now he went out and dug up five, ten, finally seventeen cases of this supposedly non-existent human ill right there in Ithaca, and the Ithaca physicians no longer gave him the horse laugh. Ithaca's milk supply was at this time not pasteurized. All the folks who'd come down with the fever, the pain, the nervous worry . . . all excepting one, had been drinkers of cows' milk, raw, and from Bang-infected herds. That one exception was a microbe hunter who'd messed with millions of abortion microbes in the laboratory.

Ithacans began asking for pasteurized milk. (Carpenter'd proved it was easy to kill the most ferocious Bang bugs in milk by pasteurization at 145° F.)

IX

You'd have thought this would have rocked medical circles and made a hero of Evans but it didn't. I remember with what whispers (very portentous) the affair was spoken of in agricultural and dairy circles in 1927. It was considered too dangerous to talk about out loud, let alone publish broadcast. . . .

Nobody can blame an industry with as much at stake as our dairy industry for not liking to believe that milk—the most nearly perfect food—might be dangerous and even deadly! It was human to not want to believe it. And now all kinds of arguments whizzed round Carpenter's ears. Only the goat microbe could cause human sickness. *But none of these people had been near a goat, none had drunk goat's milk.* But wait, Theobald Smith, the dean of American microbe hunters, had looked into this business, and had given it as his opinion that if any Bang bug at all was dangerous to humans, it was the kind that aborted pigs, not cows.

It must be said in defense of Carpenter that it was no impudent disrespect for so great an authority as Smith's that now made him go on with it. But Carpenter couldn't get it out of his independent, fact-respecting, farmerish head that none of these fever-smitten folks in Ithaca had had anything to do with pigs. There was no pig-abortion around Ithaca. These people weren't pig-butchers, handlers, or fanciers, but were students, housewives, even professors—the dignity of whose callings made intimate contact with pigs unthinkable!

And they'd all drunk the raw milk from infected cows.

Carpenter now shot Bang bugs he'd fished out of the blood of five human cases into pregnant heifers—who'd never been exposed to natural abortion infection—and promptly these heifers lost their calves before term. All excepting one of the calves was born dead. Carpenter kept plugging along answering arguments with experiments; slow, enormously thorough, they were the hardest answers to make but also confoundedly embarrassing to mere argufying critics.

Yet it seemed a hopeless fight with just Miss Evans and young cow-doctor Carpenter trying to *sell* a now undoubtedly prevalent human affliction to a hundred thousand American doctors who weren't interested (yet) and to a several billion dollar industry that just didn't like it, naturally. . . .

Now help came from across the water, from Doctor B. Bang's own country, Denmark, from little Martin Kristensen of the State Serum Institute in Copenhagen. Kristensen had begun examining blood samples that came to him at the Serum Institute from all over Denmark from folks suspected of typhoid. . . . It was funny how many Danes suspected of typhoid were turning out not to have it. . . . Kristensen now began testing all those bloods not only for typhoid but for Bang infection. . . .

In the first year he dug up more than five hundred cases of undulant fever: more than there were of typhoid and paratyphoid fevers in the whole of Denmark. Well . . .

This same year Carpenter had opened up a new terrible possibility. In New York he'd fished the microbe of Doctor B. Bang from the still-born child of a human mother who'd borne her baby too early. Long before, the New York doctor,

De Forest, had found abortion among farm women on farms where herds were infected with Bang bacilli. How many human mothers all over our country were losing their babies by abortion sneaking into them through the raw milk of infected cows?

Now came sinister news from Kristensen. Eight Danish women were known to have been pregnant at the onset of their undulant fever. *Seven of these had promptly lost their babies. . . .*

X

Now things began happening so fast all at once that it's impossible to get the exciting events in their true chronological succession. In Iowa the industrious searcher, A. V. Hardy, began turning up scores of cases among obscure residents of small towns, among farmers, meat handlers. It was still generally pooh-poohed about, not so much, now, by dairy men as a whole as by people who didn't want to see milk pasteurized, who honestly didn't think it had to be. After all, if undulant fever did occur, it wasn't much worse than a bad cold, argued one stockman.

"No statement could be further from the truth," Hardy said. Cases he'd had in Iowa were lasting three-and-a-half months, some ten months. . . .

"I will assure you," Hardy said, "that no one needs to see very many of these cases to appreciate . . . the utter disappointment and despair with this seemingly never-ending disease. . . . It is urgent that every means be taken to prevent its occurrence."

But it wasn't fatal. But it could be fatal! Hardy began turning up fatal cases, two, three, four, and here were reports of several more from Kansas, dying, obscurely—but dying. But from a part of Hardy's work the anti-undulant fever obfuscators now took courage. Many of Hardy's cases were among farmers, meat-packers who'd handled and cut up pigs, some infected. Pig infection again became the smoke-screen of these obfuscators. And the unknownness of the miserable folks who'd not handled pigs but only drunk raw infected milk was a great help to them.

Then, annoyingly, news came from South Bend, Indiana, of a most prominent surgeon who'd fallen ill in the Autumn of 1917. He'd had aches in the front and back of his head, couldn't eat, couldn't sleep, lay all night sweating with strange nervous fears, thought he was better and tried to go back to cutting people up and got exhausted and had to go to bed again. Being so prominent, he was a puzzle of the best of the South Bend faculty. . . .

Right then there were thirteen other (less prominent) South Bend people like him. These the faculty had diagnosed among other things, focal infection (two cases), syphilis, inflammation of the gall bladder (two cases), rheumatism, and two cases had been called typhoid and two more tuberculosis. These folks were given the proper treatment for these various maladies—without result, and that was too bad for them. But here was a prominent surgeon!

The top-cut of the South Bend faculty gathered round his bedside, fished every last trick out of their diagnostic cupboard, ransacked the resources of medical science, in short, putting it plainly, they gave this prominent surgeon the works.

At last he was tested for Bang bug infection.

Yes, he'd been drinking "an abundance of cream and unpasteurized milk from a herd of twenty-one cows . . ." of which three were now found to test YES for contagious abortion. . . . And all of those other thirteen, and now twenty-one more mysteriously sick folks were found—by the keen South Bend doctors, Giordano and Sensenich—to test YES for Bang infection of undulant fever. *These people were none of them pig-handlers or fanciers,* but obscure raw milk drinkers.

In addition to that prominent surgeon, another prominent

raw-milk-drinking South Bend doctor now came down with undulant fever and this was too much and now you had what headlines call a "thoroughly aroused medical profession."

Beginning January, 1929, a city ordinance was passed requiring *all* South Bend milk to be pasteurized.

It was nice for South Bend people (though tough on those two doctors) that prominent people happened to have drunk so much raw milk. But, so far—our country being a large one—it was nice for South Bend people, mainly.

XI

Meanwhile by a roundabout way the Bang bug had come back to the red brick building on the hill, not to Evans, but to Eddie Francis. Along with Goldberger and George McCoy the director, Edward Francis, formed a veteran three-musketeer trio of hard-boiled death-hunters, whose nonchalance had given Spencer his first inspiration. When Miss Evans had first come up the hill to the red brick building, Francis (to put it mildly) had thought not much of her fantastic story about the Bruce and Bang bugs being twin brothers. It wasn't lack of respect for Evans (though he's not a man to hold with the idea of women's importance in science). It was a matter of his being inherently doubtful of any fact he hadn't seen himself.

It's a fair treat to listen to Francis, to watch him working in his profoundly unhygienic paper-strewn little hole of a room in the old Hygienic Laboratory. He gesticulates. He roars with sardonic laughter. He wrinkles up his round face till his eyes peer at you through narrow slits while he propounds profane and even obscene skepticisms about some alleged discovery by this or that eminent scientist. . . .

"They don't work with their hands. There's too much *brains* used in science! We none of us work enough with our hands! Work with your hands!" So . . . Eddie Francis. He had certainly taken his own prescription. With his own bare hands he'd uncovered the new, widespread, mysterious sickness, tularemia—rabbit fever. Through those bare hands he'd himself caught this savagely infectious illness, kept working though dreadfully ill and half out of his head and racked with the pain of it, not caring a hoot in hell about it. And nobody'd ever punched the tiniest hole in his tularemia facts. The work was a classic before he'd finished it. . . .

It was a compliment to Evans that, as far back as 1926, Francis guardedly and with gesticulating, head-twisting reservations, told me, "Well, we-e-e-ll, I be-*lieve,* no, we-e-e-ll, *may*-be she's got something . . . big . . ."

Now, January, '28, a funny little epidemic flared among the students of Earlham College in Richmond, Indiana, and as usual the successive cases were called this and that and the other thing till the college lady-doctor, Marian Farbar, sent the blood of the fifth case to Francis in Washington, asking wasn't it tularemia—rabbit fever?

Francis was as proud of finding new cases of his own pet rabbit fever as an Indian is of hanging new scalps to his belt and in his messy little room he made the blood tests and, no, it wasn't tularemia at all—but the blood of this college boy tested YES, absolutely, for the bacillus of Bang.

This little epidemic was going great guns, case after case exploding among the boy and girl students and less importantly, a laundress. In a quick exchange of letters Francis saw the lady-doctor, Farbar, had bumped bang into one of those experiments—*made by nature*—that's better than any the brainiest searcher could rig in a laboratory. . . .

All these boy and girl students (and the laundress) had drunk the milk of the prize Earlham College herd of registered cattle that were almost a greater pride to the authorities than the college's deserved reputation for learning. They'd drunk that milk unpasteurized. Quickly it was proved by microbe hunter Mathews from Purdue that certain of these sanitary and highly manicured cows were pouring out the bug of Doctor B. Bang in their nutritious milk. Farbar stuck to her guns through a sharp battle with the authorities, and after twenty-eight had got sick, this epidemic suddenly snuffed out by pasteurization of all milk drunk at the college.

In this unhygienic hole in the Hygienic Laboratory Francis now rolled up his sleeves to dig (bare-handed as was his custom) into this new danger in milk. He began working with virulent goat strains that had come out of humans, and pig Bang bugs got from the blood of people, and other Bang microbes that had come out of cows. He knew mighty well that the obfuscators weren't by a long way through with their smoke screen in spite of Ithaca, South Bend, Earlham . . . and the rest of it.

There were terrifically eminent scientists who'd advocated trying to wipe out contagious abortion from cattle by vaccinating them with *living* Bang bacilli, and now . . .

There was the certified milk association justifiably proud of its t. b. testing, milkers with scrubbed hands, cows with washed udders, barns flushed out with water, animals chaperoned so their milk wouldn't have to be heated, so their milk could be sold at a high premium. . . .

There were queer people who believed that natural milk was healthier than milk that had been raised to the heat (not high) needed to kill the Bang bacillus. . . .

There was the immense amount of milk furnished raw all over our country by perfectly honest dairymen who just didn't think pasteurization was necessary. . . .

All these would be glad of the pig Bang bug fierceness and the cow Bang bug gentleness—if true. . . .

"After all has been said and done, the slippery place is in identifying in the lab a (microbe) culture as to its original porcine or bovine source," wrote Francis.

What Francis wanted to know at bottom wasn't any abstract or hair-splitting science in regard to this question but just simply whether the Bruce or the Bang bug (pig or cow origin) could be found in cow's milk and could be tracked from there into the suffering bodies of folks with undulant fever.

XII

In August, '28, he went at it, and on the 5th of November of that year he began to be feverish before five in the afternoons, with darting pains in his chest, a dry cough, and nasty pains back of his eyes and in the front of his head, and on November 13th he helped his pals fish the undulant fever microbe out of his own blood. That winter it settled into him and he went on the operating table for a serious operation in March, after limping round on crutches all winter keeping his weight off his left leg that played hob with him.

Spring, '29, he was back at work, tanned, filled out, looking better than I'd ever seen him, but working only half days . . . toward noon he'd get curiously tired. "You see, the (so and so) has still got me," he said, laughing.

Some will tell you the workers in the red brick building are just plumb careless—the way they're continually bit by the bugs they're tracking. Others—we won't go into their motives—say these fellows say to hell with the danger just for the swank of it. It's my idea it's only because of the self-forgetting curiosity, the intensity, with which they dig into every new mystery. Francis says it's damned clumsy to work with rubber gloves.

Francis felt uncomfortable about all the maybe's in this undulant fever business. He didn't like those argufiers. Before and during and after his own sickness with it, alone, with a peculiar secretiveness, he kept plugging in his dirty little room, finding the loop-hole, the catch, in this and that complicated test that was supposed to tell you the difference between the Bruce microbe and its pig and cow Bang brothers.

Finally he found what he called an "is" in place of a "maybe."

The Bang microbe that comes from cows—originally—*is* mighty finicky about starting to grow in the nutritive culture soups or jellies outside the animal body. Those cow Bang bugs need to breathe carbon dioxide to get started.

The Bang microbe that comes from pigs—originally—isn't finicky, grows easy, without carbon dioxide.

Bruce microbes, whether from goats, cows, or humans, aren't pernickety, don't mind growing without carbon dioxide. These are the differences you can bank on to tell the Bang bugs from their Bruce brothers.

But the Bang bugs from pigs can get into cows and pass out through the milk . . .

And Francis had fished cow Bang bugs from the blood of sick people . . . microbes identical with the ones he'd fished from the milk they'd been drinking . . .

And from the blood of a poor devil undulant fever had killed out in Iowa, he'd been sent *both* the evil Bang brothers. . . . One was surely from cows originally, needing carbon dioxide to grow it . . . the other grew easily and so it had to be the pig Bang bug or else the Bruce microbe of Malta.

But what matter? So long as all these three bugs did live in cows and pass out through their milk?

XIII

Toward Evans, who'd stirred up all this scandal, the microbes certainly did have a special animosity. For seven years they'd gnawed at her, taken the best years of her life, made a wreck of her. Just the same she was no longer a forlorn prophetess. She'd got a just (though not monetary) reward, having been elected President of the American Society of Bacteriologists. She could now speak right out in meeting, and did, and came out openly saying that if all the sick people who were still mis-diagnosed this or that, and who really had undulant fever, were counted, well . . .

The way her original cagy little prophecies have come true must make her smile and forget for a moment those Bruce bugs that lurk in her. In 1929, undulant fever was reported from every state in the Union. The cases *reported* had jumped from a few dozen in '26 to way over a thousand in 1929.

Of course Evans's part was long ago finished . . . and now it's entirely up to the public whether or not it wants to go on having undulant fever. Walt Simpson and the Dayton doctors have shown what can be done about it. Walt is pathologist at the Miami Valley Hospital in that midwest town and has a peculiar intolerance about people going on suffering from any sickness for whose existence there's no excuse. He's got the Dayton doctors worked up into the same strange state of feeling. In a few months Simpson and the wide-awake Dayton doctors turned up more than seventy cases of undulant fever in Dayton and its surroundings. . . .

In a very short while, Simpson and the best Dayton physicians had learned to spot undulant fever the way you'd spot mumps or measles. The doctors diagnosed it with their eyes and their common sense and began bringing blood samples to Simpson for the final check test.

Simpson and his enthusiastic gang of co-workers (all too plain to call themselves scientists) showed beautifully on a large scale how this nasty fever picks out the raw milk drinkers and leaves other folks alone.

A year and a half ago Dayton and its suburb of Oakwood began pasteurizing all their milk, including the high-toned, high-priced, haughty certified. . . .

Since then they've not had one case of the fever.

Of course in America Simpson and his Dayton gang are a bit peculiar, maybe even fanatical, and there are hardly more than thirty-some cities that require pasteurization.

People will jog along comforted by the fact (?) that you have to drink lots of raw milk to catch undulant fever.

It is also pretty good science that out of all people drinking raw milk not all by a long shot are susceptible.

The catch in it is that you're not sure till you're down on your back with it, in which class you belong.

Nothing is sillier than your muffler-wrapped, rubbers-wearing, umbrella-carrying health crank, I'll grant you.

But there are some precautions both easy and sensible. Wanting to live long and to stay fit and husky, I'll ask, before drinking milk: *Is it pasteurized?*

6. McCOY

SHOULD GENERALS DIE IN BED?

~~~~~~

"But why do YOU have to do this work," Mrs. McCoy
asked her husband.

"If the rest of them don't handle the sick birds, I be-
lieve they'll be safe," McCoy said. . . .

"But why do you have to work all alone with it?"

"If I go on working with it . . . with what we know
about it . . . I believe I have just about fifty chances
out of a hundred of being alive thirty days from
now . . ."

"That's all right. I see. It's all you can do," said Mrs.
McCoy.

~~~~~~

THIS is the last of the present stories of the adventures
of the men and women of the red brick building on the
hill. I must warn you of the insignificance of the death-fight
it tells of. We are all not much safer for the pother that was
raised over it, nor for the risks run during the desperate
three months that it lasted. But it was pioneering.

If the science of death-fighting isn't pioneering, to my
notion it's nothing. Any trail-blazer, no matter how much
the leader, has to take equal risks with his followers no matter how humble. That way all pioneering is like warfare
used to be—in the braver days when generals frequently
didn't die in bed.

Nowadays, laboratory directors (generals in death-fighting
just as Pershing was generalissimo of the A.E.F.) run about

as much chance of dying from the deaths they fight as generals in the last war ran of being knocked off by a bomb or a whizz-bang. Much modern death-fighting has become so complex, involving so many workers, that it seems plain sense for a director to stay back, saving his brains for directing. It's really no different from the circumstances that forced generals in the last war to fight from châteaux and deep dugouts. . . .

Brains have got to save their own skins or the cannon fodder millions up forward would fall into confusion.

In view of this necessity in modern wars and in death-fighting, the conduct of McCoy—Director of the Hygienic Laboratory of the United Public Health Service—seems to me to have been not only quixotic, but downright preposterous, and against the best interests of the nation he works for. It would be next to impossible to find another man with his brain for science and shrewd common sense.

Yet, what he did wasn't only like a general going up the line where the crumps were falling thick and the machine gun bullets whining and snapping. It was as if the general had gone up there, then sent his doughboys back to the safe S O S, and decided to fight it out all alone. . . .

This story (in consequence) is not so much a tale of the brainy way men against death are working to keep us living longer. If it has any merit or significance, it's because it gives you a close-up of the origins of the spirit that makes the cockroach-infested old red brick building unique as a den of scientific romance.

II

Early in January, 1930, the administrative offices of the United States Public Health Service at Washington turned into a bedlam. ". . . REQUEST INFORMATION REGARDING DIAGNOSIS PARROT FEVER. . . . WHAT INFORMATION AVAILABLE REGARDING PREVENTION SPREAD OF PARROT FEVER. . . . CAN

YOU PLACE SUPPLY PARROT FEVER SERUM OUR DISPOSAL IMME-
DIATELY WIRE REPLY. . . ."

In the offices at Washington stacks of yellow and blue
slips of paper, begging, asking, demanding, piled up on the
desks of the Public Health officials, who had hardly so much
as heard of parrot fever. Most of them had probably forgotten they'd learned, in medical school, of an obscure ill
caught from parrots and bearing the scientific name "psittacosis"—in which the "P" is silent. Knowing that word
didn't help them answer those telegrams, and of course it
was up to McCoy and his men at the Hygienic. There was
hurried telephoning.

McCoy (tall with a gnarled Lincolnian face without Lin-
coln's melancholy) called in Charles Armstrong—who was
thickset, with reddish hair and round china-blue eyes set
wide apart in a face that couldn't keep from smiling.

"Armstrong, what do *you* know about parrot fever," Mc-
Coy asked.

"What do I know about it? I don't know a *thing* about
it," Armstrong said.

Neither did McCoy and they had plenty of company in
their ignorance. The ill, when it first popped up in our
country, hadn't been diagnosed by medical scientists but by
a housewife, who'd spotted it not with the help of a medical
book but from reading a section of the Sunday New York
Times. This woman's husband was an Annapolis, Mary-
land, doctor, who'd been coming home worried, those De-
cember days in 1929, because of three cases of a peculiar
pneumonia. . . . Or was it typhoid? . . . Or possibly flu?
. . . No—these people's lungs were filling up. It was pneumonia . . . but not typical, peculiar . . .

This Mrs. Martin had read how folks in Germany that
Autumn had been getting parrots from South America, how
those birds had got sick, and then their owners. Mrs. Martin knew her husband's patients had a parrot in their home

and the bird had been poorly lately and so she put two and two together.

Now this day early in January as McCoy and Armstrong sat in the red brick building, twenty-six cases had been reported that morning, and there were deaths, three deaths from parrot fever in Baltimore, alone, and new cases were exploding all over the country, and there was a fine start toward one of our American hysterias. . . .

So this day Armstrong packed his satchel. The day before he'd been miles below the surface of the hurly-burly of everyday life, deep in fumbling with the mystery of post-vaccinal sleeping sickness. That was really important business, affecting the health and the lives of hundreds of people vaccinated for smallpox. It was a threatening business, beginning to shake health officers' sureness when they told folks that smallpox vaccination was entirely harmless. Now Armstrong had to ditch it, and it was lamentable and seemed frivolous, because only people with parrots were in any danger, and didn't people who kept parrots deserve it?

Armstrong was imperturbable. He and his right-hand man, Shorty Anderson, shut up their vaccine shop and went out chasing parrots, masquerading as parrot fever experts, which was really laughable. And Armstrong did laugh about it.

III

It was now the 16th of January and Armstrong and Shorty were in the dingy basement of the Hygienic in a couple of dank, frowsty little holes hardly bigger than coal-bins, an insult to offer any self-respecting microbe hunter for a laboratory. They practiced getting parrots in and out of cages they'd rigged up from garbage cans with wire-mesh covers. Going by the doors of their rooms in the cellar you sure got an earful while Armstrong and Shorty got over being hams as parrot-handlers. Shorty worshiped Armstrong, who'd taught him all he knew of microbe hunting. Now it was exgob Shorty's chance to teach his boss what you say (in the Navy) for spiritual relief in difficult situations. Armstrong was a fine pupil.

Telling me the whole story, afterward, Charley Armstrong tried to justify himself. . . .

"Those parrots were sure *mean* bastards," Armstrong said.

Right off the bat—with wonderful luck—they got parrot fever going among the screaming, yawping aviary they'd turned those cellar rooms into. Armstrong had hurried to Baltimore and got a bird dead of it from William Royal Stokes, the City Bacteriologist. (That was before Stokes began developing chills and a bad headache and pain in his chest.) Along with the bedraggled carcass of that parrot Armstrong brought what he'd scraped off the floor of the cage of another parrot who'd been sick. Now, instead of having to fool round months as you often do to get the hang of passing a new disease through animals, right from the gong it was a go. . . .

Armstrong and Shorty were both excited. Here were birds who a few days before had been clawing green devils. Now when Shorty lifted the covers off their cages they just stayed sitting there, kind of thoughtful. They sat hunched back with their heads bent forward, not moving. They breathed with a funny sort of grunting gasp.

Some of these had been given food sprinkled with a wee bit of the stuff Armstrong had scraped off the floor of the Baltimore bird cage. Others Armstrong had shot in the chest muscle with a tiny bit of mashed-up tissue of the dead bird Stokes had given him. Meanwhile Shorty was mighty handy at grabbing and holding parrots without getting gaffed by them and was proud of it. He was really an extraordinary lab-swipe, never watching the clock and always wanting to know what the experiments were about and *getting the point of them.* . . .

They were both parrot fever ignoramuses and for both

there was a wallop with them getting less ignorant, feeling they had control of this weird disease, by a little jab of the-next-to-nothing through a needle making those birds sicken and die, the very first experiment they made. By now there were good reasons for their knowing they shouldn't get gay with it. . . .

Back in '79, seven parrot owners had got sick in Switzerland—three dying; in 1902 in Paris, out of seventy-eight folks who had the peculiarity of being parrot lovers, and getting sick because of it, twenty-four had died. Armstrong had read that all up nights. "Pretty much day and night we were at it," Armstrong explained to me. More and more people were dying in America right now with the newspapers helping along the hysteria. Maybe Eddie Francis who always scoffed at rubber gloves (saying they made your fingers all thumbs) kidded him in his rough buffoonish way, but you couldn't kid Armstrong and he bought extra heavy ones for Shorty and himself.

You understand that, at this time, their precautions weren't extraordinary . . . they never are in the red brick building where those searchers have always been *in*-fighters, never back-peddlers or cautious left-jabbers. "If we'd got too careful, we'd have spent all our time being careful and how could we have found out anything about it?" asked Armstrong. But anyway every morning they swashed down the floor of their horrid little studios with compound cresol. They put a cresol-soaked mat just out the door so the whole basement (which ordinarily had a mixed bouquet of dog-monkey-goat-rabbit-guinea-pig) now *smelled safe*—with cresol.

Now more and more birds changed from screaming varmints to what looked like sick philosophers. Even so, every now and again they'd stage a comeback and then those heavy gloves weren't enough to keep Shorty and Armstrong from getting a nasty clawing. Neither of them were a bit worried.

Parrot fever might be extremely fatal, but who'd proved it was very contagious? It was mighty funny the way newspapers were reporting more and more people dying. . . .

At this time it was Armstrong's opinion that these must be peculiar people who let parrots kiss them and even take food from between their lips. He said this with a snort and was definitely not the kind of man who would even own a parrot let alone kiss it. Now their knives flashed and gleamed with an always greater precision, lovely and satisfying after their hick beginning, as they slit into one dead parakeet after another. They grunted monosyllables, they laughed, they were serious as they shot new healthy birds with the sick tissues of dead ones, as they delicately (tongues out the corners of their mouths) touched tiny bits of sick parrot onto this and that succulent culture medium—

About all that was known of this mysterious sickness was that a Frenchman, Nocard—who was no fool, having been Pasteur's pupil—said the culprit was a bug he'd baptized *Bacillus psittacosis.* And now the first new fact they found was that the little that was thought to be known about this parrot fever just wasn't so. The alleged *Bacillus psittacosis* was a bogey, a phantom!

They were careful, and with reasonable precautions Shorty wiped his feet on the cresol mat as he hurried out the door to carry new racks of culture tubes upstairs to Sara Branham who was the Hygienic's shark at telling this bug from that one. But they weren't showy or dramatic or idiotic about their asepsis. How the devil can you get to know a sickness when you hold it way out away from you on the end of a pair of long tongs?

IV

From coast to coast the Health Authorities (which made them parrot fever authorities without having to know anything about parrot fever) were coming out in newspapers pooh-poohing the now nation-wide silly parrot panic. One

January day there was a big picture in a Washington newspaper of Dr. William C. Fowler, who was health officer of the District of Columbia and looked every inch of it.

The picture showed the doctor with his own pet parrot. "I see no justification at this time for any widespread activity," Fowler oracled.

"Get rid of my parrot?" Fowler bellowed. "I should say not. That bird and I are good friends!"

It was good human interest stuff that every day when the doctor came home to dinner the bird squawked, "Hello, Bill!" and ordered the hired girl to dish up the dinner. It was pretty cute.

Out in San Francisco the *Call-Bulletin* exhorted its customers not to get in a cold sweat about it. "Dr. Karl F. Meyer scouts theory that parrots carried recent deaths in East." And K. F. Meyer was one of the top cut of America's microbe hunters. And Dr. Geiger posed for a press photographer (who must have reveled in it) holding a parrot and looking— or trying to look—nonchalant.

Geiger was wearing a rubber glove though.

On the morning of January 25th, when, for only nine days Armstrong and Shorty had been at it in their stinking cellar, Armstrong came up the hill to the red brick building, feeling fine. He found Shorty seedy. He walked in the lab door to find Shorty slumped in a heap at his desk holding his head in his hands. "Rotten headache, blankety-blank-blank," Shorty mumbled.

He'd always been a bear-cat for work. He was only an eighth grade graduate but had more microbe-hunting savvy than most professors. Here was the work going great guns and that was when Shorty (invariably) was all smiles and cheerful profanity. At the best of times he wasn't much to look at. He was thin-haired and had a big nose in a sort of battered face. Now he looked awful. "God, he *was* an assistant," Armstrong said.

"You know, he was one of those *honest* guys. I could always bank on him. If he killed an animal by accident in an experiment he'd come right to me telling me. He'd never try covering his tracks," Armstrong said.

"And then sorry? Lord, you'd think his heart was broke. He was a bear at handling animals. He hated to bitch an experiment. He understood what I was driving at. I never saw such a guy for wanting to know . . ."

But now, January 25th . . . "Christ, I'm cold," Shorty said.

The 27th of January they had him between sheets under nice warm blankets in the Naval Hospital next door to the Hygienic. His headache would have liked to split his skull now. The X-ray plates of his chest taken by the Navy doctor, Peterson, showed enlarged glands round the roots of his air-tubes, but otherwise nothing. . . .

At this moment Armstrong had a new helper. George McCoy—Director of the Hygienic Laboratory—was pinch-hitting for Shorty down in the dingy basement, holding the birds for Armstrong, who had a private chuckle at what a ham his boss was at this new job.

"Of course now we knew we really had parrot fever in our birds," Armstrong told me. "It was parrot fever Shorty had, all right."

The whole Hygienic Laboratory gang of microbe hunters were in a stew about their boss going down there with Armstrong. McCoy was partly serious and partly laughing and with his characteristic funny motion of his hands waving the bunch of them away.

"Let *me* take a whack at it," Dyer begged. (Dyer was the man who later found the Rocky Mountain spotted fever killing folks in the civilized East.)

All the others crowded round McCoy—Eddie Francis, Roscoe Spencer, Badger, Lillie, and Harrison (who'd had his own private hell with the undulant fever)—all the rest of them.

"Why, Mac, you're the *director* here. It isn't *intelligent* of you," said old Dr. S. P. Kramer. Kramer was the wise old volunteer searcher. He needed only a beard to be the very type of a benevolent Jewish patriarch and was all for intelligence (like many Jews) and was a shrewd counselor McCoy was likely to listen to.

"No. . . . No. . . . No. . . . Go on with you!" McCoy said.

He waved his hand to back them away and went down in the basement in the door across the cresol-soaked mat and loomed tall, pompadour-haired, gnarled, contrasting to Armstrong's stockiness. Things now went fine in that cellar. In their garbage can homes many birds were now breathing hard with grunts, not moving except for a dip of their tail-feathers as they gasped for air. They looked pitifully moth-eaten (even if you didn't like parrots) as they sat with heads drooped down in front of their green bodies all hunched up in bunches.

Since the *Bacillus psittacosis* was hooey, was it maybe a microbe too little to see, maybe a filter-passing ultra-micro-scopic virus that was at the bottom of it? Was it subvisible life down in the mysterious sub-cellar of life (where only the most primitive ooze of life stuff stirs, merging into the inani-mate protein matrix of life)? There was nothing profoundly original about asking such a question. It's the stock thing to ask of any disease where you can't spot a microbe. It's that kind of infinitely tiny, murderous, maybe formless, certainly invisible life that kills people with yellow fever, rabies.

Now things went worse with Shorty at the hospital next door to McCoy and Armstrong. X-rays showed a sinister cloud gathering low down at the base of his left lung, and gradually widening. Shorty's headache was awful. He tried to eat the swell food the Naval Hospital dietitian coaxed into him and then vomited. He felt sickish all the time and began coughing and Dr. Peterson didn't like the looks of that growing, denser and denser shadow that peculiarly crawled up and up, creeping up his chest in the X-ray pictures.

Next door McCoy and Armstrong were wiping their feet on the cresol mat, going out and in the door experimenting and seeing Shorty and experimenting. He was their friend. He became part of their experiment, an experimental animal much more important than the parrots or parakeets, with Armstrong jabbing his arm vein for blood and gathering rusty stuff—sticky like glue—that came up from his lungs. Armstrong then hurried back to shoot the blood and the sputum into parrots, monkeys . . .

That was one thing you always had at the Hygienic—plenty of animals. McCoy didn't give a hoot for fine brick buildings or lava-topped lab tables . . . but you had to have plenty of animals, even human animals if it came to a pinch. Now McCoy and Armstrong expanded, being as you might say in full production. In the little room just above their basement dens the two of them made mashes of the livers and lights of dead parakeets, made extracts, sucked them through an earth filter so fine it would hold back any bug big enough to be microscopically visible. . . .

The clear fluid that came through the filter they now shot into the chest muscles of new healthy birds, and in a couple of days these unhappy beasts stopped yawping and squawking and became philosophical. . . .

Never have experiments succeeded so quickly, so prettily. It was one of those rare rewards of your searcher whose bane and usual experience is a long succession of experiments that are negative, or go hay-wire, or come out (idiotically) two contradictory ways simultaneously. But now McCoy and Armstrong were just happy boys telling each other. . . .

V

"We've got the virus, we've got it!"

McCoy was happier than he'd been in years, never minded at all being only assistant, or *garçon de laboratoire,* or *diener,* or lab-swipe. He got very good at snaffling parrots when those devils (still full of fight) butted their way out of their garbage-can cages. They could do it even when you weighted down the wire mesh tops with a brick and it was a wallop to catch them when you knew they were infected.

They didn't let janitors or animal men or any kind of attendant come in there. McCoy fed the animals and cleaned the dung from their cages. Way past fifty, he was a boy again . . . away, at last, from his roll-top desk as director. Armstrong let it be known that McCoy—while not so handy—was a pretty good pinch-hitter for Shorty.

But Shorty was bad. It was the 3rd of February, with his pulse faster and faster and thready and his fever 104. Peterson and other Naval doctors hung over him. They shot glucose into his arm vein and talked about using oxygen. It was the 4th of February. The upper part of his left lung had filled now and there was a shadow (ominous) at the base of his right. He was so drowsy. Everything seemed mixed up and floating round in his head like one of those crazy movies going backward. He was stuporous and that was a help to him but then a gagging cough would bring him out of it.

Armstrong bent over him. "Anything we can do for you, Shorty?"

Shorty was groggy but opened his eyes recognizing Armstrong. By God, there was a boss—a guy you could trust.

"Will you pay my bills for me, Doctor?" Shorty mumbled.

Armstrong and the whole room dissolved into a crazy dream for him. Shorty was peculiar about his bills, which were the comic relief of the austere doings of the Hygienic.

"Shorty, just like all of us, had thirty days leave a year," explained Armstrong.

"Every month he'd take half a day off that leave to go round paying his installments. He had a wife and two kids and what a bunch of installments! He had the usual fourteen-hundred-and-forty-dollar-a-year man's installments, and then a lot of fancy ones besides," Armstrong said.

"He was so damn' serious about it. Made a regular ceremony about going round every month, biting a little bit off each month."

Now Shorty woke up again with Armstrong dissolving in, looming over him. "Just see those bills are paid. . . . (Coughing) . . . You know, I've got lodge insurance. . . ." More coughing and then stupor again. Armstrong knew Shorty's head wouldn't hurt him with him unconscious. That is one of the merciful provisions of Nature that optimistic theologians tell you proves something or other.

It was now the 6th of February. There were seventy-five cases of parrot fever in fourteen states of the Union and twenty were dead already and more dying. McCoy and Armstrong (sunk in a pit of taut experiment) forgot there was any nation. Now they were set to repeat, to check it, to cooper it up with gold-headed nails proving how tremendously little the parrot fever virus actually was. And to see how one parrot caught it from another, they put parts of dead parrots in cages along with healthy birds. And now guinea-pigs added their idiotic chittering to the parakeet's screams in that small first floor room and in the still of the night you could hear the low scuffling of white mice in their glass battery jars and below in the basement monkeys added to the parrots made you think of an incipient zoo. Armstrong and McCoy were cooking up experiments to see whether they could guard parrots from this sure death by serum of sick folks who had (by the Grace of God) got over their fever. The two of them were now hardly human and no better than a pair of excited beagles hot on the scent, with the rest of the world blotted out into a blank or at best just a blur.

VI

Here it was 6th of February. That morning Armstrong came up the hill feeling fine with his head running over with new experiments. Then a little shiver shot through him and his skin—this was funny!—felt tender all over.

Here it was February 7th and Armstrong who always had too much of an appetite couldn't look food in the face. He got off by himself and stuck a thermometer in his mouth. It came out saying 102 and as he read it he felt a shooting pain in the front of his head.

Then he walked into the Naval Hospital knowing very well he had about seven chances out of ten of coming out in a box. The day Armstrong went in there, McCoy went down into the stink of the old Hygienic Laboratory cellar with those sick parrots, alone.

Francis, Dyer, all the rest of them, tried to come down there but all of a sudden McCoy the director (who never directed) became their boss and shooed them all away from him. Then he went in the door over the cresol-soaked mat and had the very hell of a time trying to catch and hold parrots and inject them and operate them all alone. He whistled and scratched his stubbly pompadour hair (not being a man to blaspheme like Shorty Anderson or Armstrong). All at once he laughed out loud. He got one of the parrots into a glass jar. He tied a bit of cotton to a string. He soaked it in ether. He let it down right close to the parrot's beak. A faintly etherized, slightly ether-drunk parrot can be handled without the usual danger of mayhem. So he went it alone.

Here it was February 8th. When Armstrong had walked in the door of the Naval Hospital his fever was 104. Peterson looked at an X-ray picture showing the lower part of Armstrong's left lung filling up. . . .

Shorty died that morning at 6:15. At seven his body was on the autopsy table in the deadhouse for Peterson and all of them to study just how this creeping parrot pneumonia had killed him. This was Shorty's last experiment.

McCoy came to cheer up Armstrong. Then he hurried over to Shorty's family and saw about all those installments Shorty was so het up about and to help pay them up the whole Hygienic gang (of course) chipped in. It was nice that Shorty wasn't in the red when they buried him. McCoy and all the folks who could get off their work at the red brick building helped Shorty's family to put him away (without music) in his gob's suit in Arlington Cemetery right in the same ground hallowed by generals, admirals, and W. J. Bryan (who was a kind of a colonel). Shorty's family had eleven dollars left over.

VII

. . . (Decoration Day, three years ago, I looked out the window of the room in Washington where I was then sketching this story. Along the street between the Treasury and the White House, came marching, under the sun of that lovely May morning, first a corporal's guard of Civil War soldiers, limping and tottering. They choked me up a little. Back of them came a gang of Spanish War (?) veterans walking straight. Then a band of World War bozos in yellow imitation tin hats marched blaring "John Brown's Body" and then another band of similar young bozos in red imitation tin hats marched playing "Over There" and they all walked showing they knew they'd been heroes. I was right then full of telling about Shorty and like a fool I found myself crying. Whizz-bangs hadn't killed Shorty so it was all right for him not to have music. . . .)

VIII

"But why do *you* have to do this work?" Mrs. McCoy asked her husband.

She wasn't being unreasonable but only asking him.

"If the rest of them don't handle the sick birds, I believe they'll be safe. Working with them, I guess I have, well . . . maybe . . . about eighty chances in a hundred of getting it," McCoy said to his wife.

"But why work alone with it?" she asked him.

"Well, if I go on working with it . . . let me see . . . I believe I've about fifty chances out of a hundred of being alive thirty days from now," McCoy said.

"Oh, I see. Yes. It's all right. It's all you can do," Mrs. McCoy said.

So he went back down cellar autopsying parrots suddenly dead. Then he carried them up to the little room above to make cultures. Then he carried what was left of the birds down to the incinerator, picking up food left outside the doors of the basement room as he went back in. Pretty soon he came out the door carrying cages birds had died in and cleaned them, not letting the darky swipes touch them till he'd autoclaved them in steam under high pressure. He was now Shorty and Armstrong and himself all in one. He kept hurrying back and forth between the cellar and Armstrong —who was too cool an egg to bother much about his own chances and anyway too sick to worry even if he hadn't been the phlegmatic man that he was.

McCoy now checked their filtration experiment . . . doing it all over. Between the experiments and Armstrong visits he had long talks (over the telephone) with Assistant Surgeon General Stimson over at the Bureau.

"Isn't there a chance for a serum, Mac?" Stimson kept asking. "I've heard they're using convalescent serum over in Baltimore," Stimson said.

They were using it right then on William Royal Stokes, the bacteriologist who'd got Armstrong started with that first dead bird, who was now desperately sick with the same creeping pneumonia that had got into Shorty and Armstrong.

"You can go the limit, no matter what it costs to buy serum from people who've got over it," Stimson said.

Now if there's any microbe hunter living who's more skeptical than George McCoy is about serums, I'd like to have you name him. McCoy is the final authority, has the final say-so about the Government licensing of vaccines and serums allowed to be peddled in the United States of America. Many a time I've seen him shake his head and laugh tolerantly about serums invented in labs of the highest scientific reputation—serums for meningitis, pneumonia. He makes you think he's just being good-natured letting them by and has to do it because of pressure of medical opinion only. You understand he has no inherent prejudice against serums but he's from Missouri about them. You can't stop all quackery but McCoy does stop a lot of it.

Now McCoy thought of Armstrong. Peterson had just told him the X-ray showed a patch on Armstrong's lung creeping up and up. McCoy went over to see Armstrong and Armstrong told him he was having the most crazy ideas of what was happening to him. "I seem to be floating right up off the bed to the ceiling. I've got to snap out of it," Armstrong said, smiling.

McCoy didn't smile but called Roscoe Spencer, the Rocky Mountain spotted fever fighter. Here it was the 9th of February and Spencer was in Baltimore before you could say Jack Robinson, right after his talk with McCoy. He had a little satchel with syringes and alcohol and absorbent cotton. Now it was evening just before supper and Spencer'd gone round begging for blood from folks—five of them—who'd come through parrot fever. He hadn't got a drop of it.

"We don't *know* your blood will cure Dr. Armstrong," Spencer told each one of them. "But it's all we can think of to try to save him."

But one was only just getting better and another needed all his blood to get his own strength back and so on. Here it was evening with McCoy in Washington knowing he wouldn't fail to come back with it. Now he was talking to a frail old lady, just over parrot fever. . . .

"Yes, if there's chance of saving a life, I'll give it," said the old lady.

"I took care to wrap the blood flask in a towel so she wouldn't see how much she was giving," Spencer said, telling me long after.

Spencer told her he would pay for her blood but the old lady answered no, not if they were going to try to save a life with it.

It was now eleven in the evening and Armstrong had never felt quite like this nor heard of anything like it. He seemed to be getting bigger and bigger, swelling into a fantastic balloon till he wasn't human any more but something globoid and enormous, up and up off the earth away and away. All that evening McCoy had kept calling up Peterson.

"They gave me that serum at eleven," Armstrong said. "Just before, it was all I could do to shake myself out of that awful balloon feeling. They told me afterwards that in less than two hours I was sleeping like a baby."

McCoy kept on working and couldn't understand about himself. Why wasn't he getting chills and one of those sudden headaches? Up in New York at the City Health Department Laboratories, four workers in Dr. Krumwiede's laboratory were already down with it. Krumwiede (to my notion) was as near as you'll come to the kind of men working in the red brick building on the hill, and already he'd proved, just as McCoy and Armstrong were doing, that the *Bacillus psittacosis* was nonsense and that it was a business of a virus too little to see. . . .

But then four of them had come down with it and now the work had been transferred to the Rockefeller Institute laboratories where they had all the money in the world to take every precaution so no one working with it could possibly get it. . . .

It is reported that they put on rubber hip boots and walked round on floors flooded with disinfectant and wore rubber gloves all the way up to their armpits and head covers with windows in them through which to peep at their dangerous pets, the parrots. . . . It must have felt very safe but also (technically) must have been something like a man in a deep-sea diver's suit trying to mend one of those lady's Swiss wrist watches.

Up in the New York State Health Department, the lady microbe hunter Ruth Gilbert was down with parrot fever and not far from death. All over the nation parrot lovers and their families were sick with it, and better than thirty were already dead, and dying. Now the newspapers weren't kidding it. If he'd been asked to go down in the cellar to help George McCoy now, I wonder whether Hank Webster the cartoonist would have kidded it with his picture of the Timid Soul holding his handkerchief to his nose going past a birdstore window where a parrot sat perched behind a thick plate glass?

IX

"But I never felt better," McCoy told everybody.

"What you're doing is an absolutely unjustifiable waste," old Dr. S. P. Kramer told McCoy.

Francis, Dyer, Lillie, Badger, all the rest of them didn't know what to make of him. . . . McCoy was ordinarily genial and not really bull-headed. Now he shook his head and closed the door of his little room behind him. Was it because he'd been sitting too long by, while the rest of them had been tasting the salt of life taking chances? Was it just the wallop of his old days, when he hadn't been a director but only a microbe hunter fighting bubonic plague in California . . . was it the kick of the memory of that half-forgotten danger stirring him?

Ah . . . this was excellent. Pigeons, guinea-pigs, white mice, monkeys . . . all were immune to parrot fever. And wasn't this peculiar? He could leave dead parrots in cages with healthy ones, and nothing happened whatever! It couldn't be very contagious after all. . . . Had Armstrong and Shorty just been—careless? Here was a lovely accidental experiment to confirm it that it wasn't easy for the ill to go from bird to bird. A sick bird escaped from the infected bird room (McCoy just couldn't watch everything) and had got up on the healthy parrots' cages polluting them. But the healthy birds kept yawping and stayed chipper.

Here it was February 13th. With McCoy (the serum skeptic) urging him, Peterson had slammed bigger and bigger doses of convalescent serum into Armstrong. This morning Armstrong's chart showed a temperature normal and it said under REMARKS—"Feels fine."

Already Armstrong—an unkillable bundle of bull-necked energy—was yelling to get out of the hospital. "Just wait, Mac," Armstrong told McCoy who'd come into his sick room. "Wait till I get back and we'll give 'em hell again!"

On the morning of the 15th of February McCoy was up to his ears in experiments in the cellar with his zoo of healthy, sick, dying, and dead birds and mammals . . . it was bizarre that he felt fit as a fiddle. His pals were worried half sick by his aloof refusal to let them into it. . . . "I believe Mac would have been actually glad if he'd caught it!" one of them (who was exasperated) told me.

And who knows if this is so far from the truth? His old friend Goldberger had caught five of the sicknesses he'd hunted, among them dengue fever and the terribly dangerous yellow fever and typhus. Eddie Francis had had tularemia twice and undulant fever, and Alice Evans had never gotten over the body-punishment the Bruce bug had given her. Then there were McClintic, Gettinger, big Henry Cowan and the rest who'd gone West in line of duty from the bite of the Rocky Mountain spotted . . . Well . . . McCoy, looking more than anything else like a very competent country schoolmaster of the old days, may finally have *resented* his own safety and in a half-mad burst of exasperation gone off the deep end. . . .

But the fantastic events now on the verge of happening made his own seeming immunity to this creeping parrot death all the more incredible. It was a weirdly impossible fact about this mysterious parrot fever that McCoy now discovered . . . in an experiment that was none of his planning (in fact he'd done everything possible to prevent its occurring). You can imagine . . . mulling the significance of the events that now exploded . . . how furious it must have made him. The whole business (in view of his sincere self-immolation) was in the highest degree ironical.

On the morning of the 15th of February, Lanham, the laboratory night-watchman, took sick with the parrot fever. . . .

"We knew exactly where we were before then," McCoy said long after, "but from that day on you simply can't know how we all felt here. It was spooky. . . ."

McCoy couldn't believe it. There was no doubt of it . . . when you once saw a case of parrot fever with those strange chills and sudden terrible headache. . . . But Lanham had never been inside those two parrot rooms in the cellar, or in the laboratory on the first floor just above. He was a burly honest fellow with a wife and two children to take care of and McCoy knew Lanham wasn't lying.

At the same time Lanham was getting very sick, very quickly Dr. William Royal Stokes went to join Shorty. There was nothing to show that this creeping pneumonia sneaks from one human to another but only that it goes from parrots to humans. None of them at the Naval Hospital had got even a touch of it taking care of Shorty, who coughed all over them, or from Armstrong. . . .

None of Shorty's own family had come down with it, or

any of Armstrong's. There was nothing in the learned books about its possibly extreme contagiosity, but here Lanham had it, and how he had it!

"Better locate more convalescents for serum," McCoy ordered Spencer. That's all McCoy said and then went back into his room closing the door after him.

When Jimmy Leake was just about ready to tell McCoy that Lanham might pull through, Mrs. Sadie Carlin came down with a quick headache and felt cold. She was a microbe hunter. She did work inside the red brick building, it's true. She'd worked with cultures that had come from sick parrots, admitted. But these were random bugs that had nothing to do with the creeping pneumonia. . . .

McCoy did a frantic Sherlock Holmes on all Carlin's movements. Yes, she'd had occasion to go into a room in the cellar *next* the parrot rooms. But no virus could sneak through a thick stone wall. . . .

Now McCoy wabbled. "I'd better close down the work," he told Armstrong.

Armstrong only laughed. "Don't do it. In a couple of weeks I'll be back there giving it hell again. . . ."

Meanwhile Spencer was scuttling to New York and Long Island and all over eastern America, sitting in kitchens of the humble homes of parrot owners (it was queer how many different kinds of folks owned parrots!). He dashed about over Massachusetts and Pennsylvania with his satchel, arguing, pleading, cajoling luckily recovered parrot-fever people. He was open-faced and disarming and anyway it's always much easier to ask for something *for somebody else* who's desperately up against it. . . .

He brought home great flasks full of blood and Mrs. Carlin was certainly feeling better and McCoy was breathing easier again.

X

Then everything went hay-wire. On the 10th of March Hasseltine, one of the red brick building veterans, went home for supper feeling ravenously hungry but before he sat down to supper he was shivering and the sight of his food gave him the nausea. . . . Hasseltine had had nothing to do with the parrot fever . . . his workroom was just across the hall from the little room where McCoy autopsied his dead birds. . . . Next day big Morgal, the foreman, turned up with a rotten headache, and he'd never been in either the sick or the healthy parrot rooms in the cellar. He'd only put food outside the door for McCoy to pull in for the parrots. Now Morgal refused to go to the hospital. . . . If he was going to die, no strangers around him, no, sir. . . .

"Badger, you'd better ask for travel orders," McCoy said. So Badger got orders—no limit—to go on the blood hunt.

It was now the 12th of March and Ernest Miller, who made the culture medium for all the microbes of the Hygienic, felt awful. Like Morgal and Lanham he'd had nothing to do with the parrots and was husky, an expert oarsman with enormous neck muscles and was never sick but now he had a high fever. . . .

At the Naval Hospital next door, Captain Richards told McCoy they'd always be one bed ahead of them . . . there'd always be a bed waiting. Meanwhile in the red brick building it was comical how McCoy was the only one in a stew about it. All the rest kidded about it till McCoy had to join in the ragging . . . it was what you saw in bad places in the Line in the war.

"How's your headache this morning, Dyer," McCoy (after a night of bad sleep) would ask Dyer, very early, by telephone.

Dyer would laugh, asking McCoy if he'd taken his temperature. It was now March 13th and they'd been coming down at a rate of one per day but today was a record. That day the darky cleaner, Blackwell (who had by this time developed superstitions about proximity to any sort of feathered creature and had been nowhere near parrots . . . no, *suh!*), got suddenly so sick that he nearly joined Shorty a few days later. And that same morning, battered Eddie Francis came in, grinning and laughing to hide the way he was feeling and said to McCoy: "Well, Mac . . ."

It was the joke of the laboratory about Francis being the chief experimental animal up there, but this wasn't so funny. From Europe reports were now coming of the fever killing four, even five out of every ten it sneaked into. . . .

The day after Francis had gone (twisting his head round characteristically and waving his arms and swearing and laughing . . . Pshaw—it—was—nothing—blankety-blank—et cetera . . .) the day after that, distinguished old Dr. Ludvig Hektoen had been taken to the Providence Hospital. He'd absolutely no contact with parrots, had only worked afternoons in Spencer's room. He'd got no nearer any parrot than going past the open door of McCoy's little autopsy room. . . .

Hektoen is gray-haired with a brown face that has a quick kind smile and the whole gang up there looked up to him and loved him, admired him not only because he was such a pathologist but because he was just Dr. Hektoen. He was pretty old to stand the parrot fever that had killed Shorty and Stokes and nearly got Lanham, and right now had the darky swipe, Blackwell, looking into the Valley of the Shadow. . . .

"I've never seen the worst kind of a jam leave McCoy anything but cheerful, smiling," Dr. S. P. Kramer said.

But the next day still another darky cleaner came down with the creeping terror, and now McCoy didn't smile.

XI

That Saturday afternoon if you'd been standing by the red brick building, and looked up at the sparrows flying over the roof, you'd have seen them suddenly hesitate in their flight, then nose-dive down onto the roof, dying. No . . . not from parrot fever.

That day, for the first time in all its grisly history, the old Hygienic had shut its doors, and sealed all its windows. All morning the gang who weren't yet delirious and coughing in the hospital had turned to and carried more than a thousand of every kind of animal down the hill with great care not to mix up the labels. That morning McCoy went alone as usual into those two basement rooms (not saying anything to anybody, not even Armstrong, Dyer, or Kramer). He'd shut the doors and chloroformed animals, chloroformed and chloroformed and chloroformed till he himself was groggy and woozy . . . every last one of the parrots, sick or healthy, all the guinea-pigs, the mice, rats, pigeons, and monkeys, who'd none of them caught it, couldn't possibly get it. He murdered and murdered and made a slick and clean job of it. He never smiled nor even muttered but just killed and killed and at the end of it swashed out every last cage with cresol, and gave all the dead bodies of those assorted unhappy experimental creatures a decent and thorough burning in the lab incinerator. . . .

Then in a half daze he went to the telephone and that afternoon fumigation experts turned loose in the tightly sealed old red brick building enough cyanide gas to kill every cockroach and bed-bug in three ships the size of the *Leviathan*. . . . Enough so that sparrows flying fifty feet above the roof of the tight-sealed building (grotesquely, as I've told you) hadn't liked it.

McCoy felt tired but otherwise fine. He'd made his experiment. So he called it a day.

XII

This cyanide business accounts for the following headline which appeared in *The Washington Post,* on Sunday, March 16, 1930:

PARROT FEVER PANIC SEIZES LABORATORY

The paper went on to tell how the Hygienic had "closed its doors." Maybe the reporters thought the doors should have stayed open and all the workers (who weren't in the hospital) should have stayed at their benches during the cyanide fumigation. That would have made them real heroes. Three hours after the fumigation was over they were all back opening the windows and the next day it was business as usual with them doubling up on the work that had been dropped by the dozen who now lay with their lungs filled up, coughing. You can imagine how McCoy felt about that headline.

No, they all had stayed (excepting one assistant who early in those horrid days had suddenly developed a sick grandma or something)—even old Dr. Kramer. He wasn't an officer of the Service, only a wealthy volunteer worker, who could have gone to Kamchatka to get away from it. . . .

"Why should I have gone?" Kramer asked me. "It wouldn't have been *intelligent.* I'd been exposed. Well . . . staying there I was near the serum!"

Kramer maintained it was the very opposite of heroic for them all to have stayed, because the serum . . .

But who knew that the serum from convalescent parrot fever people did really save them?

Well, all who got that serum so frantically gathered all over by Spencer and Badger, swear by it.

All excepting Shorty got the serum and Shorty was (amazingly) *the only one who died* . . .

I will be the target of statistical biometrical wranglers,

because there were lots of sufferers all over the country who didn't get serum, yet lived.

I have only the *feelings* of those fellows of the red brick building to go by, and though bad science, they may cut deeper than the most mathematical statistics.

Armstrong felt it, that night of February 9th, going downhill fast with pneumonia and his head all crazy and then serum and then off to sleep like a baby. . . .

It was quick like a lift from a dry Martini and you don't need statistics to prove the kick *that* gives you evenings when you're at a hard day's end.

No, they all swear by the curative effect of the convalescent blood those poor people gave (many gratis) to Badger and Spencer.

All but McCoy. He is your incorrigible skeptic. You'd think, in view of the disaster that followed his insisting on going through with it, that he'd at least claim the serum as one of the results. No. . . .

"They may have got better because we got them to bed so quickly. We aren't *sure* it was the serum," McCoy said, smiling again.

So, all he had, all the net result of the disaster that so nearly sent the Hygienic Laboratory on the rocks for keeps, was this . . .

Parrot fever, from parrot to man (not from man to man) is probably the most catching sickness known to medical science.

The practical deduction is obvious to all of us—except to those who love parrots ineradicably.

This deduction was generally perceived even by parrot lovers in our country and the plague soon faded.

As soon as Charlie Armstrong got better he and big Lanham (who'd so nearly cashed in his chips with it) went to work at it again . . . way off from everybody in an old deserted building at Curtis Bay Quarantine Station near Baltimore.

Armstrong thought it was silly to put them away so far. "The way our gang came down proves you're all right if you just aren't in the same building with it," Armstrong said.

Armstrong invited me to run over to see his new laboratory. I talked the whole business over with him. In my head a dozen reasons popped up that made it impossible for me to go . . . right now.

I never did get there.

"I don't think you've got cold feet," Armstrong said, and he wasn't smiling when he said it.

Just the same I didn't go to the Curtis Bay parrot fever station and you can make what you want of that.

ENVOI

Pellagra kills only poor white folks down South. Tularemia is nasty only to rabbit hunters and rabbit-cooking housewives. Undulant fever kills not so many and only sickens many thousands for from a month to seven years. Jake paralysis does nothing but cause a funny dragging of the legs of drinkers of Jamaica ginger. Rocky Mountain spotted fever only ambushes sheep-herders and other hill-billies of America. All these negligible malaises and deaths have been conquered by the men—and woman—of our old red brick building.

BOOK III
MACHINE MEDICINE

7. SCHAUDINN

THE PALE HORROR

~~~~~~

"There is no alleviation for the sufferings of man-
kind except veracity of thought and action and the
resolute facing of the world as it is, when the garment
of make-believe by which pious hands have hidden
its uglier features is stripped off . . ."

T. H. HUXLEY

~~~~~~

IT all began in a topsy-turvy fashion with Fritz Schaudinn
forced into a job in which he had no interest whatever.
The modern fight against humanity's most treacherous affliction began that day, late in February of 1905, not long
after the Imperial Health Office ordered Schaudinn to drop
his own independent researches.

He was a bushy-bearded German giant of a man, hot first
of all for his scientist's right to search out just what he
wanted to. Here the nabobs of the Health Office were wanting him to check up on the preposterous science of this fellow, Siegel, who claimed he'd uncovered bugs causing not
only the smallpox but the great-pox, to say nothing of foot-
and-mouth sickness, and even scarlet fever. Who blames
Schaudinn for his disgust at being ordered round like any
lab swipe?

But at this detestable job he spotted the pale horror that
writhed, twisted, drilled back and forwards—invisibly—in
the bodies of uncounted miserable human millions. . . .

It's incredible that Schaudinn (who didn't *want* to) should
so quickly discover the tenuous demon that had dodged the

eyes of all searchers from Robert Koch onward. But then, the whole history of this so human affliction is full of surprises, and shot through with the positively outlandish. Four hundred years before Schaudinn it had exploded in Europe amazingly, coming—in historic probability—as the most important gift brought back from the New World by the sailors of Christopher Columbus. Its sneaking through Europe had been unbelievably rapid and horrible. The way of its spread had from almost the beginning made its name unmentionable. Yet, to the confusion of all who would divide humanity into good and bad, or high and low, it soon became plain that this scourge was no respecter of persons. . . .

So, through those centuries before that March day in 1905 when Fritz Schaudinn stumbled onto the strangely fragile cause of it, syphilis permeated humanity. It hid in the bodies of bishops and bankers of the upper ten as disastrously as it gnawed at the less distinguished vitals of the millions of the lower five. Saddest of all, apart from those whose sins it rewarded, myriads of innocent ones were (and still are) done to death by its slow, cruel lurking.

The modern fight against the curse of it is surely as strange a scientific saga as any. It began with the chance that turned Fritz Schaudinn from a disgruntled protistologist into a medical immortal. That ill-starred man was hardly cold in his grave before his fellow countryman, Wassermann, applied to it (on a wholly mistaken notion) the theoretical science of the dreamy little Belgian, Bordet—who wasn't concerned with it. Half a dozen years later the bizarre chemical antics of the gay Jew Ehrlich brought hopes of smashing at one fell swoop this pale horror. Then those hopes died. And now here's hope once more, solider and surer—rising out of the desperate adventure of an Austrian psychiatrist that's been capped by the weird discovery of an American engineer.

There's no need to apologize for the triviality of this pale horror that these men have groped, peered, sweat, and cudgeled their brains to master. It's now fairly sure that this scourge of the (till recently) unmentionable name outranks both tuberculosis and pneumonia as a cause of our human mortality. Of course the mortality tables give no inkling of its prowess as a killer—the why of that is clear to anybody. Before he died, the great William Osler put it down as first among all medical causes of death. John Stokes believes (conservatively) that from seven to ten out of every hundred hide the horror within them. He says it's very nearly the commonest and easily one of the most fatal of all the ills that plague us. John Stokes should know. . . .

It is treacherous. It is tenacious. It is ubiquitous. It is supreme among all ills as a degenerator, a sapper of life-stuff. It is altogether remarkable that the enormously tiny cause of it should have been found by Fritz Schaudinn—who didn't want to. . . .

II

There is a great deal of mystery about Fritz Schaudinn that makes me hesitate to try to tell about him in detail. Long ago, on what was certainly most dependable (though unpublished) authority, I wrote about him as "a fantastic fellow who drank and saw weird visions." Then, a short time ago, a letter came to me, signed by the director and seven of the associates of the Hamburg "Institute for Ship's and Tropical Diseases" where Schaudinn toiled in the short months between his discovery of the pale horror and his death. Several of the signers of this letter knew Schaudinn and loved him, and now politely protested he was not especially given to alcoholic indulgence nor was he a "fantast." They explained that his fantasies (when he indulged them) were only those of a vivid imagination giving him the key to many unsuspected relations in the mysterious sub-visible world of little animals he was incessantly peering into. . . .

So I apologize to Schaudinn's memory and to Giemsa, Fülleborn, and all the rest who signed that letter.

It's hard to come by facts about Schaudinn, even about such a simple matter as the occupation of his father. It seems to be agreed by everybody that he was born at Roeseningken in East Prussia in 1871. But one of his biographers says his father was a husbandman, another that he was a "goods inspector," while the famous American medical historian Garrison says he was the keeper of an inn.

Schaudinn went up to Berlin to study to be a philologist but before he knew it found himself fascinated by the microscopic loves, hates, and other adventures of those little animals known as protozoa. And here again I'm baffled. My friend the noted protozoölogist, Dobell, assures me I can't possibly write about Schaudinn because nobody but a protozoölogist can understand him—and protozoölogist is the last thing I'd claim to be. Nor would I want to be, since my nature is peace-loving, and among searchers it seems to me that protozoölogists are excessively disputatious, rowing and battling like mediaeval schoolmen.

In his article, "Protozoölogy," in the *Encyclopaedia Britannica*, 1922, Dobell ignores Fritz Schaudinn completely—though I've seen him referred to as "the father of modern protozoölogy." The eminent Doflein in his textbook about the protozoa refers to Schaudinn on no less than one hundred and eighty-two occasions. Yet Dobell (who ignores Schaudinn) had great respect for Doflein! I leave you to gauge Schaudinn's rank in this highbrow scientific realm. Incompetent to judge, I'll stay on the side-lines benevolently neutral. I will limit myself to telling those adventures of Schaudinn that can be understood not only by protozoölogists (who don't understand each other) but by plain people everywhere.

III

Before he was thirty Schaudinn was one of the protozoölogical big shots. He landed a job in the Imperial Health
Office in Berlin, never realizing how he'd be bored with it,
or what an amazing death-fighting adventure it would
bring him. He was lucky to begin with. Right away the
authorities sent him with his newly-wed young wife down
to Rovigno in Istria by the shore of the blue Adriatic. Here
he was happy. Here—away from the bigwigs—he was free to
piddle and dabble protozoölogically at anything he wanted
to, and how he dabbled.

Though some might deny it, there was a bit of the Leeu-
wenhoek about Schaudinn, for he turned his microscope
onto everything impartially. He spotted a little animal—
coccidium—that set up a dreadful inflammation in the bowels
of ground moles. Three times a week he'd sweat ten kilo-
meters up hill from Rovigno to the miserable twelve house
hamlet of San Michele di Leme, where the illiterate villagers
were shot with malaria. Through his lens he peeped at the
blood of these forlorn folks and thought he'd spotted strange
antics of the malarial parasites that even the famous Battista
Grassi had overlooked. The unhappy inhabitants of the
Istrian coast were washed out with dysentery and from them
Schaudinn fished out a crawling wee amoeba, that he was sure
he could tell from mere harmless amoebae, that he was certain must be the villain. . . .

He swallowed great doses of amoebae, gentle and ferocious,
got sick as the deuce for his curiosity, and there are those
that hint this was the beginning of the end, and the foundation for that disaster following so quickly on his sudden
triumph.

By patient peepings, by ingenious theorizings, he explained how mosquitoes itch you when they bite you, and
delved into the miniature hydraulics of the way they suck

your blood. He was always hustling his great burly body back up that hill in the white heat to help those no-account natives of San Michele di Leme try to get rid of the malaria that sapped them and he'd hurry back down remembering he wanted to look at those hemogregarines he'd found in the blood of a lizard.

It wasn't enough for him to probe into human malaria; he began peering at the malaria-like microbes that lived out their futile lives inside the blood cells of the absurd little owl—*Athena noctuae*. Half the night he'd stay peering through his lens at the blood of this bird, believing its parasites worked day shifts and night shifts . . . so he himself worked most of the night as well as all day. . . . Yet he found time to be lovely to his wife, and pretty soon he was a father as well as a husband, and they were so happy. Now suddenly the intestinal unhappiness of ground moles, the crawlings of amoebae, the secret doings of hemogregarines in the blood of lizards, the dilapidated condition of the folks of San Michele . . . all were blotted out for him. . . .

Now he went about in the daze of (what he thought) was a revolutionary discovery. Here was this idiotic little owl, *Athena noctuae,* with bird malaria parasites swarming inside the red corpuscles of its blood. Now Schaudinn let mosquitoes suck that blood from this owl, Athena. Now, when he cut up those little blood-glutted insects and peeped through his microscopes at their insides, instead of bird malaria parasites . . . *he found that blood swarming with snake-like creatures . . . trypanosomes!*

Here were great clumps of them, arranged in pretty rosettes, each creature with the curious fin called an undulating membrane. . . . Remote kin, they were, to those trypanosomes that David Bruce had found doing African cattle to death with the Nagana. . . .

For years he'd been fussing with protozoa that had a strange trick of changing their shapes (completely) depending on the animal they lived in. Now Schaudinn jumped at it. Of course! These snakes, these trypanosomes, were just another stage in the life of the microbe of bird malaria! This was revolutionary. . . .

Longer, longer, and again and again he peeped at more blood samples from more and more mosquitoes who'd feasted off malaria-infested owls . . . and yes! Those owl-malaria microbes didn't only turn into trypanosomes, when they got into mosquitoes, but into spirochetes! . . . Through his lens in the blood of those mosquitoes, mixed up among the slowly writhing trypanosomes, he could see those thin spiral-shaped beings, darting, looking like animated loosely coiled springs, very thin, pushing ahead in pretty spirals through blood cells and between rosettes of trypanosomes. . . .

Didn't kin of these spirochetes cause the human disease . . . relapsing fever, to say nothing of the fever of the domestic goose?

Again, he jumped at it. If trypanosomes were really only a stage of bird malaria, then these spirochetes were only another stage or form of it, and all three were different appearances of the very same malarial being! This was momentous. . . .

IV

And it was tremendously erroneous. Far away from Istria, in Ann Arbor, Michigan, there worked a tall, gray-eyed, Czechish man, whose eyes were as hawk-eyed as Fritz Schaudinn's, and then some, maybe. . . . This was Frederick G. Novy, and a pupil of Robert Koch himself. While Schaudinn had been peering and sweating in Istria, Novy on his own had made a fundamental discovery in Ann Arbor. For the first time in history he'd succeeded in growing protozoa, trypanosomes no less, outside the bodies of any animal, in test-tubes holding mixtures of blood and agar-agar. . . .

And now Novy read Schaudinn's report of his momentous

discovery, and Novy became excited . . . (if excitement could ever come to such a grim cool man as Novy undoubtedly was). If trypanosomes were only a stage of malaria then, by all the gods, he could cultivate malaria outside the body of an animal, outside mosquitoes, pure, uncontaminated with anything living! It would be a great step forward, this getting malaria (even if only of birds) to growing in a test-tube. . . .

Novy knew Schaudinn's great reputation, believed him absolutely. And now with his strange eyes showing his exaltation, he began growling plans for terrific experiments at his big, tough assistant, Ward MacNeal. And you needed to be tough to keep up with Novy. Now Novy and MacNeal went out and gathered what was literally a zoo of lovely songbirds . . . it was enough to send shivers up the spine of any bird lover. Into the blood of blue-birds, golden-winged wood-peckers, mourning doves, Baltimore orioles, brown thrashers, red-shouldered hawks, and many other feathered creatures they probed, and yes: many harbored parasites of bird malaria. . . .

Now for the pure culture experiments. . . . MacNeal cooked up great stews of nutrient agar-agar and bled rabbits for blood till his hands must have been numb holding the big bleeding pipettes. Novy planning vast tests in his clear almost microscopic handwriting. And alas . . . for Fritz Schaudinn. . . .

From the blood of many of those birds they could grow trypanosomes, no doubt of it . . . exactly like the beasts Schaudinn had described. But alas, often they grew them . . . *from the blood of birds that had no malarial parasites whatever.*

From the blood of many other birds, try as they would, they could grow no trypanosomes at all. *But the blood of these same birds teemed with the malarial microbes.*

And when they shot their pure cultures of trypanosomes into birds who had no malaria—*no malarial parasites ever appeared within their blood corpuscles.*

And the long slender spiral creatures that Schaudinn had seen in the blood in those mosquitoes, weren't spirochetes at all, *but only a form of a trypanosome.*

Poor Schaudinn! He'd been working with a mixed-up lot of different microscopic creatures in the bodies of his mosquitoes. . . .

It was ruin for him. You could find birds that had trypanosomes in their blood but no malaria and others with malaria in their blood but no trypanosomes whatever. And what was more there were trypanosome-like creatures in the stomachs of mosquitoes that hadn't been fed on birds. And when you fed artificially raised mosquitoes on hawks whose blood was infested with malaria . . . *no trypanosomes showed up in those mosquitoes at all!*

And it was terrible the number of different kinds of parasites that owls could harbor in their blood all at the same time. . . .

For such a severe man (scientifically) as Novy is known to be, he now let Fritz Schaudinn down very kindly.

It wasn't, you understand, that Schaudinn didn't see the things he said he saw. It was only that he thought that all the really different bugs that he saw were the same. It might have wrecked him . . . scientifically. Yet strangely, it got him ready for the famous day of March 3, 1905, that made him immortal.

V

Now it was 1905 and Schaudinn was back in Germany at the Imperial Health Office and no longer so happy. They had built a fine laboratory for him in Berlin, and he was the director, but on the 24th October, 1904, he had been officially informed that it was his business as head of protozoölogy in the Health Office to check up on other men's work

. . . but not do new work of his own. Schaudinn was (privately) furious and to his friends he is reported to have said: "But this is spiritual castration for me!"

He calmed down when he thought of his wife and babies. He went to work like a good trained seal to find if that fellow Looss had really been right about hookworms . . . the Westphalian miners were bothered with something said to be hookworm infection.

Now it was February, 1905, and here was another silly chore, with him wanting to get back at what he still thought was his deep discovery about malaria, trypanosomes, and spirochetes. Here came a call from the Health Office in the matter of the reputed tremendous discovery of that protozoölogist, Siegel, and his alleged important protozoan microbe, *Cytorhyctes*. This dubious bug was supposed to be the cause of four different diseases, of which by far the most important was syphilis. Now there was a conference, with old President Köhler and Lesser, the famous skin doctor, and the microbe hunter Neufeld, and last of all . . . Schaudinn.

It was disgusting. They all thought the business so much tommy-rot and a waste of time and energy. Siegel's reports were vague, confused. His pictures of his alleged bug looked like nothing whatever. It is (you may have already gathered) not common for protozoölogists to have high regard for each other at best, and now poor Schaudinn—put to work to check up on these imbecilities! Never was there a more astounding example of bureaucratic stupidity. . . .

Schaudinn remembered his job and his wife and babies and got ready his microscope. He got ready to find out how terribly wrong this fellow Siegel was about this supposed *Cytorhyctes* causing, particularly, syphilis . . . that darkest, stealthiest, and very nearly most dreadful of all human afflictions. For years parasitologists had been probing into the horrid manifestations of it, only to find . . . nothing. It had become axiomatic that, with the most powerful microscopes then known and the strongest staining fluids available, *this mysterious microbe could not be discovered.*

Here it was March, and big Fritz Schaudinn began carefully cleaning his microscope lenses. About no major human malady was there at this moment less known, scientifically. From the day old Diaz de Isla had climbed aboard Columbus's ships at Palos, in 1493, to treat the explorer's sailors loathsomely sick with it, this scourge had been an enigma. . . .

Here Fritz Schaudinn sat, neatly wiping piles of microscope slides and cover-slips, to find out that, once more, Siegel had failed to achieve what was anyway impossible. What you could say about this disease was—that it was horrible. But that had been known in 1493 when the town crier of Paris was directed to order from the city all afflicted with it . . . on pain of being thrown into the Seine. . . .

With resignation Schaudinn now prepared his little bottles of staining fluid . . . to look for what was in all probability not there at all. For the ignorance of its cause was still as abysmal as that of old Emperor Maximilian I, when, for the first time in history, he mentioned it in writing in his "Edict Against Blasphemers" in 1497.

Now Schaudinn packed up his microbe-hunting tools to go to Lesser's clinic where rows of sad, tainted people came begging to be healed of this horror. Well, Lesser could give them mercury. . . . But jolly red-nosed Girolamo Fracastoro, the learned physician by the shores of Lago di Garda, had done that too, in the early fifteen hundreds, when he'd written his strange medical poem about that shepherd, named Syphilis, who took care of the sheep of Alcithoüs. This shepherd had profaned the holy altars, and had been touched by a hideous leprosy, covering his body and accompanied by frightful pain, torturing his limbs, driving sleep from his bed. . . .

Now at Lesser's clinic, Schaudinn, not a physician, only a protozoölogical dabbler and peerer, asked the Medical Assistant, Erich Hoffmann, for his first specimen. What was known about this scourge was . . . that it was *catching*. This had been proved scientifically (and horribly) when the Anonymous One of the Palatinate had demonstrated that you could inoculate it from a sick to a healthy man. Who knows what disaster later happened to this unknown martyr? Who blames old Dr. Julius Bettinger for keeping his experiment a secret all his life? . . .

It's true that just two years before this March day of 1905, Metchnikoff, the wild Russian Jew, and Roux, the cool French searcher, had succeeded in giving it to apes. But a microbe? They'd found . . . nothing.

So here sat Fritz Schaudinn, ready. It was March 3, 1905. On March 1st, just two days before, Frederick G. Novy, the Michigan hawk-eye, in an austere scientific report had publicly blown Schaudinn's most ambitious theory . . . about malaria, trypanosomes, and spirochetes . . . to smithereens. . . .

Schaudinn fingered the micrometer screw of his microscope. He had no expectations. He felt no thrill of "What's—round—*this*—corner?" . . . that draws your searcher onward. Here he sat, with no illusion of his power to find what was at the bottom of this dark human trouble.

He was nothing in the face of this danger whose entry into its victims was so stealthy, whose first attack often so insignificant, flaring up, then dying down to fool its human prey into a sense of safety . . .

Then coming back, years later maybe, more hideous than leprosy; or stopping the hearts of men unsuspecting and in the prime of their vigor; or turning sure-footed runners into shambling tabetic wrecks; or slowly addling the strong brains of shrewd men; or bringing men of genius to dim-witted, slobbering, paretic death. . . .

Fritz Schaudinn hunched forward over his micro-scope. . . .

VI

Case No. 1. A. K. 25-year-old girl. Never sick before; since 20/1/1905, hard, painless nodule . . . since 22/11/1905, eruption and headache. . . .

This was Dr. Erich Hoffmann's matter-of-fact record of a now forgotten human history that went on to tragedy or happiness? . . . Nobody's bothered to record it. Here under Fritz Schaudinn's lens was a wee bit of stuff from that erup-tion. . . .

Well, one thing was certain . . . there was nothing here at all resembling that alleged syphilis-microbe, Siegel's *Cytor-hyctes*. . . .

There's no record of what Medical Assistant Dr. Erich Hoffmann at this moment thought of Fritz Schaudinn's way of looking. Hoffmann himself, three years back, had looked and looked for microbes in such people . . . finding just exactly nothing. And he'd gone at it properly in the ortho-dox manner, dousing strong staining-fluid onto the sick stuff . . . to paint, to make stand out, any wee microbe, if there was a microbe there. But here was Schaudinn (only a protozoölogist) looking down his microscope barrel at fresh, living stuff, unstained entirely. . . .

It was funny about Fritz Schaudinn. He was known as an artistic gay man, "foaming over with joy-in-life," as the Germans like to say it. Now here he sat bent over, and quiet, for a long, long time, not moving, not even muttering, just looking, looking. . . .

There's no record of it, but mustn't Erich Hoffmann have wondered why Schaudinn stayed there so very long not say-ing a word, just looking? Why didn't he call for material from Case No. 2? Why didn't he get through this idiotic business of proving Siegel was wrong . . . pronto? Why didn't he demonstrate quickly on a lot of cases in a row that what Siegel said was there, was only moonshine? Why did he keep at it and at it?

If you knew Schaudinn you'd understand it. No matter that he'd gone, bored, at this trained seal research job. At bottom he was only like your bird-dog starting out at random ranging, and then, suddenly . . .

Wait . . . this *was* curious. Here in the dim grayness, the quivering uncertain dimness of the field of the highest power of his microscope was . . . something!

Among débris of sick tissue, and random red and white blood corpuscles, and no-account microbes, contaminating skin bugs that any tyro would know meant nothing, there was a *new* something . . . moving. . . .

Now you saw it twisting, drilling back and forward, lashing. You'd turn your focus ever so wee little and you'd lose it. Wait, there it was again, drilling back and forward, hardly different from the dim nothingness in which it swam. Damn! Gone again. Now here again . . . so thin, so absolutely immeasurably thin you couldn't even guess its thickness in fractions of a micro-millimeter. But it was drilling back and forward, moving. You might say it had length but no breadth. It was like a long nothing, moving. . . .

And here another. And pretty soon another. How'd you describe it? Well . . . it was a corkscrew without a handle. It was like the very pale thin ghost of a microscopic corkscrew. . . .

At last Schaudinn called Hoffmann, and Neufeld and Gonder the microbe hunters who were experts at bacteria—not protozoa. They looked and looked and had the devil of a time to see anything. But, yes, at last, each one, focusing and focusing, would catch just a hint of that faint spiral moving, and then fading, and then swimming back for a moment

into focus. God . . . Schaudinn must have had a hawk-eye
to have picked it up!

Well?

Well . . . it wasn't anything. Schaudinn stretched his
great body, laughing. He explained to them. Those pale
corkscrews they saw, were *spirochetes*. He'd seen spirochetes
before . . . in mosquitoes' stomachs. Then there were also
spirochetes in the domestic goose. He explained to Neufeld,
Hoffmann, and Gonder that he believed these spirochetes
were just one stage of malaria, and he'd got up a theory
about them down in Rovigno. They were scientifically very
interesting.

"I'd much rather work at these spirochetes than try to
find the cause of syphilis," Schaudinn said to Neufeld. Then
he laughed. He also became sarcastic, probably. Now he
wasn't working at what he wanted to. He was doing what
the so-and-so Health Office Authorities told him to. So he'd
just have to forget about these (scientifically) interesting
spirochetes.

VII

But now it was March 20, 1905, and for Schaudinn all
purely scientific academic interest in whether malaria microbes might turn into spirochetes or vice-versa was blown
clean to blazes. Here in the past week were three more cases,
an unfortunate widow, aged 58, a blighted girl, aged 25, like
the first one, and now another girl, aged 22, with a bad rash
and headache and a sore throat and her hair coming out in
bunches. And in all of them, in the sick stuff from every
one of them . . . he'd seen those strange delicate microscopic corkscrews, long but with no breadth, moving. It's
true he'd seen them mixed up with other microbes, with
bigger spirals, that any amateur—not a hawk-eye like Schaudinn—could detect not half looking. But those big spiral
bugs were only in part of these sick people, and then on the
surface of the eruptions only, and not deep in them.

But these wee ghosts of microscopic corkscrews . . . those were the dandies, the strange ones; those were the beauties it was fun to look for, and not find, for hours maybe, till suddenly . . .

And they were always there, always in every one with the sickness . . . and never at all in those without it. You could stain them too, with the powerful azur-eosin dye invented by the microbe hunter, Giemsa. But how pale they always were! Even when Schaudinn stained and stained them. Now, first to himself, and then to Hoffmann, Schaudinn began calling them *spirochaeta pallida, "the pale spirochete."* Sometimes he could only find a few of them, but now here in this fourth girl, with the sore throat and bad eruption . . . she was *loaded* with them!

Hoffmann and Schaudinn went into a serious huddle. Siegel'd been fooled. Dozens of microbe hunters had been fooled finding bogus causes of this dreadful sickness. Both of them knew the simple fact that on the surface of anybody's body all kinds of microbes may lurk invisibly. And finding even such a fantastically different bug as this pale spirochete undoubtedly was, just in a surface eruption, might mean nothing . . . or everything!

They went into a huddle and what Schaudinn now wanted was a very new case of the sickness, just starting, but where the living poison had already got as far as the glands.

Long before, in one of those desperate experiments that seem to surround this sickness of the unmentionable name, old Geheimrath von Rinicker had demonstrated that those swollen glands (from the beginning of the sickness) *were infectious.* He'd proved it by cutting one out and injecting it into the arm of a young healthy man. "In men of good constitution it is easy to heal . . ." that was the way von Rinicker justified his experiment. . . .

Now if Schaudinn could spot his pale corkscrew deep down in one of those newly swollen glands . . .

It is not at all certain that at this time Hoffmann thought anything at all of this strange new microbe of Schaudinn's. But wait. Here was a real test of it. Three years before, Hoffmann had had just this kind of case . . . and from it he'd cut out a lymph gland, and from the stuff of that gland he'd made smears, dozens and dozens of them, on thin bits of glass. He'd stained and stained them with every kind of powerful dye. He'd looked till his eyes were red-rimmed. He'd seen . . . nothing. But wait . . . up here in the cupboard were a few of those three-year-old no-account bits of glass, smeared with the gland stuff . . . but not stained. Now, if Schaudinn thought it worth while . . .

Worth while? Well! So Hoffmann reached up in his cupboard, very likely feeling sorry for poor Schaudinn starting out on this wild goose chase. . . .

"I remember it was a Sunday," Neufeld wrote long after. "And Schaudinn and I were alone in the laboratory."

There sat Fritz Schaudinn, alone, before his microscope. All night those bits of glass, old neglected thin slips of glass saved up in that cupboard all these three years by some whim of Hoffmann's, had lain there soaking in Schaudinn's Giemsa stain. There couldn't be anything! Hoffmann had looked so carefully . . .

Now Schaudinn hunched forward, looking . . .

It was always good for quiet long looking alone there, Sundays. . . .

All at once he was up. He was running out, calling: "Neufeld! Neufeld! . . ."

VIII

So, on the very first day on the very first case on the 3d of March he'd seen the pale spirochetes. But this day, Sunday, March 21st, he knew he'd *discovered* the pale horror at the bottom of syphilis.

There's never been a fact of death-fighting science so quickly confirmed, so quickly said "Yes, of course" to by

everybody. It was the very opposite of the drubbing he'd got
from Novy, the Michigan hawk-eye, in that matter of his
wrong theory that malaria microbes might turn into spirochetes. It was like Robert Koch's demonstration of the tubercle bacillus, no less. Nobody in all the world could see
for the first time this thin pale horror, excepting Schaudinn.
Now, once he'd spotted it, had told them what to look for,
even a fair-to-middling microbe hunter couldn't miss it.

In May Schaudinn and Hoffmann got up before the Berlin
Medical Society and spoke their little pieces, very modestly,
not claiming anything, just saying that in so many cases of
the sickness they'd spotted this absolutely unique, extremely
thin, pale, tight-spiraled, very active corkscrew microbe . . .
in every true case of the disease in which they'd looked for
it. And in no case of any other kind of malady had they
seen it.

They didn't say it was the *cause,* but . . .

It was grand for them. The biggest scientific shots in Germany were up on their feet, saying, yes, they'd seen it. . . .

It looked like triumph for Schaudinn, when up jumped
one of Siegel's followers—Dr. Thesing—making the most
idiotic objections. Thesing hinted he had the backing of
Schaudinn's old master, Schulze, at the Zoölogical Institute,
no less. Now both Schaudinn and Hoffmann lost their
tempers and hinted Thesing had no credentials to shoot off
his mouth on such an important occasion. Then there were
catcalls and yells about "FREEDOM OF SCIENCE" and the whole
solemn occasion began to take on that air of imbecile futility
so frequent in human gatherings, religious, political, or scientific. . . .

Old Oskar Lassar made matters worse by uttering the
solemn wise-crack that, after all, h-m-m, in the past twenty-
five years, twenty-five causes of this sickness had been discovered.

The session began to dissolve into what was next to a riot.

To end it, the President of the Berlin Medical Society, the eminent, celebrated, Excellenz von Bergmann got up and made an immortal ass of himself by pronouncing:

"Herewith the discussion is closed, until *another* cause of syphilis is brought to our attention!"

Schaudinn was now beginning to feel seedy. In July he left Berlin for the Ship's and Tropical Diseases Institute in Hamburg on six months' leave of absence . . . planning to organize an expedition for Africa to study the sleeping sickness. There's never a doubt that he was a peculiar man, still much more fond of his wrong theory about malaria microbes and trypanosomes and spirochetes being all one beast really, than about this marvelous find of the pale horror.

"The whole thing's caused me nothing but annoyance," Schaudinn said.

All the time he was getting more and more famous. From all over the world Yes—Yes—Yes poured in, confirming his discovery. Metchnikoff had spotted the pale horror in his apes to which he'd given the loathsome sickness experimentally. It was found in the organs of little babies, born dead, whose poor mothers (not knowing) were tainted with it. By October there had been more than one hundred scientific reports absolutely confirming Schaudinn.

Now he wasn't the gay Fritz that he'd always been. He began sagging and losing his burliness . . . and here he was hardly thirty-five. He hated his job at the Health Office, though President Köhler had really done everything to back him.

All the while it began to get plainer and plainer how enormously practical this discovery of Schaudinn's really was. The Austrian, Landsteiner, quickly invented a most amazing easy way to spot the pale horror—by the dark-field microscope. It was a very simple business . . . just shooting a strong beam of light against those microbes cross-ways. That lighted them up, exactly as a sunbeam lights up dust-motes, as the sunbeam shines through a chink in the curtain of a darkened room. . . .

Now with this dark-field microscope even your rank and file skin doctor could spot the pale horror in patients who might come (worried) and conscience-stricken at the very first tiniest sign of trouble. With this new gadget the pale horror stood out, a lovely silvery tight-wound spiral, whirling round and round as it drilled backward and forward, bending, twisting, lashing. It was unmistakable, once you laid eyes on it. . . .

Metchnikoff was wild about it when Giemsa showed him these silvery demons whirling against a background of blackness.

"I'd never thought to have lived to see such pretty luetic fireworks!" the famous Jew shouted, laughing.

Schaudinn moved his wife and three babies to Hamburg, where the folks of that good Hansa town had given him a swell job at the Tropical Institute . . . just pure science, and plenty for his wife and children. Plenty . . . if he'd only get to feeling better. Down deep in him pain kept gnawing him. "Maybe it'll rest me to go to the Congress at Lisbon," thought Schaudinn. He went, feeling rotten.

Now searchers all over began to feel that, at last, here was a chance really to get at this sickness of the unmentionable name . . . now you could really collar the cause of it, see it, handle it, play with it. . . .

That same Austrian, Landsteiner, who'd invented showing it up in the dark-field microscope, now explained (what could be more hopeful?) how tremendously fragile this pale demon was. Raise the temperature of it ever so slightly above the heat of the human body, raise it no higher than the heat of a good high fever, and those pale corkscrews would spin faster and faster, and then die . . . miserably. . . .

Schaudinn was what you'd call a wow these days . . . the English (of all people!) were wanting him to come over to be a professor. He hoped his trip to Lisbon would chase away that pain that gnawed and gnawed at him.

Everything searchers were finding all over made this worst of sicknesses seem less formidable . . . now they had hold of the demon of it. This fellow, Roscher, showed how, if you just blew a current of hot air onto the first sore of the sickness, those spirochetes would curl up, die, disappear. . . . Of course that didn't cure it. Already they were finding how quickly those devils drilled their horrid way all through the body, away from the place where they first showed their gnawing. Yet . . . if just that little heat would shrivel them . . .

Schaudinn got a great hand at Lisbon and started back for Hamburg sicker than ever.

It was hardly a year after his discovery, and the whole medical world was hoorahing for him, with him really beginning to worry about his wife and babies now. You see, somehow, he'd always been too busy to feather a nest for them. Now they had to operate on him on the boat on the way back to Hamburg. He certainly wasn't the gay giant now.

It was marvelous the way searchers were discovering how easily these spirochetes were killed even by mild antiseptics, or by drying, or by the tiniest bit of heat. It made you stop looking at this sickness of the (till recently) unmentionable name, from the moral angle entirely. It was plain now that if Schaudinn's pale corkscrews hadn't been so fragile . . . this disease would be universal, like tuberculosis, and not confined to spread by such intimate contact of human beings only.

As John Stokes said, in substance, it wasn't divine moral purpose nor satanic punitive ingenuity that made this sickness the reward of sin . . . "But a mere biologic accident no more significant in the last analysis than the fact that potatoes grow in sandy loam . . ."

When Schaudinn got off the ship they hurried him to Eppendorf and did a desperate operation on him and he died . . . hardly thirty-five years old.

His wife and babies were penniless but all the scientific world was still excited about his discovery so it was in a sense lucky (if he had to die soon) that he died so very soon as he did. There was a great collection . . . a kind of benefit like they give for families of indigent actors and other Bohemian kinds of people. It was a triumph for him again . . . though posthumously. They collected 87,710 marks and 90 pfennigs . . . in 1906 when a mark was real money.

All over hope was stirring. In Frankfort on the Main another gay man got ready his experiments. He shouted at his lab-boys, bawled for his lab-assistant, the Jap Hata, urged his chemists on to cook up more and more complicated dyes, chemicals, assorted arsenicals. He would annihilate at one shot Schaudinn's pale spirochete. . . .

Of course Schaudinn had done his bit, and all he could (remembering he was only a protozoölogist) in this particular death fight. It had all been a curious business . . . uncomfortably illogical. If in the horribly wrong theoretical mix-up he got himself into in that matter of malaria and spirochetes . . . if then he hadn't got his hawk-eye used to spotting extremely tiny, almost non-existent spirochetes in the stomachs of those mosquitoes . . .

But now what matter that idiotic theory? Now with searchers all over finding his pale horror, who'd ever forget Schaudinn?

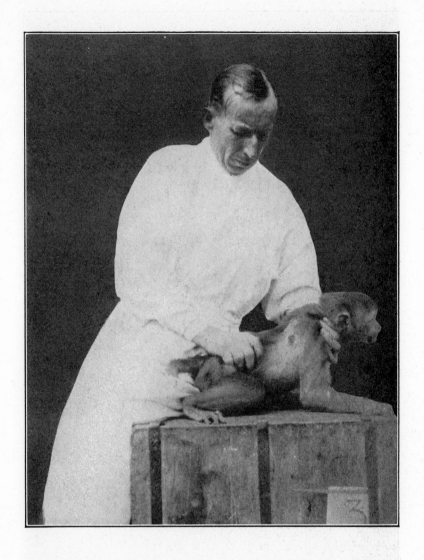

ANDERSON—"—*God, he* was *an assistant*—" *Armstrong said.*

SCHAUDINN—". . . *an artistic, a gay man foaming over with joy in life.*"

8. BORDET

PROPHET OF DOOM

~~~~~~

Are not discoveries frequently unexpected? Do not experimenters find that their researches overthrow expectations which seem quite reasonable, and is it not evident that logic totters when it would force facts?

JULES BORDET

~~~~~~

JULES BORDET is as little and as Latin as Fritz Schaudinn was German and gigantic. To the highbrow few of the top-cut of microbe hunters his fame is prodigious. To the suffering millions he has given a chance to ward off the final stab of Schaudinn's pale spirochete his name is unknown.

This isn't surprising, for about this small blue-eyed Belgian there is something too careful, too exact, too remotely scientific and coldly brainy to invite even the austerest scientific notoriety. Fundamentally, it was Bordet's blood test that made Schaudinn's sensational find of his spirochete *matter* . . . to those millions in whose bodies that pale horror lies lurking. . . .

Before the hoorahs for Fritz Schaudinn's discovery had entirely died away, it was clear to the men against this loathsome death that the fight was a long way from over. The microbe the big German had found was only a pale one, yes, and weak, no doubt of it. At the first outbreak of the sickness it was marvelous how easy it was to spot the spiral demons drilling back and forward in a silvery shimmer

229

against the black background of the dark-field microscope. At the outset . . .

But then this most dreadful of human sicknesses had the trick of fading away for a while into a treacherous sleeping. In a few months you'd no longer find its pale spiral microbe teeming. After the general flaming of the first violent eruption had faded, Fritz Schaudinn—even with his hawk-eye of the master observer—could find never a spirochete. Yet his pal, Erich Hoffmann, or any expert watcher of this so human trouble, could tell Schaudinn that somewhere in many, in most, of these stricken people his horror *must be* hiding, only waiting . . .

Even in those who thought themselves healed of it . . .

John Stokes, who has a marvelous gift of words to describe it, tells how this sickness moves "like an ice-berg, nine-tenths below the surface." Of all microbes that torture humanity, this corkscrew pale demon of Schaudinn's was unique. When it swarmed through the body of its victims in its first spectacular outbreak . . . it was least dangerous. Then when these tiny marauders were so depleted in numbers even Schaudinn couldn't find them (years after their first swarming) . . . this rearguard of assassins could awake to a ferocity that was not only horrid but deadly. . . .

This, then, was what made something like the marvelous blood test invented by Jules Bordet absolutely necessary. Granted that Schaudinn did begin everything hopeful when he first found the pale horror, somebody had to find the trick of tracking down that horror in its so ominous hiding. And that happened thanks to the watery blue-eyed dreamer, Bordet.

The story of Bordet's adventures in the fight against syphilis is romantic and not without irony, and not to be understood at all, without knowing the excessively cautious, icily logical searcher that he is. Long before Schaudinn, this little Belgian actually had the pale spirochete trapped under his microscope. But Bordet was your type of intellectual Walloon, out-Frenching any Frenchman, with a more than French horror of being mistaken. So he was too cautious to denounce it as the villain. And while it was his science that made the hidden (and most dangerous) nine-tenths of the evil ill detectable, world-wide notoriety for the blood test went to Wassermann. Super-French, Bordet was too logical, with a French passion for what's called scientific *élégance*. So he made just one experiment too many, and muffed it.

Yet, without Bordet, Wassermann wouldn't even have dreamed of it.

II

There is something droll in the thought of Jules Bordet as a knight of death-fighting science, tilting against this most formidable of diseases, or against any human ill for that matter. Son of a Belgian schoolmaster of Soignies, and poor, he came as a cigarette-smoking insignificant youngster with curious wool-gathering disposition to the Pasteur Institute in Paris in the early nineties, with Pasteur incredibly famous and dying, with fights against deaths boiling . . . as they would seethe (spectacularly) in the tradition of Pasteur's grand manner. The young Walloon Bordet got the privilege of fumbling with pipettes and test-tubes in the very shadow of the beard of the Russian, Élie Metchnikoff. There was something so gala and absolutely terrific about the way this famous man tackled every mystery, that Bordet for all of his clear head must have been awed and flabbergasted. In dangerous experiments more perilous because of their Oriental hecticity, Metchnikoff was right now explaining how it is our bodies can become immune to the deadly Asiatic cholera.

Metchnikoff was battling not only against the cholera murder, but against the German searcher, Pfeiffer, who'd have none of Metchnikoff's phagocyte theory. In some ways it was the worst of starts for a young searcher like Bordet.

Because when Metchnikoff couldn't answer Pfeiffer with brilliant experiments, he had a trick of demolishing him with unanswerable epigrams. It was certainly big-league science Bordet had got into.

But now, instead of yessing Metchnikoff's phagocyte science (it was expected of him!) . . . within a year he was off on a hunt that was absolutely his own. With little weirdly clear-headed experiments he was getting a peep at the way our bodies fight off murderous microbes . . . and it had little to do with Metchnikoff's benevolent army of white blood cells—the nice phagocytes.

It all began theoretically, it was very much "pure-science" (whatever that is), and Bordet never dreamed that the fight against the scourge of the still undiscovered pale horror *depended upon him, absolutely.*

Here sat Bordet, dabbling with serum bled a few weeks before from a remarkable goat, and with a tube of cholera microbes fit to do a husky man to death (with incredible suffering) inside twelve hours, while close by there chittered a not at all remarkable guinea-pig idiotically unaware of its fate. The goat was remarkable because in its blood there was a weird power of preventing cholera infection. The guinea-pig was negligible because like any normal rodent its blood had next to no cholera-killing power whatever.

Metchnikoff's enemy—Pfeiffer—had just been impresario of a drama that went on inside the belly of a cholera-immune guinea-pig when you shot deadly cholera vibrios into him. A man-killing dose of those comma-shaped devils, when they got into this immune rodent, instead of assassinating him, stopped suddenly in their tracks, curled into no-account granular globules and then exploded completely. You didn't have to vaccinate your guinea-pig to pull off this show; all you had to do was to shoot into him, a little while beforehand, the serum of a cholera-vaccinated goat. What was dreadful about it (for Metchnikoff) was that the whole disaster to the cholera-microbes in this guinea-pig's belly happened without Metchnikoff's pet phagocytes being on hand to eat them. . . .

Pfeiffer insisted that this cholera-killing test *had* to go on inside a guinea-pig's belly. There was something mysterious inside there, that the preventive goat serum needed, to help explode the vibrios. Right away Metchnikoff came back at him bellowing orders to his assistants in strange French mixed with Russian that had a strong kosher accent. He experimented . . . brilliantly. True . . . when you mix the cholera bugs with the preventive serum in a glass, nothing happens. But just let Mr. Pfeiffer try adding a few white blood cells—phagocytes!—to that mixture and he'd see the deadly cholera microbes blow up, pronto!

Here sat Bordet alone; he loved to work nights, and he had an entirely proper awe of his Russian-Jewish master. But wait. If the white cells would do it, why wouldn't just a guinea-pig's blood, or even just his blood serum, do the trick as well? It was heresy. Bordet had this grandest of all human instincts (and rarest) . . . he knew only one way to answer any question: by experiment.

Accurately now he mixed just so many drops of grayish fluid teeming with fatal cholera comma-microbes, plus exactly so much of that preventive goat serum. Then every so many minutes he peered at samples of that mixture through his microscope. Nothing doing: the vibrios went on swarming in their deadly dance. . . .

Pfeiffer was right. Now, wait. Now to the mixture Bordet adds a few drops of the serum of the blood of that negligible guinea-pig—a normal rodent with no cholera-preventing power in its blood at all.

What now happened was utterly unheard of, and fundamental. Alone, the cholera-preventive serum of that immune goat could do nothing. Now, just a touch of the blood serum of that normal guinea-pig added to it . . . and this mixture blew those deadly cholera vibrios to smithereens.

III

Bordet was alone there in his laboratory immensely untidy with its litter of bits of paper scrawled with his hieroglyphic plans for experiment, experiment, always experiments, mixed with half-smoked cigarette butts and abandoned test-tubes and the hairs of guinea-pigs gone West in the cause of science. He was alone there, a little bolshevik against the phagocyte science of his immensely famous master. His absent-minded head was as clear as his laboratory bench was messy. . . . Why wouldn't the cholera-preventing goat serum that was so powerfully bug-killing in a guinea-pig's belly, do nothing when mixed with cholera microbes on a bit of glass? . . . Why did the serum of a normal guinea-pig (in itself harmless for cholera microbes) awaken that goat serum to bug-killing power?

Bordet's head . . . natural as a fish swimming in water . . . seemed to ask only those questions that experiment could answer. . . . Wait. He had it. The cholera-preventing goat serum they used in their experiments was almost always old, had been drawn from their immune goat weeks beforehand. Or, if not old, then it had at least been heated, to 60° Centigrade, to keep contaminating bugs from spoiling it.

And the normal guinea-pig serum he'd used had been fresh, always, warm from the unhappy beast he'd just killed to get it. Why, of course . . .

It was a blur for him going from that quick hunch to the cholera-immune goat in its stable. A quick jab into its jugular vein with new fresh blood welling up into the big syringe. The hum of the centrifuge machine separating nice straw-colored serum. Quick mixing together of the savage cholera vibrios and this *fresh* goat serum . . .

Of course! Got fresh from the goat, preventive serum blew the cholera vibrios to the devil—without having to add any guinea-pig serum at all.

And, yes! Just heat your fresh guinea-pig serum to 60° Centigrade . . . and it loses all its mysterious power to stir the preventive goat serum to bug-killing action.

Here was the first blood test in human history, for the spotting of a dangerous microbe. Here was something practical, life-saving. For there were many comma-shaped vibrios so exactly like the deadly cholera microbe—so far as mere looks went—that it was impossible to tell a harmless germ from a savage . . . microscopically. And here was a test to douse the first smoldering of one of your dreadful cholera epidemics! For it was only the true cholera vibrio that would blow up when you mixed it with cholera-preventing goat serum and the fresh serum of a guinea-pig. It was revolutionary. . . .

IV

Bordet just mentioned in his scientific report that it was practical, but did absolutely nothing more about the death-fighting angle of it. What he was vastly more excited about was something not practical but highly philosophical. What he kept wool-gathering about was this: That the bug-killing wallop of a preventive serum may be restored by mixing it with any fresh normal serum which itself has almost no bug-killing power. Wasn't it wonderful that two serums, neither of them dangerous to deadly microbes, should make a mixture that was nasty against such a deadly germ as this cholera assassin. . . .

"Our science," said Bordet years later when he was summing up what microbe hunting had done for humanity, "is the most stirring of sports!"

When you looked into his laboratory, regarding its appalling messiness, you'd wonder at the sureness of Bordet's facts. (But the insides of his tubes and pipettes weren't messy.)

When you looked into his dreamy blue eyes you might wonder how he noticed anything. . . .

But there was nothing that got by him, and now, wasn't this funny? That old preventive goat serum—when you mixed it with cholera bugs—couldn't kill them, no. . . . But watch it now. It did do something marvelous. It made those swarming devils stop right in their tracks as if they'd been shot. Then they began gathering into little clumps that flowed together into larger and larger masses till you could see these agglutinations, each one made up of hundreds of thousands of microbes . . . with your naked eye, finally. The clumps looked like flakes of snow as they settled out of the salt solution to the bottom of the test-tube. Serum from a goat immune to cholera clumped only cholera microbes . . . no others. It was *specific*. It was a still simpler way to tell a dangerous bug from one that might be harmless—not by groping and dabbling inside a human animal but in a little glass tube, in a jiffy. . . .

It is now used more than any test in microbe hunting . . . to tell this bug from that one.

But it wasn't only microbes that clumped up in goat serum. Here was something really peculiar. Here was an old discarded tube from a bygone experiment . . . it chanced to have serum from a goat immune to cholera mixed with the serum of a guinea-pig immune to nothing. . . .

By accident a few guinea-pig red blood corpuscles had got mixed with the guinea-pig serum . . . Bordet had been a bit careless drawing that serum off the clot. Now look . . . here were clumps, not of microbes, but of guinea-pig red blood corpuscles. . . .

Nothing was too trivial to set this strange man off onto new experiments. Did goat serum always clump guinea-pig blood? Experiment. Yes. It seemed silly to desert his tests with the deadly cholera. It seemed foolish to probe into this clumping of the blood of one animal by the serum of another. But what *matter?*

For Bordet anything inexplicable mattered. He peered, he argued at himself, he conjectured, he ended—always!— by testing. Take your cholera microbe. Any horse serum, even from horses not vaccinated, would clump your cholera microbes a little. But vaccinate a horse with cholera and the cholera bug-clumping power of that serum shot up enormously. Take your rabbit blood. Any guinea-pig serum would clump rabbit blood a little. . . .

But what would happen if you *vaccinated* a guinea-pig with the blood of a rabbit?

Could any question (seeing Bordet was a death-fighter in the Pasteur Institute with its tradition of life-saving and with millions dying from every imaginable ailment) . . . can you imagine any experiment to have been idler, more devoid of importance, more really nonsensical?

But Bordet when his curiosity was roused had no altruism, nor was he . . . theological. Any ordinary searcher would have argued that you'd expect the serum of a man or an animal to stop savage microbes in their tracks, to ball them up into clumps. That might be God's way of helping His creatures combat microscopic marauders. But what reason or purpose could there be (divine or diabolical) for the serum of a guinea-pig to clump the blood of a rabbit?

Bordet never asked what might be the good of it. He only asked himself . . . would it?

It was lucky for the millions whose bodies hide the pale spirochetes lurking for that last fatal stab, that Bordet wasn't theological. Here's the fool test all rigged up to answer the silly question. Here's a row of small glass tubes. Each has in it a little opaque, brick-red-colored suspension of the washed red blood corpuscles of a rabbit. Each has a bit of serum—less and less down the row of tubes—of a guinea-pig he has vaccinated against a rabbit's blood.

V

The serum ought to clump the corpuscles of the rabbit's blood. Bordet busies himself at lab chores that are like the duties of a kitchen-mechanic or a housewife. Now and again he wipes his hands on his dirty lab coat and bends over peering at what goes on in the tubes in the rack. Yes, the clumping's begun. He goes back to his lab chores. He turns back to the tubes again. He picks one up, shakes it . . .

What's this? What the devil? Look at it. Look at all the rest of them—down to the one holding the least bit of guinea-pig serum. The opaque brick-red color of the fluid in the tubes has faded. It has dissolved into a perfectly clear, transparent, red—like raspberry syrup or grenadine!

Now quick, a bit of it under the microscope. The red blood corpuscles have gone. He sees only ghosts of them, just shadows. . . .

The fresh serum of a guinea-pig vaccinated against rabbit blood blows rabbit blood corpuscles completely to blazes . . . exactly like the fresh serum of an immune goat blows to smithereens the deadly vibrios of Asiatic cholera.

The same simple laws hold for the two of them. To prove that, Bordet sinks himself into a maze of precise experiments whose absolute newness make him never mind their entire uselessness. Sure: when your immune guinea-pig serum ages, it won't blow up the rabbit red blood cells. When you heat it to 60° Centigrade, it loses its blood-dissolving power. But add just a little fresh not-heated normal guinea-pig serum and the heated immune serum blows up rabbit blood cells as well as or better than ever. It's a perfect resemblance. . . .

The bug-killing wallop you remove from a fresh immune serum by heat, you put back by adding a little normal serum which itself has no bug-killing power. The blood-dissolving action that vanishes when you heat the serum of a blood-vaccinated guinea-pig, comes back by adding a little fresh

normal serum—which in itself has no blood-dissolving wallop.

It all sounds so easy and simple and it had taken five years
of incessant experiment to find it. The net of all this labor,
of these rabbits done to death, those guinea-pigs bled white,
those goats gone West . . . was something drolly philosophical. No more. . . . Any fresh, normal, non-immune serum
of any man or animal has an "X." It's a mysterious something that will explode your dangerous cholera microbe or
blow up your harmless blood corpuscles of another animal
species. But this "X" can't do these things, it is absolutely
powerless, until you *sensitize* your microbe or your blood
corpuscle . . . with the serum of an animal that's been
vaccinated with that specific microbe or red blood cell.

Here was what was philosophical, funny, against theology
and sentimental notions about God's goodness. This "X,"
this marvelous bug-killing power of blood serum, would
have existed in animals if there'd never been deadly microbes at all! Bordet laughed. What proved that, was the way
any fresh normal serum could blow the perfectly harmless
blood corpuscles of another animal species to smithereens
. . . once they'd been sensitized.

VI

But was this mysterious cholera-smashing and blood-dissolving "X" . . . was it really one and the same?

"It is open to experimental demonstration," said Bordet,
and anything that wasn't, you'd never catch him touching
with a ten-foot pole. The little experiment by which he
answered it led directly to the marvelous blood test that
smoked the sinister spirochete, the pale horror of Fritz
Schaudinn, out of its hiding.

If this powerful "X" was just one thing, then, when fresh
guinea-pig serum got through blowing up cholera microbes
you'd sensitized by cholera-immune serum, there'd be none

of it left to blow up sensitized rabbit red blood corpuscles when you added them to the mixture. . . .

Bordet tried it. Hoorah . . . there *was* nothing left. When fresh guinea-pig serum had got through exploding sensitized cholera microbes, it had no wallop left in it when you added red blood corpuscles that had been sensitized with the guinea-pig immune serum. It was a really lovely lab test. It was so easy to read it. The suspension of those sensitized rabbit blood corpuscles stayed brick red and opaque.

Your true searcher is always hot to discover that what he's found for one bug will hold for all of them. What tickles him most vastly is not some cure or preventive of death, but establishing what's called a generalization. Now Bordet is on the trail of it. He's big enough stuff now at the Pasteur Institute to have an assistant. Now he has the extremely serious capable Belgian, Octave Gengou, to help him. Right off the bat they run into a snag. Take the typhoid bacillus or the dreadful microbe of the bubonic plague. Alas . . . when you mix them with the fresh preventive serum of a beast vaccinated against them, they refuse to blow up. But wait . . .

Just sensitize them with their own specific immune serum that you've got from a beast vaccinated against them . . . and they'll still pull that bug-killing "X" out of the fresh serum of a guinea-pig. In a flash Bordet saw it. Here was a beautiful way to demonstrate it . . .

All you had to do was to add some sensitized rabbit red blood corpuscles to your mixture. If they didn't dissolve, if they stayed opaque, brick red . . .

It proved your microbe had been sensitized, and had sucked the bug-killing "X" from the fresh guinea-pig serum.

This set-up gave you a delicate, subtle way to find out whether this or that animal was immune to such and such evil microbe. It might tell you whether this or that microbe was still lurking in a man's body. Hammer and tongs, Bordet now went at it. Why he picked out such a deadly microbe as the black plague bacillus I can't imagine. But now he let the fresh serum of a normal guinea-pig work on a few billion of these plague-assassins that he'd sensitized with the serum of an animal vaccinated against them. . . .

It worked. When he added the sensitized rabbit red blood corpuscles they *didn't* dissolve into the lovely clear grenadine color but stayed brick-red, opaque.

Now the check test. He let the fresh serum of that normal guinea-pig work on another few billion of plague assassins, *not sensitized,* but mixed with the serum of a beast not vaccinated . . .

Of course. Now, when he added the sensitized rabbit red blood corpuscles, like a shot they blew up, turning from their opaque brick red to the clear grenadine color. The not-sensitized plague bugs couldn't take the "X" from the fresh guinea-pig serum. It was a lovely test. It was tremendously delicate, and you had to use just the right number of drops of everything.

Here was a great chance for searchers everywhere to spot whether this or that deadly microbe had been gnawing at a man or might be still lurking in him. Such people's blood-serum should *sensitize* the species of microbe you suspected was biting them. . . .

VII

Bordet loathed everything merely practical. He tried it out on just two people who were convalescent from typhoid fever. He found it worked. Then he dropped the whole business to delve into mysteries of how we're immune to pestilences. His marvelous little experiments had switched the attention of very nearly the whole microbe-hunting world off Metchnikoff's pet phagocytes. Now it was little Bordet and not the sensational Russian who was scientifically battling with those Germans about the how and why of what makes us fight off deadly diseases. . . .

It is not surprising to find him no longer in Paris, but head of a little Pasteur Institute of his own in the Steam-Wagon Street in Brussels in his home country of Belgium. It was here he first ran across the ugly trail of the pale horror of syphilis. There's no doubt he'd taken the play away from Metchnikoff, but now he showed in what awe he still held that old microbe-hunting master. . . .

Schaudinn was still muddling with malaria and trypanosomes and spirochetes down in Rovigno with never a thought of the disease of the (till recently) unmentionable name. Now one day Bordet sat hunched over his microscope in his own Pasteur Institute. He was peering at the oozing from a sinister sore on a man suspected of coming down with the terrible sickness. He'd streaked that stuff on a thin bit of glass and stained it with a dye called carbol-methylene blue. . . .

Now, out of the vague grayness of his miscroscope field there dissolved into the focus, very faintly colored, the tight corkscrew spirals of a spirochete, new, unknown, peculiar. The eye of no searcher (in human record) had ever seen it. Bordet was vastly excited about it. But wait. This was a momentous business. This wasn't quite up his alley. So he packed up that bit of glass carefully, and sent it to Paris to Metchnikoff, to his master. Wasn't this strange new pale microbe mighty worth while getting on the trail of?

"Metchnikoff couldn't see very well through a microscope," said Bordet, smiling, long after. "He said it was nothing, so I dropped it. . . ."

VIII

Then right after that, Fritz Schaudinn did spot the pale horror and convinced the whole scientific world of it, even Metchnikoff included, in a jiffy. Again Bordet had the best chances to tie his name (notoriously and immortally) to the loathsome sickness. You remember how, before men against this death had got through hoorahing for Schaudinn, they realized that the fight was really only started. You remember how it was plain you could only spot the pale corkscrew in the first spectacular part of its horrid activity, how it then faded, buried itself, went away into its dangerous hiding . . .

But here was the greatest of all chances for Bordet's delicate blood test to prove its death-fighting value. Here you had a sickness with its microbe buried away—itself undetectable—in your sufferer's body. But if that microbe was there, its victim's blood serum should show it. Its victim's blood serum should *sensitize*. . . .

Hammer and tongs again, Bordet went at it. There was this against it, that you couldn't get pure cultures, in test-tubes, of Schaudinn's pale spirochete. But look, you could get human tissues in which it was swarming. . . .

So here's the little immunity master bending over his set-up of little test-tubes. Here's the ground-up first sore of syphilis, swarming with spirochetes, and a bit of the serum of a patient known to have the sickness. . . .

Into this mixture he drips just so many drops of the fresh serum of a normal guinea-pig. . . .

It's in the bag, this experiment! According to the laws he'd himself discovered, the serum of this patient should *sensitize* those spirochetes. And, thus sensitized, they should take the blood-dissolving "X" out of the fresh guinea-pig serum. . . .

Here sits Bordet, sure of himself, waiting while this mysterious chemistry takes place, invisibly. Now, to prove the spirochetes have been sensitized. . . .

Into the mixture he drips just so many drops of the brick-red, opaque suspension of the sensitized red blood corpuscles of a rabbit. Then he waits. . . .

Absolutely. He's got it. The tube stays brick red, opaque, the red blood corpuscles not dissolving. The serum of the diseased man has sensitized Schaudinn's spirochetes. But wait . . .

Here's another tube, again with that bit of ground up first sore of the sickness, swarming with spirochetes. But this time the serum of a lucky person *who's never had syphilis.* . . .

This serum *shouldn't* sensitize the spirochetes, and now he adds just so many drops of the fresh serum of the normal guinea-pig, and waits again. . . .

Now to this tube he adds the brick-red-colored opaque fluid of the suspension of sensitized rabbit red blood corpuscles, and he doesn't have to wait long. . . .

Presto. In a few minutes that dull brick red grows brighter. The opacity begins clearing. He has it. Look . . . the tube's clear now, and lovely with its transparent color of grenadine. The spirochetes—*not sensitized*—couldn't take out the blood-dissolving "X" from the normal guinea-pig serum. . . .

Here's the most marvelous of chances to spot the pale horror's lurking. You rig up the test just as Bordet has done it. Then side by side you rig up another, with the question-mark serum of your anxious patient suspected of having the dreadful sickness. . . .

At this moment Jules Bordet teetered on the edge of fame, not only among the highbrow searchers to whom he was already famous, but among the rank and file of doctors all over, and among the millions to whom yes or no of the blood test, means happiness, or worry, or the prophecy of a doom that may be utterly inexorable. . . .

At this moment Jules Bordet went scientific and made one test too many. . . .

IX

He must prove that this test is absolutely air-tight, theoretically. So, as a final ultimate check on its scientific rightness, he takes another little tube, and into that tube goes the ground-up skin of a creature *that has no spirochetes.*

BORDET—". . . *something droll in the thought of Jules Bordet as a knight of death-fighting science.*"

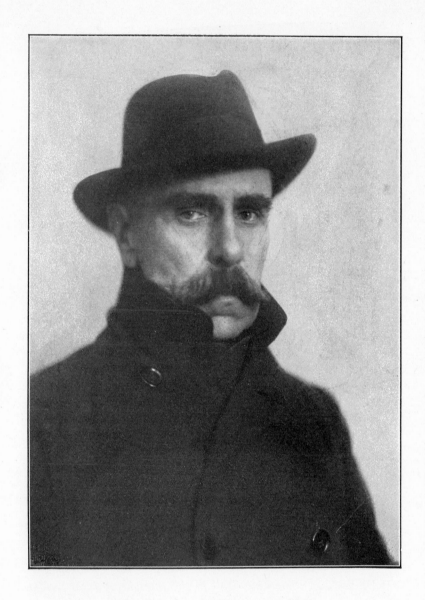

WAGNER-JAUREGG—". . . *would have made an excellent Oklahoma sheriff—of one of its tougher counties.*"

It's normal skin and perfectly healthy. It's the kind of control test your ultimately accurate searcher—and only such a searcher—would think of. To this healthy ground-up skin (with no spirochetes) Bordet now adds just so many drops of the serum of a patient undoubtedly tainted with syphilis. And then into this mixture he drips a few drops of the fresh serum of a normal guinea-pig.

Now there's never a doubt of what (by his proven theory) *must* happen. There are no spirochetes in that normal ground-up skin. So (there's no doubt of it) the blood-dissolving "X" in the guinea-pig's serum can't be used up. . . .

Into the tube he drips just the right number of drops of the sensitized red blood corpuscles of a rabbit. Then he waits—expectant. In a moment that brick-red opaqueness should be clearing. . . .

He keeps waiting and nothing happens, nothing whatever. It's absolutely against his laws of immunity. The serum of this diseased patient had taken the blood-dissolving "X" out of the guinea-pig serum . . . without any spirochetes there, to be sensitized. . . .

According to his theory, the test can't be specific. He drops the whole business. . . .

So it happens that the famous Wassermann blood test wasn't called by the name of Bordet.[1]

He made one experiment too many.

X

1906—one year later, in Germany August von Wassermann tried the Bordet blood test on the serum of apes he'd infected with Schaudinn's pale horror. He can't have been quite so careful as our super-careful Belgian. He definitely stated that it was only when you used tissues with Schaudinn's spirochete, only then would such tissue, sensitized with the

[1] Bordet has never published the history of his attempt to apply the Bordet-Gengou reaction to syphilis. The present account is based on personal conversation of the writer with Bordet in 1930.

serum of a sick patient, take the blood-dissolving "X" out
of the normal guinea-pig serum. The very next year, searchers not only in France, but in Austria, found that Wassermann had slipped a cog on that particular detail of it. Bordet
had been right on that last check test he'd made . . . super-
careful. Extracts of hearts, livers, of perfectly healthy people
or animals, mixed with the serum of folks tainted with the
trouble, *did* take the blood-dissolving wallop out of the normal guinea-pig serum.

But here was the joke of it (on Bordet) . . . those same
extracts when you mixed them with *healthy* serum, *didn't*
remove the blood-dissolving "X" . . .

So it was just as accurate to use them as if you'd had a
pure culture of the pale spirochete. . . .

So Wassermann who was wrong on a detail was right in
general. And Bordet—greatest enemy of all theories—had
muffed a deep new fact because it didn't fit his laws! And
Wassermann was world famous.

Now to Wassermann—just as to Schaudinn—good news
that his test could really uncover the hidden sickness began
to roll in from thousands of laboratories, hospitals. Now men
against death could really begin to look for the nine-tenths
of the terrible ill that (like the ice-berg) moved beneath the
surface.

Now they could begin to spot the most diabolical variety
of devilment . . . not having to look for Schaudinn's pale
corkscrew that grew rarer and more dangerous as the sickness grew older.

Now often they could surprise that demon's lurking, even
in the mysterious stage of the sickness, when it's not a sickness, when it's only "latent."

For the spirochete is the weirdest of all microbes at the
bottom of human misery. After its first flaring it will settle
down to be an *almost* or even completely harmless guest in
a human body. Its host *may* live to a ripe age, harboring it,

not knowing. Or it may disappear completely. Or again after a long harmless lingering, it'll rouse itself into a fatal gnawing in blood vessels, or heart, or bones, or nerves, or brain.

And before the days of the Bordet-Wassermann blood test, no human being could know which of these fates might be his. This doesn't mean it's infallible. Even when it shows positive . . . your patient may yet remain healthy. Even though it's negative, and repeatedly . . . the patient cheered by that good news may yet be in terrible danger.

Yet there's never a doubt that it's a great jump forward in the death fight against the pale horror. For it's very nearly sure now that, so long as it stays positive, somewhere the pale corkscrews are lurking.

In the old days, the deceptive disappearance of the outside signs of the sickness was all that doctors could go by. Today, the powerful remedies (of which you'll hear presently) more quickly than ever drive the spirochetes under cover . . . but don't necessarily kill the last single one of those demons.

Nobody will deny that a long record of outside good health and negative Wassermann tests, again and again and again, gives such stricken people hope, and chases fear as it could never be banished in the old days. *Especially when the test isn't applied only to their blood.* (The next story will explain the terrible significance of this sentence in italics.)

When you think of the thousands of innocent (morally) who suffer from the pale horror, not knowing they're tainted, you'll understand its use to the death-fighters. For as John Stokes puts it, almost every patient, no matter what his ailment, has had some symptoms that might occur in this loathsome malady. And many with no symptoms whatever hide latent corkscrew pale demons . . . waiting. . . .

When you remember the dreadful prevalence of the sickness, it looks pretty certain that it ought to be as much a matter of routine for doctors to blood-test your sick man or woman in their general examination, as it's routine now to examine the urine or listen to the heart. . . .

Of course it's not infallible, because now and again it does give "false positives" . . . that accuse a sufferer when he's been utterly free from the pale horror his life long. The old test invented by Wassermann is almost surely going to be replaced by the simpler, more accurate, more sensitive, much more fool-proof Kahn test.

But that's a story that lies in the future. . . .

Meanwhile, it's really Bordet we have to thank for the extraordinary science that will . . . as you'll see in the grim story that's coming . . . prophesy almost sure doom for a man or a woman years before it closes down on him. It's fundamentally Bordet these maybe doomed wretches should go on their knees to . . . for the test that'll show death-fighters the danger *in time to combat it.*

THE FRIENDLY FEVER

Just as the pale horror tricks its victims, so again and again it has disappointed the first hopes of the men who have fought it. Hardly three years after Bordet and Wassermann had found the test that would so often so wonderfully smoke it out of its hiding, Paul Ehrlich the gay Jewish chemist found his powerful salvarsan, 606. One shot of it would wipe every last pale spirochete out—of rabbits.

Boyishly fond of putting simple ideas into Latin mystifications, he hoped that this remarkable 606 would for suffering humans (as well as rabbits) be a Therapia magna sterilisans. *He hoped he had found the magic bullet. And it was almost magical. Over night, one shot of it would drive pain from the bones of forlorn folks in whose limbs the pale horror was gnawing. In a few days, one dose faded horrid leprous sores of the sort with which the sacrilegious shepherd boy, Syphilis, had been cursed in the poem by old Girolamo Fracastoro. But, alas, that one dose of Ehrlich's magic bullet never fetched every last one of the pale spirochetes.*

Just the same it was plain that the healing power of 606 was brilliantly better than anything ever tried or heard of. Dangerously powerful, in the early days of its use, one "course" of a succession of shots of it could wipe out enough of the pale microbes to make the blood test negative (with no relapse) in eighty-five out of every hundred. Again, alas, the pale germ showed its horrid resourcefulness. Through the years it began (apparently) to accustom itself to Ehrlich's magic bullet. So that, ten years later, a similar number of doses of 606 caused the blood tests of only twenty-three out of every hundred to become negative.

Relieving sufferers from outward evidence of their affliction in a few days, the tragedy of 606 lay in its lulling thousands into a sense of security. So that they neglected to submit themselves to the rigors of the long treatment of the powerful (and poisonous) drug which alone had a chance to secure them from future disaster. . . .

Even so (says John Stokes) of all who are bit by the pale horror and fail of detection within the first week of its outward appearance, at least one quarter, in spite of reasonably effective treatment, develop serious complications. And many of these are mortal. Paul Ehrlich's discovery was magnificent, but clearly not the last answer.

The way Julius Wagner-Jauregg got into the fight against the most terrible result of the spirochete's hiding, was bizarre. It was totally unlooked for, like the first song of the returning whippoorwill waking you in the gray of a May morning.

TO look at Wagner-Jauregg, you'd take him for a Viennese professor who would have made an excellent Oklahoma sheriff . . . of one of its tougher counties. You'd never think him the revolutionist who has put it in men's power to wipe out paresis, the general paralysis of the insane . . . the last consequence of the pale microbe's lurking.

That's one of the strange and hopeful angles of the long fight against Schaudinn's horror. Granted the spirochete is of all microbes the most treacherous and resourceful. Admitted the ill it causes is—with cancer—one of the two most fatal that assails humanity. But against it there has risen the motliest yet the boldest, shrewdest, most original band of men against any kind of human death. Of all these Wagner-Jauregg was as bold and surely as original as any.

His job was psychiatry—which, of all the disciplines of medicine (though fascinating) had given least to the staving off of death. Yet this gnarled old alienist has turned forty centuries of medical dogma topsy-turvy. He has proved that fever—always thought to be man's enemy—is a friendly fire that frizzles the pale cause of the most surely deadly of insanities.

You'll be amazed at the expedient he used to bring men already in the clutches of this always fatal madness back to sanity, human dignity, and usefulness. Yet that's only the beginning of the story. The friendly fever he first dared to set flaming has been shown by that other Viennese, big-hatted Kyrle, to prevent (if used in time) this brain-softening from ever starting.

What's yet more astounding is that a new kind of death-fighter—not a physician—has found a fever as powerful probably, but far safer than the dangerous fire lit by Wagner-Jauregg. Ten years after the Vienna doctor's experiment, Whitney, the engineer, by chance bumped into an electric fever, non-poisonous, and controllable.

Could you ask a more grotesque contrast? Wagner-Jauregg, crude as Prometheus, digs back into despised medical superstitions for a way to burn out the sickness that robs wisest men of their understanding. Whitney, super-modern, lights spirochete-blasting heat by invisible energy hatched in mercury-arc rectifiers and radiotrons. The machine medicine of this odd assorted pair of trail-blazers gives unexpected hope in the fight against Schaudinn's corkscrew microbe. Whitney's magic fire may really turn Paul Ehrlich's 606 into the magic bullet the gay Jew was sure it would be. . . .

II

It took thirty years of disappointment, fizzled-out pseudo-success, failure, to bring Wagner-Jauregg to the day, June 14, 1917, when he braced himself to drip a few drops of dangerous malarial blood on a scratch on the arm of a paralytic crazy actor. Wagner-Jauregg was already sixty, and his life work a failure. But he was hardly thirty when the hunch hit him that mental fogs might be heated out of people's skulls by fever. . . .

Middle eighteen-eighties—there he's standing hopeless at the bedside of a woman aged twenty-seven. Her post-child-birth madness has gone on to imbecility, incurable. He knew that any treatment in the whole psychiatric bag of tricks was futile. He hadn't wanted to be an alienist. After his M.D., he'd sweat six years at pathology to fit himself to become a diagnostician. But he was working in Vienna, the city where low medical politics and stand-pattism had defeated no less than Ignaz Semmelweis. And now wire-pulling had jockeyed Wagner-Jauregg out of an assistant's job he'd earned, a job that had been half promised him. He was bitter. He planned to exile himself to Egypt. He was conscientious, must learn a bit more medicine before treating even such people as Egyptians. Here was a place in old Leidesdorf's insanity clinic that nobody wanted . . . a snap job that would give him time to study.

So here he stood by the bedside of this woman . . . how lucky for her that she was dying. She'd come to the clinic praying incessantly, saying her milk had gone to her head, saying devils bothered her. She had become maniacal, then sullen, sitting shut inside herself for weeks till now it was five months since she'd spoken. She had gone downhill into a blank state that was worse than animal.

Then she'd caught typhoid fever, and now, *in extremis,* she'd gone into toxic convulsions, and here stood young Julius Wagner-Jauregg waiting for her to die. Now her convulsions had eased her into coma, with him hoping that for her sake she'd never wake.

She woke, to sanity.

Wagner-Jauregg didn't go to Egypt. Of course it was silly of him to change his mind. This seeming miracle was only a straw to grab at. And, indeed, the poor woman didn't even keep her sanity but slid slowly back to idiocy. And, anyway, his scientific training should have told him her recovery was just coincidence. And besides, who'd let him try to prove it wasn't—by infecting lunatics (even though hopeless) with typhoid fever that gave them seven chances out of a hundred of dying?

Just the same his experience had bit him deep. After the fashion of men who delve into psychiatry he was a little mad himself, maybe. And now he dug back into ancient books that told how Hippocrates, the half-legendary father of physicians, had seen epileptics cured by catching quartan malaria. In other fat forgotten volumes he read how, in France, cholera had swept through a mad-house killing hundreds— and leaving survivors who'd got back their wits. . . . Folklore. . . . In the light of modern science mere old wives' tales, superstition. Night after night he dug such stories from dusty books whose page-margins time had tinted yellow.

Day after day Wagner-Jauregg walked sad-eyed through those forlorn asylum wards, where you had to keep your eyes right and left and even behind you for fear of sudden violence, where the creepiness of the surroundings would make a hard man shudder. But what was this? This time it couldn't be happenstance. Here was a mother of nine children, insane at her change of life, gone idiotic, hopeless. Here she lay, her face aflame with the rash of erysipelas, almost fatal. . . .

Four months . . . and she was back home minding her family, and completely sane. And presently here popped up another case like her, and another. Now he knew the forgotten stories in those old books were not just nonsense. He dug back again into those tomes that were in these modern, *scientific* times a laughing-stock of scientific psychiatry. Yes, typhus fever had done the same healing trick, and pneumonia . . .

Wait, here was even an experiment, not an entire failure. Forgotten Ludwig Meyer had rubbed antimony salve, and kept rubbing and rubbing it, into the scalps of folks doomed with general paralysis of the insane. Their heads had got terribly ulcerated, with them feverish, and a few had come clear-brained out of their lunacy. This heroic experiment had been snorted (by scientists who did not try to repeat it) into oblivion.

In 1887 he got his own experiences of these strange natural cures together with all this mass of medical folklore. He published a scientific report in which he made the serious proposal to infect hopelessly crazy people with erysipelas, malaria. In Europe nobody listened. Reading this report in 1930—forty-three years later!—in the New York Academy of Medicine, I found its pages still uncut.

III

Nothing could stop him, not even the absence of opposition to his fool idea. He actually tried to infect insane folks with cultures of the recently discovered streptococcus of erysipelas. They refused to come down with the flaming sickness. They stayed crazy. He wanted to try malaria then. But nobody would listen to his starting such a formidable illness going in the Clinic which was in the middle of Vienna. This was long before the days when Ross and Grassi found it was spread by mosquitoes, and God knew where it might not spread to. So for three years he was stumped. . . .

Till he found a way to set fevers going in folks without letting pestilences loose all over. Here it was 1890, with Europe all excited about the new remedy, tuberculin, that had just been brewed from tubercle bacilli by Robert Koch himself. Already the first enthusiasm for it had changed to fear, to secret medical whispers of its frightful danger. The trademark of Koch's great name tied to tuberculin had caused it to be used too enthusiastically and it was known (*in camera* in medical societies) that the new poison had flared up nobody knew how many hundreds of cases of mild tuberculosis into fevers ending mortally. It had become almost a crime to use it.

So Wagner-Jauregg went at it. For ten years he dabbled with it, first in the idiotic asylum in Graz, and then after he'd been promoted professor in Vienna. It was famous the way he could send insane folks' fevers up with the first little and then bigger and bigger doses of tuberculin. He failed to help them mostly. And yet here were some . . . whose families tried to forget them because they were worse than dead . . . who'd gone home to make their dear ones happy.

Yet, in 1900, this tough-brained Wagner-Jauregg, looking back on it, had to admit it might all be failure. Cures? Yes, he could show cures that might have been broadcast as brilliant successes by a doctor less self-honest. But here was the devil of it: he'd fevered folks with all kinds of insanity . . . with that utterly vague assortment of brain troubles called dementia praecox, paranoia, acute psychosis. These names hardly did more than hide the vast psychiatric ignorance of what really caused any kind of brain sickness. And just as their causes were unknown, so their duration was variable, and they might end—*without any kind of treatment*—in idiocy, or recovery!

He had the heart to face his past failure. Now he boiled his whole future work down to one dreadful proposition. In all this jumble of vague brain diseases there was one clear-cut, sure one. Its definition, agreed to by all authorities . . .

"General paralysis of the insane is an incurable sickness, which in the course of a few years leads to imbecility and death."

From now on he'd fever none but those insane with general paralysis. He had the guts to face the almost certain ruin of this work he'd now given thirteen years to. In 1901, helped by his assistant, Doctor Pilcz, he began stoking up fever, in the Steinhof Asylum, by big doses of tuberculin, in a forlorn band of trembly-lipped doomed ones, all paralytic. Some sat always smiling vapidly. Others were potential murderers. Some were melancholy to the verge of suicide. Others were sure of their wealth, their financial genius, though with brains so addled they couldn't add simple sums of figures. Some whose sickness made them feel all the world against them, were here for the sudden ghastly murder of their own dear ones. All of them were members of a benighted rearguard of humanity. None who'd come to the Steinhof Asylum paralytic had ever left save in a coffin. All were doomed to die. That was the grim joke among psychiatrists: if these folks didn't die they weren't really general paralytics.

IV

Against the inexorability of the death he was now beginning to tackle, Wagner-Jauregg had this to encourage him: In a short while the cause of this worst of insanities was discovered. For many years it had been suspected that general paralysis was really only an end result of the ill that Schaudinn's microbe was the cause of. Then in 1906 August von Wassermann applied Jules Bordet's blood test to the uncovering of every kind of ambush of Schaudinn's pale horror.

That very year he used this test on the spinal fluid of paralytics, and found that it proved the thin spiral microbe's
lurking in their brains. By 1908 Wagner-Jauregg could be
sure that, in ninety-nine out of every hundred of his miserable paralytics, the Wassermann test of the spinal fluid
. . . showed positive. . . .

It is not the least fantastic angle of this ill's story that
Schaudinn, Bordet, and now Wagner-Jauregg, were all drawn
into the battle against it with no preconceived plan nor even
a notion they were going to fight this death. Now at the International Medical Congress at Budapest, 1909, Wagner-
Jauregg reported to the assembled great whales of psychiatric
science on what his tuberculin fevers had done for general
paralytics during the eight years he'd been at it.

To sixty-nine of these sad folk he had given long bouts
of tuberculin fever; sixty-nine others he'd watched, but left
without it. Five of those not fevered were still living. *Eight*
of the fevered ones hadn't died. It was absolutely negligible.

He stuck at it. Never has there been a more slogging, plodding following of a hope more utterly forlorn. Year after year
for a short rest every summer, lean-faced and with somber
eyes, Wagner-Jauregg left the gray barracks-like Psychiatric
Clinic. He tried to forget the gibbering crew of daft ones
for whom he could do so little. He forgot his failures in
climbing to the tops of the most unclimbable peaks of the
Dolomite Alps. He'd come back brown and leaner out of
that thin clear air, and stronger, and as mulishly determined
as ever, and always as simple. Enthusiastic again, he'd bend
over records and charts of general paralytics he had fought
so hard for . . . with so few of them living. He kept pry-
ing into every idiotic detail in the lives of those not yet
dead. His face lit up at pitiful bits of good news that would
only have brought a supercilious smile to the face of a really
scientific searcher—deeply versed in statistics. Bending closer,
his wide mustaches almost touched the jagged tracery of the

fever charts of these people. Fever: then they'd got marvelously clear-headed, even gone back to support their families. . . .

Months would pass, with these healed ones coming back,
daft, and then dying. . . .

V

In 1911 there was new hope . . . for a moment. Here was
606—the bullet Paul Ehrlich was sure was magical. And there
was then no doubt that it was ruinous to the corkscrew microbe in the early stages of syphilis. But alas, it soon became
plain that the long sleeping of these pale demons in the
linings of the blood vessels of the brains of men and women
seemed to toughen the microbes against the magic bullet.
And nothing was more grimly certain than this: That when
the spirochetes (for reasons yet mysterious) at last awoke to
do their last fatal gnawing, they were untouchable—even by
this new marvelous medicine.

Wagner-Jauregg stuck to his tuberculin fever. He added
the old remedy, mercury, to the fever. Instead of beginning
when they were totally daffy, he tried to start his cure when
folks were still in that early stage of so-called "nervous
breakdown" that's the first muttering of paresis in men hitherto iron-nerved, healthy. In 1914, he gathered together news
of eighty-six paretics he'd fevered in years 1907-9. Twenty-
one were still alive, and seven actually still working. It is of
interest to the observer of human stupidity that this good
news, in high psychiatric circles, caused hardly a ripple . . .
though all realized that the average life of *all* paretics is
hardly two years.

When any comment was offered, it was wise shaking of
heads with words to the effect that this tuberculin fever
was dangerous. . . .

That got Wagner-Jauregg into a smoldering fury. He
asked the alienistical bigwigs of Europe whether the chances

of *any* paralytic were so brilliant as far as life went that you weren't justified in trying *anything?*

He was sure now that fever helped them. Look at the case of this oil well engineer. He was awfully proud of that one. He was a most intelligent man, this engineer, who'd come sucking at trembling lips, stumbling over simple sentences, full of idiotic ideas of grandeur, sure for the mad-house. . . .

So many shots of tuberculin, with him getting each time hot, and hotter, and then his old pep and keenness back, and his silliness gone. He'd been able to go back to the oil wells in Galicia. . . .

Then that oil well engineer—the prize patient—relapsed, and died.

VI

Now it was morning in June, 1917. An assistant comes in to report to old Professor Wagner-Jauregg, who is wrinkled and with eyes sadder than ever. The sands of his hour glass are beginning to run low and he knows it, and knows his life-work is next to being finished, and knows his tuberculin "cure" is (fundamentally) just a will-o'-the-wisp he's chased through thirty years, to failure.

"Here's a shell-shocked soldier has malaria," the assistant now reports to the old alienist. "Shall we cure it with quinine?"

Wagner-Jauregg is anything but quick on the trigger. Now he waits. Then at last he growls: "No. . . ."

He has come to it finally. But does he dare? He knows there are comparatively gentle kinds of malaria, and then there's the dreaded aestivo-autumnal, often fatal. Which did this shell-shocked fellow have? After all Wagner-Jauregg was no malaria expert. But now he grunts certain low-voiced orders to his assistants. Now they're jabbing drops of blood out of this shell-shocked fellow's ear-lobe and bending over their microscopes. . . .

What if malaria should start spreading through Vienna,

with times tough enough already what with the War and food running low? He, Wagner-Jauregg, would be held responsible. . . . Now more orders to white-coated young doctors and presently you see them prowling peculiarly through the garden round the Clinic, making strange passes over pools of water under bushes. They report finally. Good! No malaria-spreading mosquitoes round here. All right, then . . .

But look. If, instead of malaria going naturally from man to man via bites of mosquitoes, you *shoot* blood loaded with malaria from one man to another, and from the second to a third, and another—won't the sickness flare up in deadliness, won't it become incurable by quinine? And then? Wagner-Jauregg knew there'd be newspaper headlines, screaming MURDER IN THE NAME OF SCIENCE. True enough. But it all boiled down, finally, to this . . .

For seventeen years a sad parade of forlorn humanity had come to Wagner-Jauregg. He had been their last hope. He had fevered them, with tuberculin, with vaccines. Where were they now? Dead mostly, or worse. Against these hundreds here were a tiny few who'd got better and stayed so. Why?

God knew why. But every last one of them, besides his tuberculin fever, had caught, *by accident,* the more fundamental fevers of pneumonia, typhoid . . .

Ergo . . .

So you see why, that June of 1917, they didn't cure that shell-shocked fellow's malaria but instead there was a quick painless jab of a syringe needle into his arm vein and a gush of dark blood pushing the syringe plunger back. . . . And quick now . . . don't give it time to clot! . . . over goes the blood into a scratch on the arm of this poor actor fellow, out of a job because he can't remember his lines any longer. And then a few drops onto that little ex-postal clerk, staring there with a brainless smile. . . . All right. That's all for today, gentlemen!

This malaria inoculation of two paretics was done on June 14, 1917. During the next two months the same thing happened to seven more confused, maniacal, or demented ones on their way to the madhouse, all hope abandoned. It was too simple to be called an experiment.

VII

Ten years have passed. 1927 . . . and what's happened is unbelievable, and against the grim science of general paralysis of the insane. Of those nine doomed, here are three completely sane, not in asylums, all home, all by their own sweat and clear brains earning their own bread and that of their wives and children. It is unprecedented. These are the first in history ever saved from this imbecilic death not by some random act of nature, but by Wagner-Jauregg.

That old-fashioned man, though seventy, was proud as a boy of these three people. They were surely curiosities. Looking at them, healthy, strong-brained, it gave you a feeling of being with folk not quite real, outside humanity, ghostlike, back from the dead. By now there are thousands like them the world over, but these first three were . . . historic. It hadn't been beer and skittles for Wagner-Jauregg that 1917 in his house of madness. All those first nine patients, with the malaria microbes multiplying in them, had become dreadfully and dangerously sick, no doubt of it. Their chills shook their beds. You'd have thought they'd burst into flames with their high fevers. Many got crazier than ever, with wild storms of maniacal madness, and from their ward in the Psychiatric Clinic there came weird wailing, whining, and now again awful screams in the night. The postal clerk—the second one inoculated—had died suddenly in a convulsion. . . .

Then just as those first three were getting so wonderfully

better, there came that ugly disaster of 1918. Enthusiastic
with those successes Wagner-Jauregg had shot what he was
sure was benign, tertian malaria into four patients. Alas,
the blood he used turned out to have hiding in it deadly
half-moon parasites of malaria tropica. Three of those folks
died and the fourth was just saved by enormous doses of
quinine. . . .

You'd have thought this would have stopped him. Austrians, and especially Viennese, have not the reputation of
being a stern, persistent people. You're likely, thinking of
Viennese, to imagine giddy folks dancing to Johann Strauss's
"Darling" waltz or languishing (decadently) to the strains of
"Tales from the Vienna Woods." But Wagner-Jauregg now
had the sternness to stick to it. There was in him something
of Semmelweis, who seventy years before, close by, had admitted he was the killer. There was in him, too, more than
a little of the fighter Ludwig van Beethoven—who ninety
years before had died in the Schwarzspanierhaus not far
away, raising up with his last breath to shake his fist at the
storm raging outside his window. Defying fate like these two
others, Wagner-Jauregg now stuck to it. . . .

Now came good news. Give your paretics the right kind
of malaria, and, though it burned them, yet this malaria got
by direct inoculation was not nearly so persistent as that got
naturally by bites of mosquitoes. It was much more easy to
cure by quinine. A few doses, and, presto, not a malaria
parasite remained in these people's bodies to make them
dangerous carriers, potential spreaders of malaria. Nobody
could have foreseen this new fact of science. But then, no
death fight would ever even get started if these Prometheans
weren't the kind of fellows who slog and plunge ahead, regardless of the most closely reasoned objections, regardless
of impossibilities, and of consequences. . . . But the best
news of all was the weird, internal somersault that Wagner-
Jauregg watched take place in the beings of these folks who

got better. It was a transformation not only of their sick brains, but the whole bodies of these paralytics seemed cleansed by the malarial fire. It wasn't sudden. Thin, washed out by the terrible fever, they came out of their malaria, and then gradually they began to turn into new people. Color came back to their pasty faces. They gained weight like healthy babies. Their trembly lips grew firm. Their stumbling footsteps changed to strong men's walking. They said they felt strangely fitter than they'd done for years before their madness started. Meanwhile they began (it was lovely) to show *insight,* to explain how sorry they now were for the silly acts they'd done when they were crazy. It was all a slow upward soaring of their whole beings that went on for months after the malarial fire had been extinguished. What was most striking was this . . . many had been sent on to the asylum as not improved, even doomed; gradually some of these had felt new strength flowing through them, with sanity returning. At last they'd been released and they'd come back to Wagner-Jauregg telling him they were well now, and working. . . .

The only bad news was that this magic happened to about a third of all those given malaria. But no wonder: brain stuff, once thoroughly damaged by the pale horror, can't repair itself like damaged bone or muscle or liver. To more than sixty out of a hundred, the malaria had come . . . too late. . . .

So now he did what was logical. He began getting hold of doomed ones who were not yet crazy, or paralytic, but who were known to hide the pale spirochete in their brains, by laboratory tests, and by the first faint evidence of damaged nerves and "nervous breakdown."

Malaria . . . and not three out of nine, *but eighty-three out of every hundred of these were well now, and working.* You'd have thought Wagner-Jauregg, old as he was, and having fought through so much disdain and sneering, would have been fanatical now about the virtues of the malaria cure he had discovered. Nothing was surer than the futility of 606 treatment of poor wretches on the verge of paralytic breakdown. There were sinister whispers that Ehrlich's "magic bullet" when it didn't cure the trouble, might actually drive the pale spirochete into folks' brain stuff. There was science (from autopsies) to show that while skin and bone syphilis was less . . . that the far more dreadful brain and nerve syphilis was on the increase, since 606 curing had been started. . . .

But, like the marvelous physician that he was, Wagner-Jauregg tried everything. And now he reported that, if you immediately followed the malaria fever with good heavy shots of 606 . . . the results were much better, and more lasting. "It's not a question of the prestige of one treatment as against another," he growled.

It's still a complete enigma . . . the way the malaria in this last most dreadful end of the loathsome sickness turns Ehrlich's salvarsan from something useless into a bullet that comes near being magic. It's known that the malaria fever alone doesn't always burn all the pale microbes, completely. Does it weaken them, so that the 606 can then come in to give them the final triumphant wallop? It's more likely (when you think of that strange upward soaring of the strength of those first three historic patients) that the fever stirs in the human body a hitherto unknown, microbe-fighting energy. It maybe helps the human more than it merely hurts the spirochete. It maybe turns degenerating, defenseless brain stuff into good healthy fighting protoplasm . . . and so gives Ehrlich's arsenic bullet, 606, its chance to wipe out every last lurking one of Schaudinn's corkscrew microbes. . . .

VIII

1927 . . . and it's the day Wagner-Jauregg, now seventy, is retiring from his professorship. In the crowded old ex-

chapel of the Clinic, eulogists have called him the con-
queror of general paralysis. He'd be the first to protest that
this is balderdash . . . for all over this final bite of the pale
horror still helps to fill asylums. Of course, by now, many
thousands of paretics who should have been dead, were back
home sane, and working. There was no longer any counting, the world over, the thousands malaria had dragged back
from worse than death. For this the Swedes have given
Wagner-Jauregg the Nobel Prize. Yet this day, honest and
tough as ever, he knows what's left to be done.

The eulogies are over. He gets up to give his swan song.
He looks like a hard-bitten small sheriff minus gun and
cartridge belt, dressed up for this occasion in black clothes
with little tie tucked under turned-down collar. His hair
is still remarkably thick and stubbly. His speech is short,
utterly without self-congratulation. He's not the kind that
holds with extended palaver. Austere, he even now denies
himself the garrulity appropriate to age and this great occasion. He admits he's nearly finished. "You do not know that
for some time now, effort and will power is, what once was
strength," he tells them.

There's a storm of stamping and a roar of cheering from
the students and even the professors forget their dignity. It's
real bedlam. They rush down the steps crowding round him.
Then he shows them all how young he is; jumping up onto
a chair to be above them, he holds his two arms high above
his head, shaking hands at all of them, exultant. No, he's
far from finished.

And he's no longer primarily interested in the possible
cure of general paralysis. . . .

1930, Vienna, Landesgerichtsstrasse, Nr. 18, and here a
high-ceilinged, old-fashioned study in an apartment I've
come into through a door decorated with a bright-polished
plate asking me please to wipe my feet before I enter. This
is the sanctum of the old searcher, nearly seventy-four now,

but not finished. The late afternoon light is still good enough to let me see something granite, something crag-like about this gnarled, hairy, lean, but not wizened old man who stands before me. Now I understand how for forty years he'd let the swirl of scientific fads, idiotic theories, psychiatric verbosities boil round him, with him not worn down, never budging, just plugging at his laughed-at fever theory. . . .

"Of course, what is most important is to *prevent* general paralysis," he said in his precise, slow French with German accent. And here he's super-modern in spite of his great age, years ahead of any other fighter of Schaudinn's pale horror. "That is the real future of the malaria treatment," Wagner-Jauregg tells me.

He reminds me of what's known to any expert who fights the loathsome sickness: that all in whom the corkscrew demon once starts gnawing can be divided into one class in which by long terrific drug treatment (begun early) their sickness may be checked . . . and into a tragic class who in spite of everything keep on relapsing, not responding. . . .

Years before its horrid outbreak, by the Bordet-Wassermann test of the spinal fluid, you can *prophesy* which ones are threatened with the doom of general paralysis. These poor devils may be reasonably healthy, with absolutely nothing showing outwardly . . . with a few of Schaudinn's demons lingering in the nerve stuff of their spinal cords and brains. For ten, fifteen, twenty years and even longer these spiral microbes may hide there, latent. . . .

In the days before Jules Bordet, you couldn't predict the possible quick stroke of paralysis, sudden seeing of things double, the lost memory, the manic ideas of grandeur, that loom (possibly) for any or for all of them.

Almost murderous doses of 606, of mercury, of bismuth, you can give them, and still, ominously, the Wassermann test stays positive, shows that spirochetes are waiting. The twilight in Wagner-Jauregg's study grows slowly dimmer, but I can still see his rugged silhouette against the window. He tells me of the marvelous adventure of his friend, the death fighter, Kyrle. . . .

Wagner-Jauregg had often talked of this fundamental: that the earlier in the sad insanity folks got their malaria treatment, the surer chance they had of being healed of it. And what if you shot them with the fever . . . in that pre-paralytic stage when their trouble still was sleeping? Kyrle was one of the chiefs of the great syphilis clinic of Professor Finger, and had the grandest chance to try it. Kyrle didn't seem enthusiastic. . . . Then one day on a mountain-climbing trip with Wagner-Jauregg, Kyrle told the old master he'd begun it. . . .

The bearded, round-faced Kyrle with the black wide-brimmed hat, by warnings, by cajolings, had got these people —still pseudo-healthy—to stake their present lives in a gamble. He gave them successive shots of Ehrlich's new 606 that bears the number 914—that's called neo-salvarsan. Right afterward, malaria, with eight or ten terrific rigors of that stormy sickness. Then quinine to cure them. Then neo-salvarsan once more. . . .

Now the remarkable events that followed began to crack the riddle of why Ehrlich's bullet wasn't always magic. The bullet's no good unless the bodies of the poor devils you shoot it into can *help* that bullet hit the spirochetes. It's that strange somersault, that life-giving kick, that upward soaring which fever causes . . . that lets the salvarsan get in its spirochete-smashing wallop. *The body itself has got to join in the death fight.* . . .

Time went on, and as these pseudo-healthy people began to get mysteriously stronger, all the tests that showed their brain and nerve stuff to be tainted grew weak and weaker till at last many of them were completely negative. Remaining so . . . a possible sign of the death blow to the last lurking spiral microbe? Wagner-Jauregg's voice lifted ever so slightly, coming exultant through the semi-darkness of his study. . . .

"Anyway . . . not one of those hundreds, and it's eight years now, has ever come to the psychiatric clinic with general paralysis."

And again . . . those rescued people hadn't taken such a terrible gamble; again it shows how your man against death can never know till he *tries* it. Kyrle knew when he began it, that many a general paralytic snuffs out suddenly in the middle of one of his malarial paroxysms. Maybe two or three out of every hundred die so. But when their insanity was marching ahead to certain death, wasn't that chance worth taking?

But what of these latent folks, not yet crazy—only threatened, maybe?

Well, you had to try it! And what Kyrle found out was that in such people the malarial fire wasn't near so deadly. They did shoot appalling fevers, have frightful agues, a dreadful siege, in short, but yet nearly all get better. Only two in all had died. . . .

It was plain horse sense that now led Kyrle forward, or, really when you come to think of the topsy-turvy history of it, *backward,* closer and closer to the start of the horrid sickness. Now Kyrle didn't need Wagner-Jauregg to urge him any longer. And now, just as the old master had found the earlier he gave his crazy doomed ones the malaria, the better, so Kyrle found, too, that the earlier you lighted the malaria fire (sandwiched between Ehrlich's salvarsan before and after) the more completely this fantastic combination treatment wiped out every sign of the pale horror.

What now began in Vienna was almost as incredible as Paul Ehrlich's original dream of his magic bullet . . . when he'd hoped one shot might wipe out every spirochete for always. Kyrle now cajoled unfortunates in the first year of

their trouble to submit to the heroic ordeal of this purifica-
tion by the malarial fire. Eloquent, with the super-fanatic
sureness of an apostle, he showed them that when you have
this ghastly trouble, it's your future much more than your
present the doctor must think of guarding. He explained
patiently to them how, once their sickness got past the first
stage of its entry into their bodies, those spirochetes pene-
trated, gnawing, boring back and forward, lashing, poisoning every nook and cranny. . . . They were shot with it.
. . . And no drug, no magic bullet alone, not the most expensive doctor, could now promise them safety from its
awful consequences. . . .

Hundreds of them—it was really wonderful—consented
(for their future) to take the harder road toward possibly
perfect healthiness. So now: six shots of salvarsan. Then hospital and fire of malaria. Then salvarsan again, 'right after.
And that was all. . . .

Out of two hundred and fifty brave ones to whom Kyrle
gave this *one* course of sandwich treatment, all excepting
three had every last sign of syphilis possible of scientific detection wiped out of them. Down to the extremely delicate
Müller precipitation test (twin of our Kahn test) . . . and
much more sensitive than the best Bordet-Wassermann reaction, no trace of the pale horror was left in them. And of
the three who relapsed, all three had refused, after the hell
of their malaria, to come back for the after treatment with
Ehrlich's now really magic bullet. . . .

It was almost unbelievable. It was so dark now in the
study that Wagner-Jauregg's shape was ghostlike. His voice
came through the dimness a bit unreal. He stopped talking.
He groped about with a long stick, like that of an old-fashioned lamp-lighter, reaching for the gas-jet high above him.

Kyrle had died in 1926. That Bohemian-looking man,
debonair in his broad-brimmed hat, had gone too soon to
know the real triumph of his dangerous experiment.

Year after year its results became more brilliant. 1930 now, with eight years gone by. Yet no relapses in any that had taken full treatment—not even doubtful, tiny flare-ups just detectable by the most sensitive test of blood or spinal fluid. . . .

Yet we must be cautious in predicting . . . the scourge of the pale horror is of all human sicknesses by far the most lingering, tenacious. . . .

Just the same each year that goes by with all these people staying healthy, makes Kyrle's new treatment more astounding. . . .

Wagner-Jauregg's long stick had made contact with the gas-jet now. He isn't unreal any longer and the story hasn't been just a dream. Here was the fundamental: "Not one, of all those hundreds, has ever come to the Psychiatric Clinic with General Paralysis."

IX

But alas. Here you have what's far and away the greatest promise of demolishing, obliterating, wiping the pale spirochete out of your sufferer . . . early, in a few months, without the years of gnawing worry and uncertainty, with an enormous saving of time and money, without the danger of the long poisoning with the enormous doses of arsenicals that used to be necessary. . . .

But alas. How are you going to get your suffering millions in the early less desperate stages of this sickness to go to the hospital, to face the ordeal of the fierce rigors and the fire of malaria? How are you going to convince your rank and file of doctors that this is necessary? And, if convinced, how—practically—are they going to keep the malaria virus going, ready to inoculate, when it's known the malaria can't be grown in glass in cultures like ordinary microbes? When you have to keep it living, shooting it from one human being to another. . . . Alas. It's Utopic!

Now comes the engineer, the physicist Willis R. Whitney,

to help Wagner-Jauregg and Kyrle . . . and maybe all these suffering millions. Maybe . . .

In Schenectady, New York, worked Whitney. He was worried by certain bizarre happenings in one of the workrooms of the General Electric Company Research Laboratory, where he is director. In this room was a powerful high frequency oscillator, a short-wave radio transmitter. It was a maze of radiotrons, rectifiers, and other electric gadgets whose buzzing sends news of disasters, the blah of politicians, the degenerate cacophony of jazz orchestras, the idiotic simperings of high-priced crooners, to Australia or Alaska.

Every time Whitney's electricians tinkered at this powerful broadcasting monster, they got uncomfortable. They snapped on its switch. There was a low humming. And presently they got hot and bothered.

They didn't have to be in contact with the machine or any of its gadgets, mind you. All they had to do was simply to stay in that room while there was this low humming . . . to get really feverish! Whitney stuck a clinical thermometer in one electrician's mouth. He snapped the oscillator's switch. In fifteen minutes the man had 2.2 degrees of fever. The room itself was not so hot. There was only that low humming. It didn't sound formidable. But to detect the terrific invisible energy that the broadcasting oscillator was hatching, you could wave a neon bulb near the machine's antenna. The gas inside that bulb then glowed a lovely red and rose and blue. It was spooky. . . .

You'd say Whitney (not being a biologist or doctor) had no business meddling with it. But now he had one of these machines built in miniature. It was 750 watts instead of 20 kilowatts. Instead of radiating its energy off an antenna, this little one bounced its power invisibly back and forth between two metal plates placed parallel. You could pass your hands back and forth between these plates in the field of this short wave energy, feeling nothing. The air stayed cool. You could put a little tube of water—pure—between them, and nothing happened. But wait: turn the water in this tube into a conductor by adding just so much salt, and the unseen energy would heat the fluid to any temperature up to boiling. It was mathematical, predictable.

In place of putting salt into a vessel of water, Whitney now put a tadpole, and the switch snapped, and there was that low humming, and in a few seconds the tadpole in that vessel of water between the two plates began to get anxious, then hot, and then, alas, he died. The air between the plates wasn't hot. The pure water in the vessel stayed cool. The tadpole simply got too hot to live. It was weird. Now Whitney (who was after all not a biologist but only very curious, inquisitive) hired the physiologist Helen Hosmer. Hosmer knew the ins and outs of animals. What did go on inside various beasts when this energy oscillated back and forth through their bodies?

Into a glass battery jar Hosmer now put a white rat, snapped the switch, and while the air in that jar stayed cool, the rat's fever went up one degree per minute, up and up, till his ears began to blister, till his legs began to stiffen from the fever flaming *inside* him. . . .

Here's what was remarkable. Set the two plates just far enough apart. With just the right amount of energy zipping from one plate through the glass to the opposite plate and back the same way to the first plate *at the right number of million back-and-forth zips per second* . . .

You could keep that rat exactly as hot as you wished for as long as you wanted, not hurting him.

Whitney (though only a physicist and with no right to dabble in medical mysteries) saw the point of it. Here was fever . . . absolutely controllable. Here was fever . . . not from shooting in poisons like tuberculin or inoculating microbes like malaria (and then having to pray that everything would go nicely)—

Here was fever you snapped on with a switch and dosed with an ammeter. . . .

Whitney had this advantage over Wagner-Jauregg. He hadn't, like that old heretic, had to spend his life fighting to break down four thousand years of medical belief that *fever, per se,* is pernicious. Whitney in his layman's way had heard of the marvel of Wagner-Jauregg's healing of general paralytic doomed ones by malaria. Being simple and not too well versed in all the complicated science that had already grown round Wagner-Jauregg's plain discovery, Whitney jumped to the conclusion that what the malaria must do was simply to heat these people.

Even Wagner-Jauregg wasn't sure this was the whole story. And indeed, that careful, never-theorizing searcher had a notion that it wasn't the fever alone that brought his people back to sanity. If Whitney had looked through Garrison's "History of Medicine," he would have found scores of references to "fever," and if he'd then tracked those references down, he would (alas) have found not one word hinting that fever is anything but dangerous—and something for physicians to try to douse if possible. . . .

Now Whitney didn't bother with old medical dogmas or modern complicated scientific confusions about it, but just shoved off from Wagner-Jauregg's malaria cure of general paralysis with the firm notion *that fever is one of nature's ways of fighting death.*

Now things moved swiftly, as they have a trick of doing in those laboratories which professors are wont, with a certain degree of academic sniffishness, to call "commercial." Now to the Albany Medical College came Charles M. Carpenter—that same young doctor (of cows, horses, and philosophy) who'd helped Alice Evans fight the undulant fever. Into his laboratory came troops of rabbits . . . Belgian

Hares, New Zealand Reds, Flemish Giants, and albinos. And from the General Electric Laboratory in Schenectady, close by, came the radio-transmitter, the high-frequency oscillator . . . in short this machine that could so weirdly stoke up any degree you wanted of *electric fever*.

It was going to be a very simple experiment. Whitney, who was simple (in the sense of not being tangled up in a lot of medical ifs, buts, and theoretical balderdash) . . . thought that maybe malaria had just made things a little too hot for Schaudinn's corkscrew microbes. Well . . .

Now, day after day in that laboratory in Albany, in glass battery jars between the aluminum plate electrodes of the high frequency electric fever machine, there sits a succession of Belgian Hares, Flemish Giants, New Zealand Reds . . . all getting hot.

They've all been infected in their testicles with the cork-screw spirochete of Schaudinn. Day after day the switch snaps, the oscillator starts humming. Carpenter and his assistant, Ruth Boak, wave the long-handled neon-gas bulb between the plates. Yes, it's working. In the field of terrific energy that's zipping back and forth through the glass and through those rabbits at so many zips per second, the gas inside the bulb glows rosy red, then fades to nothingness as they take the bulb away. It's eerie with more than a smack of Rosicrucian necromancy to it. But it's entirely exact and prosaic the way you can absolutely dose and control the fever in your rabbits—heating them to 106° Fahrenheit, or 108° . . .

The result of this (and many another) experiment was very pretty. In only one out of twenty-five rabbits inoculated with the corkscrew microbe was there any sign of the small-est lurking of the pale horror. All these twenty-five had had electric fever.

In a like number not fevered there were the ulcers of the

terrible sickness in every one . . . teeming with back-and-forward drilling, lashing spiral demons.

Here was the pale horror killed . . . by energy.

Whitney hadn't been too simple.

x

Of course you're ahead of me, already. You're saying . . . of course the thing they did then was simply to repeat the wonderful experiment of Wagner-Jauregg and of Kyrle, giving folks in early stages of syphilis the sandwich treatment of Ehrlich's salvarsan and fever. Only now they'd use this electric fever, this new radiothermy (so Whitney named it) and not the terrible, difficultly controllable microbes of malaria. But alas . . .

You'd have thought great research foundations, university hospitals, laboratories everywhere, would have grabbed at the chance to use the oldest (but just discovered) death-fighting weapon of nature . . . now that you could turn it on with a switch and dose it with an ammeter. But human progress is rarely so direct and simple. . . . It's nothing new for fundamental discoveries to kick around for a long time, neglected.

Logically, Carpenter had lighted this weird new fever in rabbits *before* the pale microbes had got a good foothold, right after he'd infected them, before the sinister ill's first outward eruption. He'd succeeded—brilliantly.

Wagner-Jauregg and Kyrle both knew, and had dinned it over and over in scientific papers, that the earlier in the human sickness you use Ehrlich's arsenic bullets, *made magic by the malarial fever,* the more devastating the effect on Schaudinn's spirochete . . . and the greater your chance to wipe it out completely.

You'd have thought men against this worst of deaths everywhere would have jumped at this chance now, would have put two and two together. As long ago as 1929, Whitney's safe, controllable electric fever was common gossip in academic circles. And surely some of them at least must have read Kyrle's final paper . . . published as long ago as 1924.

But then the grim history of men's fight against the stealthy sickness has always been topsy-turvy. So now you find this fever stoked up by the radiotherm proving itself (just as malaria had to) against the last, most fatal consequences of the pale microbe's gnawing.

It was Carpenter (physician of the "lower" animals and doctor of philosophy) who first took the chance of lighting it in human beings. With those short radio waves zipping from one electrode through a coffin-like box of celotex into one side of a man and out the other to the opposite electrode and back to the first one at the right number of million zips per second, Carpenter and Page, the engineer, found you could get a man as hot as you wished for as long as you wanted—not hurting him.

Carpenter went to New York then—to the Psychiatric Institute at the Medical Center high over the Hudson River. He taught the electric fever to Dr. Leland Hinsie. Now Carpenter and Hinsie made fever curves in doomed paralytic humans. You couldn't tell those curves apart from the fever curves of the fierce rigors of real malaria. That was scientifically elegant.

What was really important though was that what had happened when Wagner-Jauregg shot his poor crazy folks with malaria happened now with the new machine fever.

Of course it proved that Whitney hadn't been so simple about its being just fever. It was a terrible test of his idea. The spirochetes had been lurking, soaking, adapting themselves to the bodies of these folks for years, even decades. Yet the fever stirred the bodies of many of these human wrecks to wallop them. . . .

Now came news about this other kind of short wave heat-making energy called "diathermy." You could fever folks with diathermy too—by energy shot from jacket electrodes strapped round them—not so simple as Whitney's radiotherm . . .

But both these fevers sent just about the same proportion of daft ones home sane . . . just about the same number as Wagner-Jauregg's malaria had brought back to reason and to supporting their families.

In the days of Carpenter and Page's first fumblings with the radiotherm it wasn't such a picnic for the folks they put in that coffin-shaped box. In the first place they perspired in rivers. The electric energy arced across the sweat-pools and the blisters weren't comfortable.

That's all fixed now. Boss Kettering, the engineer, the inventor, the fixer, the extraordinary, salty-talking searcher, looked at a poor devil sweating and horribly uncomfortable in the radiotherm. . . .

"We'll shoot some hot air in there to cool him down," Boss Kettering said.

Now, when the short-wave radio fever begins to make these people hot in their box of celotex, they're air-conditioned in there. A gentle current of dried air sweeps over them. It's air heated to 260° Fahrenheit—48 degrees above the boiling point! That air evaporates their sweat and they feel cool and comfortable . . .

So now, here's comfortable electric fever, ready.

Like malaria, it stirs up a new mysterious chemistry in the sick people whose bodies have been sapped by the long secret working of the spirochete. But unlike malaria this fever-machine medicine isn't a strain on the hearts of these people; it doesn't load them—already poisoned by spirochetes —with the added toxins from the microbes of malaria. It's snapped on with a switch and dosed with an ammeter. . . .

These people can now be fevered, and not even have to stay over night in the hospital.

Now who'll repeat the experiment of Kyrle?

That shrewd Bohemian-looking man always lamented he couldn't use Ehrlich arsenic bullets right along with malaria, in between the chills of it, instead of before and after. It was impossible, because the salvarsan hits malaria microbes even better than it does spirochetes, and so douses the malaria fever.

But no arsenical that Ehrlich ever invented has any dousing action on this fever stoked up by the short-wave radio. Nothing is simpler than to sandwich the 606 in between each electric fever—so they can both work together.

XI

So here are the weapons, ready. Will physicians expert in this sickness really set out now to begin obliterating the horror that—along with cancer—is one of the two worst scourges of humanity?

Fritz Schaudinn, Bordet, Wassermann, and right now Reuben Kahn have given them power to spot its lurking. Will they use the fantastic artillery that Paul Ehrlich, Wagner-Jauregg, and Whitney have discovered for them?

Will they use the friendly fever that really makes Ehrlich's arsenic bullets magic—not only against general paralysis, *but will they use it early?*

In millions (literally) round us today the spirochete is hiding, waiting for its final bite that will show up innocently in the mortality statistics as death from disease of liver, kidneys, heart, blood vessels, nerves, or brain. . . .

In New York State alone, just *one* of these last consequences—general paralysis—is responsible for the deaths of one in every nine who die between ages forty and sixty. Will death fighters set out to prove that these deaths can now be prevented?

Will they remember that up till now all their efforts have

only lengthened life in the mass by making a dent in the mortality of the first years of human life?

Do they realize that here—*for the first time in death-fighting history*—is their chance to crush an enemy that waits stealthily for the kill of its millions, most of whom are beyond age forty and in the prime of living?

BOOK IV
OLD DOCTOR SUN

10. FINSEN

THE LIGHT HUNTER

~~~~~~

Finsen the Dane, wool-gathering at his medical stud-ies, watched a cat on the roof just under him move again and again from the shade out into the sun. The sun is dim in Denmark and when Finsen wanted to invent a machine-sun to replace it, the Danish doc-tors gave him the horse laugh. So he cured his first case of skin tuberculosis in the Copenhagen electric light station—the engineers not laughing.

~~~~~~

DEATH had already tagged Niels Finsen when he dis-covered that the energy of light may be death's worst enemy.

Finsen was not only the first scientific light hunter, but the first systematic fighter of death by means of sunlight, and besides, he was the founder of machine medicine. That was all of thirty-five years before Whitney began to fight the pale horror with his radiotherm.

You'd hardly call Finsen's watching of a drowsy cat's shift-ing from shade into sun a logical beginning of medicine by machinery. But then his discovery (which was really an eleven year race with death) came about through a chain of events seemingly unscientific and medically not quite orthodox.

His funny little experiments on the ear of his young wife might be laughed at (and would be) by the high-paid search-ers of our glass, white-metal, and white-tiled laboratories—where science is really scientific. It is well for all who look for help against death to come only from such gaudy temples to remember that Finsen's first swat at the horrible, incurable skin tuberculosis took place in the Copenhagen Electric Light Station. And in that hare-brained reaching toward the light there was never a doctor but only engineers cheering him from the side-lines.

Finsen was outside the ordinary human pattern right to that day when, dying, he chuckled and said: "If I only could see my own autopsy!"

His own bizarre doings are only less astounding than our modern negligence to make thorough use of what he discovered. His machine substitute for the sun's life-giving light is the most powerful single weapon now existing for the death fight against all kinds of tuberculosis. Why, then, do so many hundreds of thousands of people still go on dying?

I leave you to untangle that puzzle, which is just as deep as the riddle of the way Finsen's curious left-handed brain dreamed out his strange scientific poem of the sun against death. It is possible that his followers, from gentle Axel Reyn down to hard-boiled Ove Strandberg, are too modest and quiet. It's a way Danes have. They're almost apologetic about discoveries that could right now save us scores of thousands of lives every year, not counting all the pain and sorrow. They're too polite to ballyhoo. . . .

II

Finsen when a boy was fired from a Danish prep school "for small ability and total lack of energy." In those days nothing could have been much blanker than medical ignorance of the death-fighting power of sunlight. Finsen's father, who was an Icelander, sent Niels up to that extremely civilized country (where they have no police or jails) to finish his prep-schooling. In Denmark they had tried to turn him into a little human parrot. The Icelandic ex-Vikings had the absolutely unique system of teaching Finsen to believe noth-

ing but what he found out for himself . . . and how he took
to it.

In the middle eighties he got to medical school in Copenhagen where the professors and students were then all on fire
over the new science of the microbe-hunting trail-blazers,
Pasteur and Koch. Finsen didn't bother but lone-wolfed it
off on a trail all his own. Here he sat wool-gathering, watching a cat on the roof just below his window. He was deeply,
mysteriously sick already, hadn't enough blood, got strange
fits of coldness. . . .

Now there lay this cat on a flat roof, part shaded, part
sunlit. Marvelously healthy, that cat lay basking. When the
cool shadow touched him, he just edged over into the sun
again . . . again, and again, and again. Well, cats didn't
seem to need doctors very often, and they seemed to
know. . . .

He couldn't get this hunch about innate cat-sagacity out
of his head and he tried to read up on it, neglecting his
studies. Night after night he bent his back over Danish, German, English medical books which like most books are fat
in inverse proportion to the real knowledge of the sciences
they're concerned with. In the portly tomes at Finsen's disposal, he only discovered that sunlight inflamed you, cooked
you, hurt you. . . .

True, there were rare references to sun being good but
he didn't run across them. . . . They weren't important
enough for the big books to notice. . . .

He couldn't walk very far without a pain jabbing him in
the chest. Now here he was, one day, easing that hurting by
leaning across a bridge railing over the canal round the Slots-
holmen. Dreaming—not thinking—he followed the unimportant antics of a lone skating bug being carried by the current
down below on the water. Funny. . . . Every time that fool
bug hit the dark line of the bridge's shadow, just exactly

there, it would shoot back upstream into the sunlight . . .
again, and again, and again. . . .

So the skating bug told him (according to Finsen's lone-
wolf way of looking at it) what the fat books of the savants'
couldn't. He began dreaming experiments, but not yet making them, and he had hands that would come in handy when
it got time to do them. He was a wizard at gun tinkering
(and a crack rifle-shot) and his hands were so nimble the
famous surgeon Chievitz wanted to make him a prosperous
knife man. He was tempted enough (though not by the
money end of it for which he had a loathing) to turn himself into an expert anatomist. And here it was 1892.

Finsen was in the garden with his sweetheart, Ingeborg
Balslev, not courting her, or only partly. For three hours the
day before he'd puzzled her by sitting burning his forearm
in the midsummer sunlight.

Now today with an impersonal entirely unloverlike excitement he was demonstrating to Ingeborg that his arm
was all cooked, blistered . . .

"Excepting where I painted this band in India ink . . ."

That, he explained, had shut out the *chemical* rays of the
sun. These chemical rays were what burned you. And that
must be why the negroes in the tropics were black. Such was
his scientific courtship. North Summer days drowsed by in
that garden with Ingeborg maybe realizing that searchers'
wives have got to be much more mothers than sweethearts.
Finsen's burned arm had turned light brown now . . . all
excepting where he had painted India ink. That was
white. . . .

Now today there he sat again, burning that same arm for
three hours once more. Next day it was only that band of
skin that was cooked and blistered . . . with all the rest
browner, not hurting. It was what any common sailor knew
and too idiotically obvious to call an experiment. Just the
same, right here Finsen took his first jump ahead of what

he'd found in the fat books. Sunlight wasn't always bad. It only hurts skin that's not tanned!

Such was the romantic prelude to his marriage to Ingeborg Balslev and now it was Spring of 1893, with them at their honeymooning. Finsen presses his young wife's ear-lobe between two pieces of glass. Will making it bloodless let the sunlight shine through it easier? Finsen (immensely delighted) shows her that sunlight shining through her blanched ear darkens sensitive photographic paper faster than it does when it shines through her pink ear full of blood. Ingeborg was patient and not too bored with it even when she had to sit stock-still for five minutes. It must have seemed pretty silly.

All this puttering went on in their flat in Copenhagen. They had no laboratory. Their only other experimental animal (besides Ingeborg) wasn't expensive . . . being simply a tadpole. Here it lies squirming, wrapped in wet filter paper on the stage of Finsen's microscope. Holding a burning glass just so, he shoots a strong beam of white sunlight onto the tadpole's tail sticking out of the filter paper . . . and now through his microscope squints at the microscopic excitement this light is kicking up in that tadpole's body. It was a kind of complicated piddling because while Finsen focused his microscope with one hand, with the other he kept pouring cold water over this future frog's tail to keep the hot light from frizzling it . . .

Now under the strong beam of light the pollywog's blood ran slower and slower through the delicate capillaries. Now in those tiny passages there was a traffic jam of red blood corpuscles. Now among the masses of them all jammed together there came sneaking a few white blood cells . . . and then myriads. They stopped, then slithered, oozed (like amoebas) right through the blood-vessel walls out into the tadpole's tail tissue.

It was . . . inflammation. It was nothing more than the

microscopic, dramatic goings-on that were at the bottom of the ordinary reddening of anybody's skin when the sun began to cook it. It was just that and then it was more. Finsen knew how Metchnikoff had proved that white blood cells swarm out of the blood-vessels in masses, like soldiers, to swallow dangerous microbes when they invade us. But here was a kind of inflammation that called out this white blood cell militia, these phagocyte minute-men, without any microbes . . . and before malicious microbes had got there.

III

This very year that his pure science was showing how light might be life-saving (for tadpoles) he turned right round and proved that even traces of sunlight might be deadly to human beings, and it wasn't pure science but practical. Here's Finsen arguing with the chief physician of the Blegdam Hospital, Copenhagen. He was trying to sell him a most fantastic new treatment for smallpox. To keep smallpox blisters from getting inflamed—*and infected*—you ought to keep all light away from people who'd broke out in smallpox's first blisters. If you kept those blisters from getting inflamed and infected—you'd keep away the fatal blood-poisoning. . . .

It was against his pure science.

You had to keep the tiniest traces of light away from smallpox people from the moment their blisters first broke out on them. So he argued to the chief physician . . . who in soft polite Danish gave him the horse laugh. But Finsen kept hammering at him. Didn't the distinguished doctor see it? Why . . . it was plain as the nose on your face. Where did people break out in blisters when smallpox started? All over. Where only did their blisters fester, scar? On hands and face . . . where the light hit them!

He preposterously held that smallpox folks should be kept shut up in rooms behind thick red curtains that let in only red rays, shut out the chemical blue, violet, ultra-violet. . . .

The Blegdam doctor snickered again and then Finsen flung out saying: "You might at least try not to laugh at me!" At this moment his status in Copenhagen was purely that of a . . . nuisance, that's the word for it. Now this same year, way up in Bergen, Norway, two Bergen doctors (who were too far up north to hear the Copenhagen guffaws) read Finsen's theory.

That very Autumn these two fellows, Lindholm and Svendsen, bundled sundry Norwegians just broken out in very bad smallpox blisters into dark rooms weirdly red from thick red hangings. . . .

Two weeks later every man jack of them blinked out into the daylight with blisters dried, no fever, no blood-poisoning, scarless. . . . And then from Gothenburg, Sweden, came a scientific report of cases of black smallpox (deadly) that had been guarded from blood-poisoning by lying in Finsen's dim red light, where the blue and the violet and the ultra-violet of sunlight couldn't get at them. For this Finsen suddenly became internationally famous, and yet deep down in him he felt sunlight was good.

He now might have cashed in on his new reputation as a doctor who'd proved light was bad. He kept sniffing into entirely unprofitable corners to try to find out how it might do good. He had no job, and heaven knows how he kept himself and Ingeborg alive those first years. He applied for a fellowship, telling the professors who had the giving of it that he felt he could demonstrate the possible death-fighting power of sunlight. . . .

"Oh, I see, you want it for something *practical,* something *use*ful," the principal professor said. . . .

He didn't get the fellowship.

Yet he was too idealistic. He was a sort of naturalist with a strong streak of poet in him that had a trick of suddenly turning experimenter. Spring, 1894 . . . it was a day when life all round was waking from strong sun breaking through on a cloudy morning. That was when you noticed the peculiar action of sunlight! All over, all at once, things got lively. . . .

Now for an experiment to show it was sunlight. Since his boyhood he'd lain—hundreds of days like this—on his back and on his belly in fields, in thickets, seeing this sudden resurrecting effect of sunlight. He'd not understood it. He had tried to write down the poetry of it . . . of sun breaking out from clouds inciting torpid bugs to crawl round happily or fly round merrily, setting grumpy birds to sudden singing and rejoicing. And himself he could even feel the feeble fire of life in his own sick body flame higher. Scientists said it was merely the *warmth* of the sun, or that it was "psychic" (whatever that is). Well, he'd show them. . . .

Finsen bent over a shallow dish standing in the corner of his study, with water in it, that held three tiny salamanders lying there absolutely motionless. Now he held a little concave mirror out in the sunlight that poured in through the window, and he turned and turned it, just so, till it shot a beam of reflected light bang onto one of those motionless salamanders. . . .

First nothing, a few seconds nothing . . . then like a flash the beast shot through the water. It was absolutely constant and consistent that he could be set swimming just by the light beam. It was machine-like. It must be chemical . . . the way sunlight unlocked energy dormant inside him. He called it "light as *incitement*" and believed it was deeply fundamental though he was absolutely ignorant of the mysterious chemistry of it. (And so is everybody down to this day.)

Now Finsen let the June sun shine through bits of colored glass onto frog embryos curled up in their eggs. For twenty-four minutes he held the blue glass steady. The blue-violet rays coming through it stoked up this future tadpole to lash-

ing violently round sixty-nine times in his egg. . . . But he
would only shimmy feebly five times in fourteen minutes
when red rays coming through red glass hit him. You can
sympathize with the Copenhagen professors who refused him
his fellowship. This was no different from a little boy, with
tongue stuck out of one corner of his mouth, fooling with
bits of colored glass and pollywogs. And if he'd been refused
his fellowship on the grounds he wanted to find out something useful (merely) . . . who'd say that these dabblings
were—academically—anything but silly?

All the time they were giving him a smoldering fanatical
up and up faith in sunlight.

He turned from his pollywog science to a funny little
miracle with a mess of angleworms that he'd intended for
food for his salamanders. The worms were obviously dying.
"I had about twenty pieces, entirely lifeless," Finsen explained. Trying to resurrect them, he'd poked them, warmed
them, sprayed water over them . . . nothing stirring. "Till
it occurred to me to see if sunlight would not . . ." Finsen
said.

Light: in a few seconds three or four of these wretched
creatures began bending, writhing, with Finsen pop-eyed,
and convinced here was a miracle. Sunlight can inflame. Sunlight can incite. Fundamental! Excellent! Everything! Without which nothing! "One can say these chemical rays are
life-awakening, energy-stirring . . . a natural force too little
noticed in medicine," Finsen wrote (on the ground of these
experiments!) . . . and then he jumped experimentally
from sick angleworms to suffering men.

IV

The Danish engineer, Mogensen, had suffered for eight
years from the horribly disfiguring burrowings of sundry
billions of tubercle bacilli . . . into the skin of his face.
This was *lupus vulgaris* and it was dreadful, not so much

because of its mortality . . . though there were plenty of lupus sufferers put out of their misery, finally, by consumption. No, the worst of it was the absolutely unstoppable spreading of these t. b. microbes through the skin of their victims' faces, changing healthy skin into one great running sore, too terrible to tell about, incurable, turning these folks into outcast beings ashamed to be seen by anybody . . . with death the best way out of it. Mogensen was on the way to it. He feared it.

Finsen had gone to the Copenhagen faculty again . . . it's a way cranks have, and now the doctors had smiled, and who blames them? Hadn't Finsen himself proved that these very rays—blue, violet, and ultra-violet—were the ones dangerous to smallpox patients' faces? Why then would they be good for lupus? It sounded like tommyrot, was certainly devoid of logic, and besides was impractical. . . . Where'd you get sun, in Denmark, in November?

Mogensen had tried all the doctors and his lupus kept gnawing, spreading. Finsen had no patients, and had never heard of poor Mogensen. He knew there was no sun in November in Denmark had hold of this fundamental . . .

The hotter you heat anything solid the redder it glows, then whiter; and the whiter the hotter, the more chemical rays it irradiates. He'd make his own sun. He hurried to Winfeld Hansen and it was luck for Finsen that Hansen was Mogensen's friend. Hansen was chief-engineer of the electric light works and medically too ignorant to know how silly Finsen's hope of curing incurable skin tuberculosis really was.

Finsen told Hansen he needed a carbon arc light . . . only much stronger than the lights used for street lighting. They had to cause inflammation, like sunburn.

"But we can't have patients running round the electric light plant," Hansen said, laughing. Finsen didn't laugh.

Didn't Hansen get it? Hadn't Finsen proved that *concen-*

KYRLE—". . . *debonair in his broad-brimmed hat, had died too soon to know the real triumph of his dangerous experiment.*"

FINSEN—*"He was a cool egg—no doubt of it."*

trated sunlight killed microbes fifteen times as fast as ordinary sunlight? And wasn't skin t. b. the very trouble on which to try it? Weren't the t. b. microbes right up near the surface where light could get a whack at them? And, since it was mostly incurable, then if they *did* cure a bad case, wouldn't that prove . . .

It is not my intention to be unfair or make invidious comparisons but I wish here to state that after reasonably extensive chance for observation it is my notion that, of all professional men, engineers are most often open to persuasion, by fanatical inventors.

To put it more mildly, among engineers a crank occasionally has a chance to come to the surface. Now all these questions of Finsen's did sound sensible. At least you could test them out. Hansen caved in and told Finsen about his friend Mogensen who'd had lupus for eight years, now, and had doctored all over Copenhagen and the doctors had given him up for hopeless.

But mind, he couldn't begin to have patients running round the light station!

To an accompaniment of the hum of dynamos and in a weird blue light, for two hours, every day from November in 1895 all through the winter till March, 1896, Mogensen sat, dead still. Onto the ulcer that was eating away the right side of his face, Finsen shot the hot light from the fiery crater of the positive carbon of a twenty-five ampere direct current arc lamp. He gathered together all that arc's rays through a clumsy set-up of lenses, shot the whole hot cone of them down onto less than a square-inch of ulcer for two hours, repeating it next day, and so on. For over a month there was nothing stirring, with Mogensen fed up with it . . . having sat still for sixty hours to suit this fanatic.

It trembled on the edge of being a complete wash-out, but now one or two days later, wait, yes . . . the nasty spot was just a wee bit smaller.

Yes! And a few more days, with Finsen never dreaming of quitting and with Mogensen the annoyed and intensely uncomfortable hero of it, and, yes . . .

There was now no longer any doubt whatever about it. And look, here's the mirror, Mogensen, you see it, don't you . . . the way the ulcer's edges have got angrier these last few days, and then blistered, and then scaled off to leave, look at it! That's healthy skin, Mogensen, I tell you!

Mogensen saw it. And now sitting there stock-still with the strange man Finsen, intent, taut, bending over him, shooting that fierce concentrated arc light just so through his lenses . . . why, sitting there so was a positive pleasure. . . . Look how that bad corner there has cleared up, gone, Mogensen . . . gone, absolutely. . . .

Till at last Mogensen . . . for years for the shame of it he'd hated meeting even his best friends because he could feel how they didn't want to look at him even while their eyes told him how they pitied him . . .

Till Mogensen walked out cured of incurable skin tuberculosis.

V

Finsen wouldn't take a cent from Mogensen but Mogensen's face made a real sensation in Copenhagen. It fired up the manufacturers, Jörgensen and Hagemann, to found the Finsen Institute. They were the real enthusiasts for this strange new science but it is pleasant to record that even four university professors consented to serve on the board of directors and give the Institute an aura of science, and now at last Finsen did have academic respectability.

It would have amused you to have been present at the first formal meeting of that board of directors. Of all people I've ever met anywhere the Danes are the most courteous, generous, tolerant, polite, and in every way the finest, and the only reason I love my own people better is not because they come up to the Danes but irrationally because they are

my own people. But now at this meeting Niels Finsen out-
did all the Danes of Denmark. It was moved that Finsen (as
director of the new Institute) should have a modest annual
salary. He got up, red in the face, and stuttering, and as
violently as his inherent mildness would let him, he protested. He would absolutely not take any salary till his
theories had been really proved valid in practice. The faith
the committee had shown in him was more than enough pay
for him. . . .

Then after the fashion of Danes who are born with urban-
ity, up got Borup, the Mayor of Copenhagen. They were
not voting Finsen his salary out of regard for him. It was
the purest egotism on the part of the committee. It was bad
for men who worked in *their* interests to be unfavorably
situated economically. . . .

This is not told in praise of Finsen but only to show what
an essentially outlandish man he was. And Finsen was a
doctor!

They hurried up to build him an institute, with him
knowing his own end was coming nearer and nearer. It was
a one-story shack in the Municipal Hospital Garden. Before
the carpenters' hammers stopped banging he was busy there.
Weaker and weaker, he'd nearly been bumped off by pneumonia while he was curing Mogensen. He wasn't kidding
himself about how much time he had left. Now for the next
eight years with his own strength seeping from him, he set
out to prove that Mogensen's cure was no accident.

It was grueling business and enough to take the heart out
of anybody who hadn't the guts of Finsen. It looked for a
while as if he'd just been lucky with Mogensen. People terribly disfigured flocked to his wooden shack. Months of light
rays . . . and why was it more than half of them didn't get
better at all? And why, when they did get better, was it that
they improved so slowly? Was it that real sunlight was better? Every sunny day in that garden here lay rows of these

wretches like lepers, patiently lying there, with nurses in funny head-dresses (like big white carnations) bending over them.

Was it that sunlight didn't penetrate? Finsen dug up that old experiment on his wife Ingeborg's ear. When he'd pressed the blood out of it . . . the light went through faster. . . . And now these carnation-hatted nurses had to cramp their hands, two hours at a stretch, to hold pressure glasses tight down over these poor folks' sore faces, to drive blood out so that the lens-focused sunlight could bite down deeper into their t. b.-riddled skins.

And now the results were a little better, maybe. But the hellish part of this sickness was that you had to wait months and even years to be sure. Many quit on him, fed up, and left while still horribly disfigured, and it was not too good an advertisement for his new science. And there wasn't enough sun. And his first machine sun hadn't had wallop enough. . . .

So next winter there grew up in his shack an enormous arc lamp with eighty amperes of current turning its positive carbon into a terrific little miniature sun. The rays from it cooked the faces and seared the eyes of Finsen and his helpers. And now the results were faster but not fast enough, and still too much this way and that. . . .

Finsen fumbled and groped and cut and tried this, that, and everything, experimenting far into the night after his young men had gone home. He laughed. He said he was his own best experimental animal because the results were always right there on him where he could observe them whenever he wanted to. It was by his own nastily burned arm that he proved rays that came out of the big arc and shot through quartz lenses were stronger than rays that went through glass. Now he thought he had it for certain. . . .

Those rays concentrated through quartz would kill microbes in three seconds . . . the same ones through glass had

taken half an hour for this murder. But trouble again . . .
with the heat of the rays causing terrible burning that
brought yells of pain from the patients and with the poor
folks not coming back . . . though there was now a much
better chance to cure them. But who'd blame them?

He didn't lose patience. He fixed and tinkered and puttered and fixed and tinkered. All the time he was himself
getting sicker, and to keep from filling up with fluid he put
himself on terrible dry diets of desiccated food and next to
no water. And in spite of it fluid kept filling up his belly
so they had to begin tapping him. It was the winter of 1902
and they'd tapped him six times and now again they were
at it and he set his lips while the needle and trocar went into
his abdomen. . . .

The doctor suddenly went white and began sweating and
Finsen knew what was the matter. There was no use camou-
flaging—the needle handle had broken and the needle had
slipped down through the trocar inside him. Finsen and the
doctor knew he was too weak to stand an operation to find
it. . . .

He was a cool egg, no doubt of it. He told the doctor to
send to the engineering college for the biggest magnet he
could find. "There's a chance the end of the needle hasn't
left the trocar entirely. If it hasn't, the magnet will lift it.
I'll stay perfectly still," Finsen said. So he saved his own life
to work a little longer.

VI

There must be some way to relieve those poor people of
the hot rays' burning. He held his own arm in the terrible
focus of his artificial sun. He poured cold water over the
burning place while the rays were still playing on him and
the burning vanished like magic, with the water blocking
out the heat rays. It was a quick jump from that crude experiment to changing the pressure glass that the nurses held
next to the patients' skin to press the blood away. Now the

pressure glasses were changed from solid to hollow with a stream of cold water running through them. It was a very pretty invention. . . .

It meant that his ulcer-tortured people could keep perfectly comfortable in a focus of chemical light that was hot enough to set wood smoking and glowing.

He was sure now he had it. It was mighty satisfactory after all this tinkering: getting one bug out of his apparatus only to have another one pop up in place of it but finally getting it practical. Now his artificial sun's rays, shining through quartz, cooled by flowing water, cleared up horrid patches of tuberculosis the size of a pea in one raying of twenty minutes. While Finsen sat up in a wheel chair no longer walking, his men were fading lupus ulcers—incurable—after a short three months' raying.

Now a fine new Finsen Institute building went up in the Rosenvaenget in Copenhagen. Into it crowded hundreds of folks ashamed of their faces. From it went hundreds proud to look the world in the face and healthy enough to support their wives and their children. It was now the wonderfully sunny summer of 1904, and Finsen sat up in his wheel chair to receive the Nobel Prize, happy though dying, and yet . . .

There was still something lacking. Here was his Finsen-made sun. It cooked your skin as much in twenty minutes as strong summer sun would burn it in three hours. Yet only fifty-nine out of every hundred lupus cases could be cured. Why not all of them?

His hands were helpless now but his head kept on asking questions. Why was it, with his super-arc lamp's rays killing microbes one hundred and fifty times faster than concentrated sunlight killed them . . .

Why was it that folks treated outdoors in the garden cured faster than the ones he'd bombarded all winter with the much stronger rays of his super-arc light?

Why were those sore-faced unfortunates *in better general condition* in the summer?

Had he been going hay-wire, shooting his light at those t. b. varmints locally . . . instead of at the whole man or woman?

Back in his hand-to-mouth, free-lance days, when he was a sort of gypsy scientist, he'd planned bathing sick folks all over in sunlight, strong arc-light. He'd thought it all out in the days when academicians were sneering at his poetry about sunlight making birds rejoice and bugs fly round happy. That light from the sun resurrecting his moribund angleworms had got him dreaming of general light baths. Then his dreams were just air-castles with those Danish scientists (who had heard of him) smiling in the polite Danish manner. Now he *had* the sun, and giant machine suns even more powerful. Well, it was too late now. But . . .

But would microbes getting into folks matter as much, matter at all, with life-giving light *inciting* latent microbe-smashing power in them?

Toward the end, that last lovely summer, Finsen stripped his dying body naked. He bathed himself in the sun in a little sun house built on his roof. His heart, loaded down with its strange casing of lime salts, beat a little stronger. He drew vast plans to treat all kinds of tuberculous-doomed ones with sun baths and arc-light baths all over their bodies. . . .

"To cure lupus by local concentrated light is all right," Finsen explained to Ingeborg.

"But light baths will be much, much more . . ."

It was a sort of testament he left with her. He himself hadn't time to try them. Ingeborg was alone with him when he died with her arms around him in 1904. It was September, just when the fogs from the North Sea were getting ready to blot out the light of that sunny summer.

II. ROLLIER

THE SUN DOCTOR

~~~~~~

For the men that worked with him there must have been something dominating and stirring, like sunlight itself, in tough-hearted Finsen. It was something that left all of them lost when he left them. How otherwise explain the nine-year gap between his plans to start light baths and their actual beginning at the Finsen Institute?

But—never knowing it—Finsen had made far-off disciples. They were both of them Swiss of the high Alps. Curious old Bernhard knew the Italian mountaineer proverb: "Where the sun is the doctor ain't." Rollier, the chamois hunter, city-hater, sun-dreamer, took fire from Bernhard, who'd taken fire from Finsen.

What Rollier did was way out beyond science and in thin air where the moles of the laboratories have hardly yet dared to go. Out of the reek of the hospitals, away from the shades of the laboratories, Rollier can show (if you'll get up early enough) a real death-fighting sunrise.

~~~~~~

UP the hill in the sunshine walked a file of nearly naked boys whose bodies the sun had turned the brown of old pennies, and it was the tough tanned look of these boys who had been so utterly puny and sickly that started me laughing at microbes. This was long before I'd met any one of my three uncles, Osborn, Jack Miner, or Corsan. It was shortly after I'd had to stop plugging at the indoor job of turning fierce microbes gentle for a vaccine to guard rabbits (possibly) from broncho-pneumonia. But here, laughing in the sun, were these ex-invalid boys with strong brown bodies that you'd know any microbe would think twice about making a pass at.

All at once I was glad I wasn't a laboratory mole of a microbe hunter any longer.

These boys had come to this hillside, pasty-faced waifs with tubercle microbes nesting in the glands at the forks of their air-tubes. Here they were now, scholars strangely not bored with their schooling, in this school of the sun-dreamer, Auguste Rollier. In 1903 that peculiar Swiss surgeon had jumped clean out of surgical respectability. It was this sun-doctor's dream that knives, serums, and new, long-named chemicals of medical science weren't a patch on the cheap, simple light of Old Doctor Sun . . .

Not when it came to checking tuberculosis.

For twenty-eight years Rollier, who is huge, brown-faced, and gentle-voiced, has stood by with outlandish patience watching the sun's energy light up a still mysterious microbe-murdering chemistry in the maimed bodies of thousands of pain-racked people who came up his mountainside pronounced incurable. His patience has done what the most elaborate scientific wits have failed at, miserably. It must be the long time needed, and the deep simplicity of his trick of turning the energy of the Alpine sun into something healing, that makes it so hard for the smartest medical scientists to get this into their heads . . .

That here is something revolutionary in the science of death-fighting.

II

Rollier himself would laugh at being called a medical scientist. He is much more a sort of prophet (no doubt with many of the short-comings of this risky profession) —way out

beyond the often cut-and-dried drabness of science. Yet what
he has done, if you believe death-fighting facts can be got
from sick *men* as well as from rabbits, monkeys, and guinea-
pigs . . . is not by a long shot purely evangelistical.

His worship of the sun began when he was a school-boy
in the eighteen-eighties on the shores of the Lake of Neu-
châtel. He was the pale son of a bookish professor and from
his first year in school he didn't like the way the brown-
faced farmer boys could lick the tar out of him. "They were
flagrantly superior to me," Rollier said. From then on he
began bathing his bare body lying like a lizard in the sun,
began turning himself into an Indian.

His spaniel taught him a lesson. That creature developed
a tumor on its spine. Rollier was already dreaming of being
a knife man and now cut this tumor out and covered it with
an elaborate dressing. "Every time I bandaged him, he
clawed those dressings off," Rollier said. Then one day he
came upon his dumb disobedient patient lying with the
wound wide open to the sun, and healing. So on, every day,
till it was completely better.

Rollier studied to be a surgeon with the famous Kocher,
one of the landmark, milestone men of that then still bloody
art, who was the first of all knife-men to dare to take out part
of the thyroid gland. The historian Garrison says Kocher was
a "careful, precise and absolutely skillful operator . . . with
whom success was an almost foregone conclusion."

Now the fate of one of his own school pals taught Rollier
how mutilation and death—as well as healing—comes from
cold steel, even in the hands of such a surgical genius as his
lean-faced, gray-bearded master unquestionably was. This
pal of Rollier's had stumbled, bounced down the gymnasium
steps on his bottom, got t. b. in his hip, had tried to cure
it by rest, had failed, had then gone to the great Kocher in
Berne, who'd cut out that hip joint—masterfully. There was
absolutely nothing of your movie surgeon about Kocher,

who was slow, precise, had a wonderful technique of asepsis, and by the minutest dissection now made sure he'd got every bit of tuberculosis out of this boy's hip-joint. . . .

Pale and with one leg shorter, the boy came back to school. He was gay, he was hopeful, he was sure the poison was out of him. Then the waxy t. b. devils set to work at his knee joint, and Kocher cut that out, too . . . in a masterful manner. . . .

By now Rollier was Kocher's right-hand man, and here who should turn up but this old pal—out of whose knee Kocher had cut every single last t. b. bacillus. The boy's face was earth-gray, and pain-twisted with hope gone out of it. . . . It was the grimmest of lessons for Rollier, when at last his boss (greatest with the knife since John Hunter) cut out his pal's shoulder joint. That was the fifth operation . . . after hip joint, knee joint, one foot, one finger. . . .

The boy thanked Kocher and Rollier for all their skill and their kindness, and left the clinic, and eased himself out of the tortured life he had left . . . by suicide.

Kocher was most marvelous of all surgeons at Ignaz Semmelweis's art of keeping deadly bugs out of people while he was slashing them, and even in his dangerous thyroid operation hardly more than four folks out of every hundred died. Now in the four years that Rollier bent over the operating tables shoulder to shoulder with that hatchet-faced wizard, he watched fifty out of every one hundred wretches with t. b.-riddled bones leave Kocher, to die. This ghastly dance of death showed Rollier what even Kocher (learned as he was) couldn't seem to fathom: *That tuberculosis of the bones and joints can't be cut out of anybody like a tumor.* It was hardly different than the pale horror of Schaudinn; it was in the blood, raising its ugly head in a hip when you'd cut it clean out of a knee. It was, fifty times out of every hundred . . . hopeless.

Then Rollier's sweetheart fell sick with serious t. b. of

her lungs, and went up for the rest and fresh air cure to Leysin, a mile high on the south slope of a mountain. There she looked across at the everlasting snow on the peaks of the *Dents du Midi*. She listened to the absurd cow bells loud as church bells tied round the necks of those Leysin cows that climb mountains like goats. She waited wondering whether she'd get better and marry Rollier, or . . .

Rollier tossed a brilliant surgical future over his shoulder, followed her up there, went back to the bottom of the ladder to start over as a country doctor. Up and down those hills he stalked from one miserable chalet to the next one: surgeon, baby doctor, gynecologist, midwife . . . everything to those mountaineers. With no chance for super-cleanliness of your modern operating room, he began cutting into these people in low-ceilinged rooms in combination barn-houses. Back to their huts through the glare of the sun on the high snow Rollier went, looking for festering wounds, for blood-poisoning, for death. He didn't find them. Extraordinary: no pus, no infection, or hardly any. . . .

Then Rollier would walk back to his sweetheart, dreaming, asking why, why . . . Now memories gathered in his head out of a vague tangle, unraveling into a clean straight string of reasoning . . . about his sun-bronzed playmates who were never sick, about his sun-bathing spaniel who was his own best surgeon, about his t. b.-riddled pal driven to suicide by the futility of the knife of that master knife-man, Kocher. How were these manure-heeled mountaineers . . . different?

Through that clear air with its champagne-like kick and under this sun that stoked up his energy and made no work seem too much for him, Rollier walked back home . . . suddenly knowing. When you know something all alone, it makes you timid to act on it (usually) but here came news from an old surgeon, Bernhard of Samaden in the Engadine across the mountains. Bernhard, purely through bitter experience, had got skeptical of knives, and had observed that his ignorant mountaineer patients bathed their meat in the mountain sun—that was all they had to do to keep bugs out of it. They got tremendously old (with absolutely no life extension examinations or health assays) and they were always making that wise-crack about "where-the-sun-is-the-doctor-ain't." In the beginning it had annoyed Bernhard, brash from medical school. But now he was old, and when those leathery-faced folks told him they knew they got so "stone-old" because of the sun . . . he was no longer so cocky about dismissing it as a superstition. Then Bernhard read Finsen (not superstitious but scientific!) and how that pioneering Dane had turned his machine-sun onto lupus. And now in less than no time the grizzled surgeon was starting his whole life over, turning high Swiss sunlight onto gaping wounds. And now Rollier heard of Bernhard.

III

Under the sun his sweetheart got better, married him, and they were happy again. Now a strange procession began trickling up the cog-road from Aigle toward Leysin to Rollier. It was a sad parade, of crippled children looking like little old men and women, many of them moaning at the slightest movement, and all with skin pasty, shriveled, flabby. Among these were older folks on crutches with every hobbling step stabbing them or on stretchers imprisoned in plaster casts that were as cruel as they were idiotic and useless. And here were beings no better than dwarfs, bow-backed, with the bitterness of their pain and the shame of their deformity plain on their faces. Those early days this parade was hopeless, gray-faced, though the cheeks of some were spotty red with the sinister rouge of fever and with eyes bright with the dreadful gleam of the tuberculous.

Those early days they all had been given up by surgeons, and had had the last proper Oslerian consolation from their doctors, and it was against the warning of their physicians, most often, that the doomed ones of this pitiful remnant of humanity's rear-guard crept up the cog-road, toward Rollier. He sunned them.

Here was the trick of it, and it was new, and absolutely unheard of in medicine: Rollier *eased* these wretches with a subtle and almost imperceptible gentleness into the strong dangerous light of the mountain sun. First they'd lie for days in an airy room with the doors wide open. Then for more days Rollier would roll them on vibrationless, big-wheeled beds onto balconies, looking south, but shaded. From their shriveled limbs, bandages horribly tuberculous and plaster casts were taken off gently, and their purulent wounds were exposed to the air . . . but not yet to sun.

Till at last, one fine morning, here were just their bare feet stuck out in the white sunlight, for just five minutes at a time, three times that first morning. And the next day three times for ten minutes—while for five minutes Rollier exposed their thin legs as high as their knees. And so up and up, bit by bit, Rollier turned the sun onto their entire bodies. He towered over them, dreamy-eyed, yet watched them, hawk-eyed, for the faintest sign of a dangerous "reaction."

So, up and up their naked bodies he let the sun bathe them till at last—with never so much as a blister or even the faintest redness of sunburn—they were brown all over.

That was the trick of it.

IV

As their skin turned light brown the pain left their bones. As the brown turned to coppery-bronze, little smiles began to pass over their faces. It was a slow, slow business, of weeks, of months, but what of it, since they felt new strength stirring in them? It wasn't brainy of Rollier. It was just super-patient. He knew nature needs time. . . .

No human wreck was too bad for Rollier to tackle. To have seen him you'd have said that this boy ("R. R." on the published records) was absolutely at the end of his tether. He'd been given up by the best surgeons of the *Allgemeines Krankenhaus* of Vienna. He was five years old, but weighed only twenty-two pounds, and his face when he came up to Leysin was ashy white, with bluish lips, and unnatural blue veins ran up his forehead. On his neck, under his arms, in his groin, were enormous tuberculous glands, discharging. Both of his legs, both of his feet, his right arm (so reported the Viennese surgeons) were utterly beyond saving. His left lung in his deformed chest had advanced consumption at its apex. In thirty-four distinct places—detectable—those t. b. Beelzebubs were gnawing, and the end bone of his right thumb . . .

But it's too terrible to tell of it.

In July, 1908, the first gentle touch of Old Doctor Sun.

June, 1909, R. R. (who'd arrived, as the doctors say, *in extremis*) was transformed into a husky, brown-bodied little imp . . . transfigured. Three years, and he's a pupil in Rollier's school in the sun . . . on skis and naked in the snow. A year later, and he's making hay as strong as any peasant boy in the sun . . .

Today, twenty-three years after, he is a market gardener husky and making his living with those feet, legs, hands, and arms the surgeons had said were beyond all hope.

The great difficulty of doctors all over comprehending and practicing it was that it was not sudden or dramatic like a cure (sometimes) following the brilliant slash of a knife or the spectacular working of 606 on the outward signs of Schaudinn's pale horror. It was slow like nature. It seemed unscientific. It was hopeful like Spring's gradual coming. It had a lift to it like the soft sweet song of the rose-breasted grosbeak and the husky short warble of the scarlet tanager who have both been singing for me for the first time this Spring this May morning. . . .

Rollier had a tough time those first years. When he made his first speech at the physio-therapy congress in Paris, in 1905, the crowd walked out on him. But time went on, and all over Europe too many folks given up by surgeons with sentence of death came down off Rollier's mountain not only alive but walking and anxious to get back to earning their livings by working. And if the mere business of their being able to walk and to work again wasn't sufficient scientific proof for their doctors, why, here were their X-ray plates . . .

Before, during, and after . . . they proved how Old Doctor Sun, given time, can actually make over a hip joint ruined by t. b. microbes. That was scientific and began to convince some of them.

What held Rollier back, and kept the sun cure from spreading all over, was the silly simplicity of the whole business. No gadgets, no complicated apparatus, just that slow, extremely careful sunning of the skin, getting it browner and browner. Rollier was an absolute fanatic for brown, velvet-smooth skin, and this, for all learned ones who believe you must probe deep for life's mystery, made his half-poetic science superficial, only skin deep. Any medical student could have told him that sunlight doesn't penetrate past the skin, can't get down into the depths of a sick human's body. And yet . . .

Yet here were facts (not poetical) to show them. Here were rows of them on Rollier's sun balconies, pain gone, discharging sores closing, joints moving again, hungry, and gay and laughing in the sun. They were transformed in what you've got to call—I know it's unscientific—their *general condition*. The trouble was you couldn't measure general condition in a test-tube or under a microscope but only by horrid wounds' slow fading. But even the celebrated Barden-

SCHOOL IN THE SUN—*"They ski away, laughing and shouting with the sun shining on their bodies brown against the snow."*

*"Then how can Old Doctor Sun's death-fighting wallop be eased
into shade-loving millions. . . ."*

Ɪⱸeuer, surgeon of Cologne in Germany, had to admit it. Head of the knife-enthusiasts, he came to Leysin to Rollier, and a day there ruined his own life's work for him. He said, man that he was, to Rollier:

"This morning I was Saul. Tonight I am Paul."

Looking at those strong brown bodies, Bardenheuer saw something weird that no knife could accomplish. Here were poor devils who'd come up there with muscles shriveled to mere cords, with them having to stay motionless. Now here they were lithe-muscled again, heavy muscled on arms and legs that had had to be held quiet for months because of infection in shoulder or hip joint, just from sunlight. . . .

Rollier didn't care a rap about the unscientific vagueness of the "good general condition" that Old Doctor Sun bronzed into his patients. The worse their general condition, why, of course, the more need for the sun to shine . . . all over them. Folks came to him, thinned to skeletons, with eyes glowing feverishly out of sunken sockets . . . they were the cases of tuberculous peritonitis, and besides had severe disease of their lungs. The sun, nothing more, at first just a few minutes at a time, but sun. . . .

Among a hundred and sixty-one of such doomed people that came to Leysin over a long stretch of years, only five have died. Nearly ninety out of a hundred are healed and working again.

v

About sunning people with consumption, with pure lung tuberculosis, Rollier has always been curiously cautious, never tackling this worst plague of all on a large scale. Maybe his Alpine sunlight is too strong? Maybe at one end or another of its spectrum there are bundles of radiations (that whole business is still mysterious!) that are actually harmful . . . for those folks who are born to have t. b. in that particular vital part of their bodies?

It would seem possible, and even very likely. For at Perrys-

burg, New York (it was amusing and instructive for anybody without pride of intellect) . . . patients themselves
have forced proof on the lung-healing power of sunlight on
Dr. Horace Lo Grasso. For years at the J. N. Adam Memorial Hospital, this follower of Rollier had been curing t. b.
of the bones and joints in the sun. He had been kept from
turning sun onto consumptives by reports of the sun cure
lighting up fevers, hemorrhages. Lo Grasso had never seen
the proof that any such thing had happened in any consumptive dosed gently with it. He knew it had happened in folks
who'd foolishly treated themselves. He knew it had happened
to the patients of doctors who were ignorantly enthusiastic.
Yet Lo Grasso was scared of it. . . .

Here now at his hospital were consumptives taking the
fresh air and rest cure. Some of these were going downhill
despite best "hygiene and general care." These people, carefully kept in the shade, saw the bronzed bodies of their
neighbors who were getting marvelously better from their
t. b. of the joints and bones, in the sun. A bunch of them
now sneaked off when Lo Grasso and his staff weren't looking and bootlegged Old Doctor Sun for themselves. . . .

They hid themselves back of barns and behind thickets
and bared their chests, and some their whole bodies, ignorantly, naked to the sun for seven hours at a stretch. . . .

There *were* hemorrhages. There were fevers following this
stolen medicine. But there were mighty few of them . . . it
was amazing. There was an upward soaring—in most of these
sun bootleggers—of their general, their total condition. Their
night sweats left them. They got hungry and began gaining
weight. Lo Grasso was not too proud to learn from them. He
actually forgave them their crime—most horrifying to doctors—of self-medication. Now he picked out a gang of bad
lung cases who were going downhill, with the rest cure not
helping them. He began dosing sun into them gently, like
Rollier. He got them brown all over very slowly . . . ex-

cepting their chests which (shrewdly) he didn't let the sun hit at all. Instead of sunning them middays when the heat might sap them, he had them out in the slanting sunshine when the dew was still on the grass in the morning. He'd put them back out in the sun again in the late afternoons when the robins began singing the shut-eye song to their young ones. . . .

There wasn't a single accident.

Dr. Edgar Mayer at Saranac Lake, New York, and Dr. Alexius Forster at Colorado Springs, Colorado, are (cautiously) trying sun treatment of lung t. b. sufferers. And yet . . .

Yet today in our country nobody knows how many thousands of consumptives go downhill for lack of sun to raise that "total condition" that's at the bottom of every fight against death. It's largely needless. It's only because they're starving for sun, shut off from life, from the free medicine of the sun, simply because it isn't yet realized that Old Doctor Sun has got to be dosed—like any strong medicine. It's lamentable (scientifically) that nobody really yet knows what mystery lies at the bottom of "good total condition." It's deplorable that for it there's no elixir, no serum, no scientific gadget doctors can use presto . . . but only the long slow sunning that was Finsen's dream, which Rollier made come true.

VI

If sunshine alone could save surely doomed little R. R. from Vienna, riddled with tubercle microbes . . .

If sunshine alone couldn't only keep him from dying but transform him into a superb animal healthier than kids considered normal . . .

If t. b., once it gets started, sends children from home and parents, fathers away from work and chance to support wife and children, for one, two, three years of the sun cure . . .

Even if Rollier, in his new International Factory Clinic, is doing his superb job of firing up the fighting spirits of his sick people by giving them the chance to work naked in bed in the sun and so become part of humanity again, supporting themselves, even their families, while the sun cures them . . .

Even so, wouldn't he have been silly to have stayed content with the *curative* power of Old Doctor Sun?

He may be called evangelistical, poetical, a little mystical by your men of science, but he wasn't silly. Now in 1910 a new parade started up the cog-road toward him, not of folks given up for doomed, but only youngsters, frail and delicate, chilly under thick clothes on days that weren't cold. There were boys pale and pepless. There were girls, green-faced, finicky, anaemic, and listless, feverish in the evenings after feeble playing that would leave normal kids just a little hungry. This was the parade of the pre-tuberculous. . . .

Infected they were with the slender waxy t. b. varmints, maybe only in the little glands at the forks of their air tubes and at the roots of their lungs. Here in these little forts of the body's first line of defense those microbes were lurking, thrusting, secretly sluggishly multiplying, waiting to find a way in. . . .

Here they waited for some mild no-account infection, like measles, or maybe just a bad cold, to knock down the already feeble total condition of these waifs . . . just enough to give them an opening. Then heigh-ho for their victim's lungs, the insides of their bones, or the delicate membrane covering of their brains. Then for murder with the assassins put under ground along with their victims . . . all of them that didn't sneak into other children.

Such threatened ones were the marchers in the new parade to Rollier. They were candidates for matriculation in as strange a school as any you could imagine. It was a Spartan kind of school . . . more primitive than any drafty pine schoolhouse on our western prairies, and the very opposite

of the expensive brick and glass monstrosities that our vil-
lages, cities, counties, have helped to break themselves building.

Now he began with these threatened children exactly as
he'd started with the really sick folks at Leysin, only not
quite so slowly, and before the week was out their bodies
were exposed entirely to Old Doctor Sun. Now Summer
fades into Alpine Autumn, and now Autumn's fallen leaves
are covered with snow gleaming in the sun. Out of Les
Noisetiers at Cergnat, the chalet for boys, tumbles a rabble
of brown-bodied rapscallions in nothing but breech-clouts
and shoes. They make the devil of a rumpus getting on
their skis. They sling their portable desks to their backs.
They ski away, laughing and shouting with the sun shining
on their bodies brown against the snow.

VII

Of the 466 t. b.-threatened boys and girls of Rollier's
School in the Sun—from 1915 to 1922—only two have died.
One developed tuberculous peritonitis and, coming back to
Leysin, has been sun-cured. One has always stayed delicate.
Two have dropped from sight leaving no address. All the
rest are in excellent health.

The Frenchman, Sergent, said you can't grow wheat on
rocks. It's rocky soil against planting of the dangerous microbe that Old Doctor Sun makes of the bronzed bodies of
these children. When you come right down to it, like the
friendly fever of Wagner-Jauregg, it all boils down to a new,
much more fundamental slant at death-fighting, not trying
to wipe out microbes directly, not trying to keep them from
getting in—*but stoking up the human body itself to fight
them.*

It's so new that only a few like these pioneers, starting
with Finsen, have hardly more than scratched the surface of
it . . . and the first of the top-cut of microbe hunters to

realize it is Thorvald Madsen. He is from Finsen's country, but not tragic like Finsen. He is a super-civilized *bon vivant*, cosmopolitan, with nothing of your austere sun-crank, like Rollier, about him. He's not fanatical. He has just finished a lot of common-sense digging in the remarkable infectious disease reports—the world's most accurate—that Denmark has been piling up in the last thirty-seven years. There—and there only—the doctors have *had* to report all cases of every infectious disease during all that time. . . .

This gay kind-hearted Madsen has distilled these sound figures and thrown the essence of them into the face of his own science. It's amazing the way the raging of this or that serious sickness doesn't depend on the microbe . . . but on the seasons.

Scarlet fever, diphtheria, tonsillitis, broncho-pneumonia, bronchitis . . . all run up to a mountain peak on Madsen's charts from November through January and February. They're all down in a deep valley in July and August. The total death rate from all diseases, year after year, for these thirty-seven years, is highest in February, lowest in September. Being a microbe hunter, Madsen at first was mighty prejudiced for this being due to the ups and downs of savagery in his microbes. But for years (knowing there was no evidence for that) he scratched his head over these mountain peaks and valleys. . . .

He found there's only one thing jibing absolutely with these seasonal ups and downs of sickness and death. . . .

The thing is hours of sunshine.

And it doesn't take a savant of Madsen's sagacity to tell Danes how their total condition ebbs with the gray months beginning in November, and surges with the bright months beginning with May. Madsen knows that it's our own total condition which after all is what decides whether those microbes will shy away or will bite us.

Of course he's got it. Rollier's boys and girls of the School in the Sun, once bronzed, get rid of their colds, sore throats, catarrhs, coughs . . . and runny noses are unheard of while they're under the sun. And when there are no colds there's no soil for some of the most deadly microbes to get started growing in. . . .

VIII

This marvelous upping of total condition by Old Doctor Sun doesn't only guard us from ills of our throats, air tubes, lungs. Old Bernhard of Samden, who, fired up by Finsen, first inspired Rollier, proved that when he turned sunlight into the horrible incurable wounds of German soldiers during the War. He turned strong sun onto wounds that were incurable by every antiseptic and germicide, wounds on which every surgical wizardry had been wasted. Soon pus began drying, the ghastly odors began fading, gaping wounds began sweating out healthy serum, began closing as new tissue started growing. It gave you a lift to watch the way those woe-begone poor devils of soldiers felt the up of their total condition, to see how they reached their mutilated bodies toward the sun's light, how they wanted to live again. And how they did live, how they got strong again, strong enough to go back to run the risk of being smashed up again. . . . Bernhard started with the XIVth German Army Corps and before the end of it he was sunning the incurable wounded of the whole German Army. . . . It was not only a lovely thing for the mutilated but very necessary for the generals and politicians who were running short of healthy young soldiers, of good cannon fodder.

Sunlight helping surgery is not yet understood generally, indeed is hardly heard of in our country. Would the lives of more people be saved (in operations not emergency) if surgeons let Old Doctor Sun first brew the medicine that ups our total condition?

And if surgeons first let the sun get sick folks' strength

soaring upward—how many would then duck operations completely?

There are plenty of scientifically sophisticated physicians who'll smile, calling all this a dream, a fantasy. They'll not deny the sun's death-fighting power. They just deny that it's practical. They'll simply smile saying Rollier (who called cities suburbs of hell) was a Utopist, a dreamer.

IX

They'll say this is all beautiful and all very well. But this idea of everybody living near naked in the sun for a couple of hours a day for twelve months a year is utterly impractical. In the first place it's too cold too many days, with many days of no sunshine. In the next place it is true (or so says H. L. Mencken) that most people are by nature shade-loving animals. They like to be healthy, but don't care to be tough.

There's only one answer. If the mass of humanity is to be put into that superb total condition that (so far as we now know) only light's energy can bring to them . . .

Humanity has got to be exposed to this energy, not realizing it, getting it free, unconsciously, just as humanity breathes free air never thinking of it.

Is that possible?

12. STRANDBERG

MACHINE SUNLIGHT

~~~~~~

Niels Finsen the tragic Dane . . . groped for the sun in the fogs of Copenhagen, didn't find enough of it, invented his carbon arc light. . . .

This was the first machine sun, man-made. . . .

Ove Strandberg had the nerve to use it to bathe folks who'd gone into the last stage of their sickness that was then recognized as the consumptive's death sentence. . . .

He turned it, hoping nothing from it, onto that little newspaper-peddling woman who with voice faded to a whisper was the sole support of four children and absolutely doomed to die. . . .

He came across her long after, running alongside a street-car yelling her papers. Long before that she should have been dead.

~~~~~~

CAN humanity get the sun's death-fighting energy, not realizing it; get it free, unaware of it, just as it breathes free air, never thinking of it?

To make this more than a dream, one thing was needed: some ill or other, desperate enough to make its conquest dramatic, had to be fought by this machine sunlight . . . and the crudity of the primitive apparatus used to generate this energy *didn't matter*. . . .

What was needed was to prove—even though the first

machine sun was ridiculous and clumsy—that man-made light could really do it.

For that proof we must thank Axel Reyn, who was very gentle, and Ove Strandberg, who was (to put it mildly) hard-boiled.

You remember that, way back in 1904 when he lay dying, Finsen had told his wife, Ingeborg, that light baths, browning people all over, would be much more powerful than raying confined just to the horrible sore spots on their skins where you could see the t. b. devils were gnawing.

You'd have thought Finsen's follower, Axel Reyn, would right away have jumped at the chance of it. When Finsen died, more than forty out of every hundred sore-faced wretches who'd come hopeful, were dragging themselves away, incurable. Was it for that very reason that Reyn didn't start general light baths? Was it because these doomed forty out of every hundred were too horribly riddled with t. b. microbes, past hope? Reyn had married Finsen's sister. He was a fanatic worshiper of that tragic man's memory. Yet he went on record saying that general light baths "couldn't be expected to do much" for these forlorn ones.

Years went by, and then Finsen's hunch while dying came back at last to Copenhagen by the strangest of routes, via Samaden and Leysin, from the mountains of Switzerland. Finally, Reyn saw what old Doctor Bernhard and the sun doctor, Rollier, were doing, what slow miracles they were making, browning doomed folks all over by mountain sunlight.

But where was the sun in Copenhagen?

II

Right after that, if you'd chanced to come into a certain room in the Finsen Institute, you'd have seen eight people stark naked—sitting in the blue glare of two giant carbon arc lamps. To protect their eyes, Reyn made them wear strange gadgets shaped like lamp shades. These were pulled well down over their heads and they made these folks look like a lot of animated floor lamps (who'd forgotten to dress) sitting there talking. Slowly they turned their bodies round and round. The light's fierce glare threw their shadows, grotesque and monstrous, onto the room's dark blue walls. It was comical.

It was comical if you hadn't seen the faces under those lamp shades. They had been shot, ruined, riddled by years of gnawing of the t. b. microbes. This was the experiment of which Axel Reyn—gentle and skeptical—hadn't expected much. And who would have? Thirty minutes, then an hour, then two hours every day this forlorn band sat there while the weird light reddened their bodies, blistered them, hurt them—though not badly—then scaled off them and turned them a rich red-brown. . . .

In a month they lost their poisoned, tuberculous drowsiness. They felt the beginning of new life flowing through them. The powerful rays of Finsen's arc lamps—played only on the hideous sores of their faces—hadn't made them feel the faintest surge of strength in their bodies. These were the rearguard of lupus sufferers—they were of that forty percent untouched by the local Finsen treatment. But now, browned and mysteriously stronger from the carbon arc light baths played all over them, now when the arc light was concentrated on the dreadful wounds on their faces, those sores began rapidly fading. It was next to incredible.

III

And now came news that was still better from Ernst, who was Axel Reyn's helper. He had bathed with this arc light people whose t. b. was much more than skin deep, with the microbes burrowing in their hip joints, rotting their spines, riddling their bones. . . . The results were astounding, and as beautiful as those from the real sun on Rollier's mountain.

But what of the most terrible sickness of all the troubles hatched by the t. b. microbe? What of consumption? Here was an ill against which, in its serious and progressive stages, even Rollier's sun seemed powerless . . . against which it had to be used with the extremest prudence and caution. What could have led Ove Strandberg to try the expedient of arc light-bathing of folks whose consumption was not only serious, but desperate?

Strandberg in the early days of Reyn's carbon arc light-bathing was only a very open-faced cub of a throat doctor, wide-eyed and simple. He was a practitioner, a surgeon fundamentally. He knew nothing at all of the mysterious new chemistry that any sunlight natural or man-made set going in sick humans. He was a naïve Dane, hardly more grown up than when, a child with chronic ear trouble, he'd made up his mind to be an ear and throat doctor. Now here was Strandberg, deviling Reyn, and pestering eminent Copenhagen t. b. specialists to let him light-bathe a type of consumptive whose death knell had as good as sounded. It was not only presumptuous but preposterous. It was making sure death surer.

IV

From his first interne days in 1908, Strandberg had been hit by the hopelessness of throat tuberculosis. In the big provincial hospital where he then began working, there was a division for folks with t. b. of the lungs and the throat. "This was at a time when . . . tuberculosis of the throat . . . was considered to be an almost terminal stage of tuberculosis of the lungs," Strandberg said.

Everything in that throat division (said Strandberg) was hopeless. These were the desperate cases of consumption, and many of these people could neither talk nor swallow because of continual pain. Was it that the head doctors of this hospital had failed to apply the most modern death-fighting science to it? Strandberg began burning the midnight oil reading every scrap ever written on throat tuberculosis. No, it wasn't the reason. "So far as treatment was concerned, this, too, was hopeless," Strandberg said.

Finally, a full-fledged ear-nose-throat specialist, Strandberg had got to the Finsen Institute. It was his job to operate and to try to locally shine Finsen arc light into all kinds of sicknesses—tuberculous and other—that might bother the insides of folks' mouths, ears, and noses. And he worked out ways of treating lupus when it got inside people's noses—it was fine the way he could cure them. But all the time that next to incurable last stage of lung tuberculosis (when sufferers began ominously to talk only in whispers) kept bothering him. He tried operations. He tried this and that treatment. He tried everything. He read the final word on tuberculosis of the throat, an excellent book written by the famous Swede, Arnoldsen. The ending of Arnoldsen's story wasn't pleasant or happy. Arnoldsen finished it by saying that—by operating—*you might cure about four out of every hundred who got it.* . . .

The other ninety-six would die . . . it was inevitable.

Arnoldsen said the death-fight against this most terrible trouble might get along faster if doctors organized special sanatoria where nothing but throat t. b. people were admitted. Now at a medical meeting in Copenhagen Strandberg proposed it, and if the subject hadn't been so tragic, the eminent members of the faculty there assembled would have given him the horse laugh. As it was, they rained all over his proposal. It was hare-brained. It was unfeasible. It was . . . inhuman.

You'd have to write over the doors of such a sanatorium: "From here all hope is excluded." Or if you didn't write it, the poor devils going in would see it in big letters—written invisibly. . . .

He kept trying everything. Right now Axel Reyn had got his first lovely results watching the general carbon arc-light-bath send the general condition, the death-fighting resistance, of his sore-faced lupus folks on its upward surging. And Ernst was light-bathing the same microbes out of folks' joints and bones. . . .

Now here was Strandberg, wanting to try it on these desperately sick, whispering wretches whose chance of ever talking again was four in one hundred. . . .

He was wanting to risk bathing these forlorn ones in the terrific energy of these rays zipping at a rate of 186,000 miles per second out of a carbon arc's fiery crater. It was folly. It was worse. It was . . . well, maybe it was unkind to call it murder. It was what not even the sun-prophet, Rollier himself, had dared to go on with, though using the sun of nature, which must be superior to any machine-sun—man-made. Rollier wouldn't risk sun-bathing people with *active* lung tuberculosis, feverish. From unwritten but grimly tragical experience Rollier forbade unconditionally the sun-bathing of consumptives whose malady was progressive. . . .

And here was wide-open-eyed Ove Strandberg proposing to light-bathe (with man-made sun surely inferior to God's sun) folks whose tuberculosis wasn't progressive but *terminal*. . . .

It was, to put it mildly . . . criminal.

V

The worst trouble Strandberg had was, of course, with the tuberculosis *experts*. They wouldn't let him have those desperate cases; knowing most about tuberculosis they naturally knew best of anybody what wouldn't be of avail in this last whispering stage of it. (They knew without having tried it.)

They knew it—as experts—on the ground that "it would be inadvisable" to subject such very and indeed hopelessly sick people to light treatments. "I received admonitions from several sides," Strandberg said.

In spite of all of it he finally started it—on folks who were too poor to have specialists to admonish Strandberg. In 1914 he led two such people whose consumption had spread from their lungs to their larynxes into that room where the machine sun's blue-violet glare threw the shadows of their thin, naked bodies on the dark blue walls. They hadn't come to him, hopeful, but only because they were absolutely at the end of their tether. Long ago they'd been told by their doctors to eat plenty of nourishing food, to rest . . . it was easy to tell that to folks whose wage was two kronen a day. . . .

Months passed, and now more coughing, whispering ones sat in the great arc's blue glare . . . naked. The throats of all of them had started hurting them so it was harder and harder to swallow, so they hardly dared eat, and of course that made the t. b. in their lungs worse, and with their lungs worse their larynxes got sorer. . . .

Till finally here were some with such ulcers at the openings of their voice boxes that their larynxes couldn't close when they tried to swallow . . . so that their food went down the wrong throat, choking and gagging them. . . .

And all who've lived at t. b. sanatoriums know what it means when, for the first time, one of their comrades whose voice has been getting more and more husky suddenly starts to have those swallowing accidents at table. . . .

They know it means that comrade won't be at table many days longer. They know it means the beginning of the finish. . . .

Such were the people who'd come to Strandberg for his light-bath experiment. It wasn't really Strandberg who was making the experiment. It was poverty, and let us remove our hats to another one of poverty's manifold blessings. This was 1914. . . .

1922 . . . and of the sixty-one whispering lost ones who'd come to him, thirty-one were now entirely healed of their throat tuberculosis . . . and there was never a doubt it was the carbon arc-light-baths that had done it. Again we must give all praise to poverty—for how, without it, could Strandberg have known it was just the carbon light that had kept them from dying?

Any doctor worth his salt knew that even in the early, still hopeful stages of consumption, rest in bed was fundamental. But of these sixty-one who were all of them peering into the valley of the shadow . . . fifty-three had had to come walking to the Finsen Institute for their light-baths. . . .

Rest in bed would have been very fine for them, but it would have been a little tough to find time for that when you had to steal time from your daily drudgery, even to hurry to Strandberg for your daily light-baths. . . .

It was the ancient law that poor folks (especially the proud aristocracy of them) must work to keep living even when dying—it was this law that made it sure the one thing that cured them was the carbon arc-light-baths.

It was his patients themselves who helped teach Strandberg that the healing by the light was more strangely powerful than even he had dared to hope. One morning a sunken-cheeked little poor lady—who sold newspapers—came whispering, asking for the light-baths. . . .

She'd heard that her friend so-and-so . . .

Strandberg's assistants had gone over her already. They'd shaken their heads to each other, and she was altogether too dangerously sick to stay on her feet at all any longer, let alone walk back and forth to the Institute for the treatment. . . .

It was plain that she had only a short time to live, and

gently they tried to tell her in a roundabout way it was too late by suggesting, maybe, that her case wasn't *suitable*. . . .

Then she'd broken past them and got to Strandberg, and began crying and begging, please, please, Doctor, could she begin those light-baths right now. . . .

Strandberg looked down her throat, and what he saw there chilled even that hard-boiled observer. She had a high fever, and her lung tuberculosis was terrible. Strandberg knew it was hopeless. He caved in a little with her pleading and pleading. . . . Well, if she went to bed for a couple of weeks, and then came back, he might . . .

The wretched little woman went down on her knees then, throwing her arms round Strandberg. "My man's dying of the consumption, Doctor, and my four children are all sick. I've got to keep selling my papers. For them, I've *got* to . . ." This in a desperate whisper.

"It was only to comfort her that I agreed to it," Strandberg told me.

In a month she was a little better. She could swallow food now without its hurting her so. She still could only whisper. She wasn't quite so thin now. She was gaining. . . .

"Now you've got to stop working," Strandberg told her. "Now there's really a chance for you."

She promised Strandberg anything. Only . . . if only she could go on sitting in that light. She could feel it making her stronger. That terrible tiredness was so much less now. . . .

Again she sank below the level of Strandberg's notice with him busy with others, and then he went away on a voyage, and when he returned, driving his motor slowly through the crowded Copenhagen streets one evening, here was a little lady, yelling her papers running alongside a trolley-car just stopping . . .

In a loud voice she was bawling her papers. . . .

It was that same little woman.

Strandberg was furious with her for disobeying that way
. . . he'd told her not to work and above all not to try to
talk and here she'd been yelling. A couple of days later,
when she reported to the Finsen Institute, that severe man,
Strandberg, began (as he expressed it) to "admonish" her.

"But, Doctor"—and her voice was entirely clear now—"my
husband has died. I had to take care of the children. . . .
And anyway, I feel fine now. . . ."

Strandberg smiled as he told me. "In this I agreed with
her, after seeing her larynx—which was cured," Strandberg
said.

VII

Aside from the lucky fact of the poverty of the folks he
had for patients, his disrespect for medical authority helped
Strandberg a great deal. When he first began reddening, even
blistering the pasty thin bodies of these poor people in the
arc light's glare, he started out with them feverish. That
was terrible to begin with. But now their fever went higher,
and by the medical canons that was alarming.

But Strandberg had an insight—it was something like
Wagner-Jauregg's—that just made him smile at it. He gave
them all a pat on the back and told them it was just what
he wanted. Fever was good. Fever showed they were . . .
reacting. If they hadn't had fever—why, then he'd really have
worried. They smiled at him, trusting him.

He wasn't foolish about it, and when the fevers began
climbing up off the chart, he'd stop the light-bathing, but
just for a couple of days, and then he'd have them back
under the strong bluish light again—dosing them shrewdly.
What happened now was fantastic to anybody who understood the full horror and hopelessness of larynx tuberculosis. While their bodies turned browner, their sunken faces
filled out. As the stabbing pain faded, they came telling him
they could swallow, and eat again, telling him first in whispers, then husky, then clear-voiced.

Hard-boiled though he undoubtedly was, Strandberg hated their poverty, and knew the light-baths alone took too long to cure them. How to hurry it? He'd learned (from bitter experience of death after death) the danger of cauterizing tuberculous ulcers in larynxes. But look! It was really a simple business, it was the old business Finsen had got an inkling of, with those lupus folks getting better in the summer while they were outside in the Institute garden. . . .

Whether they could stand an operation on their throats or a cautery to burn out those ulcers, all depended on their *general condition*. Now he knew he could shoot general condition, from the arc light's fiery crater, into the skins of these people. Now he could tell, from the way their weight came back to them, with them eating, with the color in their faces (not fever rouge), with the laboratory test of the speed of their blood corpuscle sedimentation, that his light was upping what death-fighting highbrows called their "immune-biological reaction."

That was a fine eight-dollar word—more impressive than plain "general condition."

Now he could tell whether his operation would kill them or hasten the cure. Now when the light made some unknown microbe-fighting sap stir in them, now was the time to burn out their throat ulcers. Now here you see Strandberg, bent over them applying with marvelous delicacy the searing heat of the electric cautery. So he gave a final wallop to their misery, and best of all gave them a chance to earn their bread.

VIII

1927 . . . and Strandberg was appointed to the staff of the largest private sanatorium for lung tuberculosis in Denmark. His light-baths had gotten respectable now, and here he was helping the lung specialist, Gravesen, with well-off folks whose whispering had told him all hope was going for them.

The danger of light's starting up hemorrhage had always made lung specialists shy away from sun-bathing—especially from irradiating progressive, *exudative* cases of tuberculosis. Strandberg laid that bogey for Gravesen. Here were hundreds Strandberg had bathed in the hot glow of the arc light. Out of those hundreds, forty-seven had spit blood before the light treatment began. Only eight had any hemorrhage whatever during the months they sat naked in the arc light's rays. And of these eight, five had had hemorrhage before the light-baths started.

In the past three years at this sanatorium at Vejlefjord an obscure miracle has been happening—so far hardly noticed in our country. With a mild kind of Danish fury Strandberg had always been insisting if his poor folks could only have got the kind of general care well-off folks could pay for, plus their light-baths, then you'd see . . .

It was no good just curing their larynxes only. If only they could have had rest, good food, and if those whose lungs needed it, could have had the new collapse treatment, then you'd see the figures for cure jump upward.

In the past three years that's what's happened at Vejlefjord. Of the sixty-nine well-off folks who could rest, eat hearty, and be treated all over while they browned under their light-baths . . . only four have died. And all sixty-nine were in that last horror of throat tuberculosis.

Of the sixty-five remaining, fifty-eight have been entirely cured of their larynx disease, and in not one case did they have to stop their light-bathing because of fever or hemorrhage. Their sick lungs, far from flaring up under the arc light's energy, actually got much better. At least it was that way in two-thirds of all those light-bathed—checked by X-ray and physical examination.

Nobody doubts the warnings of the famous Rollier, who'd seen strong sunlight send folks with active tuberculosis downhill to their doom. That only makes Finsen's discovery of this man-made sunlight more striking, and Strandberg's using it in such people *in extremis,* more astounding. When you think of the care with which God's sunlight has to be doled out to such people, it's no wonder sun baths are used so little in our country to fight tuberculosis.

But from all this there's only one conclusion: Finsen's machine-sun for consumption is better than sunlight itself.

Why then do folks with the t. b. doom in their throats, with their lungs far gone, have so little chance—in our country—to bathe themselves in Finsen's light, *exactly as Strandberg uses it?*

Has any t. b. fighter in America tried to repeat these marvelously hopeful experiments of Ove Strandberg, using the direct current carbon arc light, same amperage, with the death-fighting energy coming from the crater of the positive carbon?

Is there any sense whatever to any expert's denying Strandberg's discovery, till he's tried to repeat it, not with mercury vapor arc lights, not with lights from carbon arcs with alternating current supplying the energy—but with apparatus exactly as Finsen devised it, and as Strandberg has used it?

And what would happen to the t. b. death rate in our (or any other) country, if, instead of waiting till people's natural defense is so shot to pieces that the microbes have already spread from their lungs to their larynxes. . . .

If, all over, systematically, thoroughly, with the right kind of machine-sunlight, you'd start shooting this good general condition into them the moment their consumption was discovered?

IX

So one ill, certainly desperate enough to make the most self-satisfied, the most stick-in-the-mud big-wigs of the academic hierarchy sit up and take notice, really begins to be fought—by machine-sunlight.

How to make it practical—to put it in reach of everybody,

before they ever need it—so that humanity will have a chance at this man-made sunlight, getting it free, unaware of it, never thinking?

Brian O'Brien—who was Horace Lo Grasso's co-worker—has tinkered up a gigantic carbon arc light that's so nearly like Rollier's sun of Leysin that sick folks can sit outside in its light and heat even in the rain and the snow. It's a step ahead in latitudes where the sun of nature has death-guarding force hardly more than five months a year.

But I must be practical. To suggest sitting solemnly, naked, for so many hours a day, basking in the rays of such a great machine-sun, in order for those of us who are healthy to stay so . . . that's idiotic.

Then how can Old Doctor Sun's death-fighting wallop be eased into shade-loving millions, and into those other millions who've just got to like shade in order to earn their bread and butter? How can it be eased into all of us . . . with us not thinking?

The engineers, physicists, of the General Electric Company are making a start at it. They've invented a simple 500-watt lamp you can screw into a ceiling or wall-socket. Its light from a tungsten filament shining through special glass has actually cured two darky babies and one Chinese baby—of rickets. But that's only rickets, and not the terrible ill caused by Robert Koch's waxy t. b. demon. . . .

It's well known what a very little bit of the energy of a small band of the ultra-violet spectrum you need to cure rickets—and even less to prevent it.

And nobody knows anything really of what part—whether it's one definite part or the whole of the light—from God's sun, or Finsen's machine-sun, that ups our general condition to make our bodies fight the t. b. devils.

There are a lot of so-called "sun-lamps" and health-maintaining (so-called) lamps sold to folks today that give out only certain fragments of all that's in sunlight, and maybe even too little of those fragments. Maybe it's enough. And maybe it's still stretching it to say they're "health-maintaining." In the light of what's known about them that's a strong statement.

It brings me back a moment to the sun-doctor, Rollier. Half-poet that he is, he just believes with unscientific simplicity that the whole sun spectrum—from the ultra-violet to the infra-red—is what puts death-fighting vigor into his boys' and girls' fine bronzed bodies.

Maybe he's wrong. Maybe his vague poetry is a challenge to physicists like Whitney who found the electric fever, and to monkey-wrench scientists like Boss Kettering who's scheming a revolution of the climate inside our houses and factories. It's up to men like these and to the vanguard of young men against death.

The engineers—just give them a whack at it—will invent machines to pour out this, that, or any set of vibrations you can call out by striking this, that, or the other part of the great electro-magnetic spectrum—from the cosmic rays to the long-wave radio.

More and more young men against death, done with pills, with complicated chemicals, even with most serums and vaccines . . . will be working with the engineers to find what the energy of their machine medicine will do to our bodies.

By and by these machine-doctors may give us lamps to read and work by . . . whose energy will build up our appetites, raise our weight when we need it, up our red blood corpuscles and our hemoglobin, widen the blood vessels in our skin to give it the chance to pour its microbe-smashing energy through all the rest of our bodies.

At least, it would be silly to say it's impossible.

Meanwhile I'll keep as much of my body as brown as I can for as many months as possible in the light of Old Doctor Sun.

EPILOGUE

NO, I don't want to die. Since the day of this book's beginning, close to three years have passed and there's no denying I'm that much farther down the L-x line and that much closer to the inexorable.

Yet I don't feel older. The day of this book's beginning was at the end of October, a wild day with Lake Michigan raging and gnawing at the foot of our bluff. It was a sad day with the news of the strong ship *Milwaukee*, lost with all hands, and with the good beach-master William Deplidge down-hearted because the lake had wiped out in one night all that we'd fought to build that summer.

But this is a May day. Ten paces south of my open sun house, right now, a father bluebird is bringing food to his nestling children. Before me the sumach is shooting out its leaves. Round the sun house the lilacs are in leaf and ready to burst into blossom. I know I can't clamber back up Pearson's L-x line. But it is spring. Life is good. Hope surges.

It isn't only spring's tender and vibrant awakening that now makes me feel hopeful. It's the lift from all that I've learned, these last three tough years, of what men against death have done, are right now doing, to help me, to help all of us grow old more slowly and stay young very long. Provided we want to. . . .

What makes me more hopeful hasn't been only my finding out how death-fighters are making headway against this or that death now lying in wait for me. It's my slow-growing understanding of how they've won these victories. They've not done it by necromancy or by any sort of super-intelligence far above that possessed by the common man. They are not wizards. Nor would you class any of

them as "scientific geniuses"—genius being a word applied
with facility by those too lazy to dig for the plain qualities
(combined with good luck or accident) that make these men
extraordinary.

They've all been plain men finding simple truths understandable by everybody. To win their fights they've only
had—to a superlative degree—guts, honesty, and (for a moment) a quick eye to see the obvious in its mysterious obscurity. Each has slogged ahead knowing (in the words of
Boss Kettering) that his own problem, when solved, would
be simple.

When you remember how widely these simple qualities
are distributed in humanity, you understand it's no inherent
impossibility that'll keep more and more men against death
from making yet undreamed-of discoveries to help our children and those after them to grow old more slowly and stay
young much longer.

It's remembering this (and not only this Spring morning)
that makes me feel younger though older.

Though the searchers in the dead house—among whom
the lamented Warthin was the most brilliantly persuasive—
ask me to look at those inexorable ills called "degenerative
diseases" that lie in wait to ruin my kidneys, my heart, and
blood vessels . . . even here hope is stirring. You remember how Wagner-Jauregg and Whitney have brought hope
against the secret gnawing of Schaudinn's pale horror—that
Warthin himself proved to be the very Beelzebub of all degenerative microbes.

Right now other searchers have brought news of the uncovering of the manifold crimes against our fundamental
life stuff, of a sub-visible villain nearly as murderous. This
last story is tragic, yet strangely hopeful, and the book of
men against death would be unfinished without it.

II

That microscopic varmint, the hemolytic streptococcus, always did remind me of a rattlesnake. 1912 . . . when I first began squinting down a microscope barrel, the way that bug grew into chains of tiny beads made me think of the rattles at the end of a sub-visible diamond back's tail. That was long before it was known that this microbe was as treacherous, as versatile in its life-wrecking cunning, as it's right now being found out to be. It was already known to be the arch-assassin of mothers dying with childbed fever.

But it was not known in those days that the hemolytic streptococcus causes scarlet fever as well.

In 1912 this microbe was known for the murderer that killed two of my young doctor friends with blood-poisoning. But the sneaking way this same bug tortures and kills hundreds of thousands of children with rheumatic fever and rheumatic heart disease—that was then hardly suspected. Long before that, this hemolytic streptococcus was known to paint the flame of erysipelas on folks' faces and bodies. It was not then dreamed that its transient visit to our throats—here again, gone again—is almost surely at the bottom of rheumatic arthritis. Its innocent-seeming throat inflammation may leave behind it mysterious poisons that wreck hearts, kidneys, blood vessels. . . .

Will this resourceful microbe murderer be found at the bottom of many of those *degenerative* sicknesses that age us? There seems to be an excellent chance of it.

To counteract the bites of the sub-visible rattlesnake, men against death are rediscovering an old remedy prescribed by the oldest of doctors. . . . It will astound you. It is all very hopeful. It is just work in progress and none can say the end is sure. None can deny there's a new gleam of hope against suffering (to say nothing of death) that cripples more people than all forms of tuberculosis put together.

III

It has not been the discovery of any one searcher. It is the tangled story of a scattered army of microbe hunters—from Chicago to the depths of Russia—fixing for forty years at the pieces of a mixed-up puzzle that's just now falling together. It revolves round clearing up the enigma of scarlet fever.

The strangest thing about it is that a couple of Austrians had the hemolytic streptococcus spotted for the criminal as long as thirty years ago. They fished a special kind of streptococcus out of the throats of kids with scarlet fever, and even made a serum that seemed to save the lives of children from the then malignant red sickness. That ought to have settled it.

Then the Russian, Gabritchewsky, brewed a vaccine from killed streptococci and some hyper-sensitive people—into whom he shot it—got red rashes, looking like boiled lobsters, and even had the strawberry tongue you often get in scarlet fever. That should have sewed up the whole business, but then along came a lot of medical fellows giving this the lie. What mixed them up was that they didn't realize there were many closely similar families of this sub-visible rattlesnake, and they'd found the wrong criminals, not knowing it. . . .

If they'd been studying dogs and not streptococci they'd not have been fooled because you can tell a Great Dane from a poodle just by glancing at the two of them. But under a microscope any one hemolytic streptococcus looks as much like another as two peas in a pod. They tried using Jules Bordet's delicate test of a serum that would clump this microbe and not that one. But in those crude days any bug they tried looked alike to their serum—whether they'd fished it from septicemia, scarlet fever, or just a sore thumb.

The whole business was made more confusing by a German named Jochmann who claimed he'd seen fatal cases of scarlet fever where he'd found no streptococcus at all. He also held (this was not fact but philosophy) that streptococcus is too common, too garden variety a bug for a disease so *specific* as scarlet fever. That messed the whole science of it up for ten years. Scarlet fever was put down in the highbrow books as due to some mysterious microbe so tiny you couldn't see it at all. That wasn't philosophical but downright theological. So the red sickness returned to mystery.

Children died with no serum to save them, though a good one had actually been invented. So they went on dying till ten years ago. Till the Dicks—not policemen but two doctors surnamed Dick—of Chicago tried to give scarlet fever to humans. And till the searcher, Dochez, of New York, cooked up a very cunning microbe-spotting trick with pigs and guinea-pigs.

A thumbnail sketch of Alphonse Dochez would delight you but Dochez says "leave me out of it." He is—just the same—one of the very shrewdest of modern men against death, and reminds me (by his always courteous kindness) of the famous Count Arnaud, *patron* of the finest restaurant in all New Orleans.

By feeding streptococci on a special soup, Dochez got them over a great deal of their finicky unreliability about being serum tested. By serum-testing the nasty devils right after he'd fished them out of sick folks' bodies, he found there was something distinct about streptococcus you fished out of scarlet fever throats. Like diphtheria, scarlet fever always starts with sore throat; and now Dochez and his helper Bliss found if you only fish soon enough you'll always find that special hemolytic streptococcus in every scarlet fever victim.

Is this bug like the diphtheria microbe? Does the streptococcus itself stay right there in the throat—pouring out some still unknown poison through people's blood all over their bodies? Is it that way that it turns them lobster-red, gives them rheumatism sometimes, wrecking their hearts other times, and their kidneys? . . .

To spy out this possible streptococcus poison, Dochez tinkered with all kinds of animals from monkeys to mice. He tried to get the bug to locate in one spot in those animals' bodies and poison them all over. No go. The bugs either swarmed all over the beasts, killing them, or the animals only laughed at the streptococcus infection. . . .

Till at last Dochez hit on a slick trick—which really amounted to giving guinea-pigs artificial sore throats under their skins—in places (under their hides) where he'd shot a little of the nutritive jelly of agar-agar. He shot it in liquid, and it jelled right under the spot he injected it and now right into that mass of jelled microbe food, Dochez injected his special scarlet fever streptococcus. . . .

It was especially pretty in pigs and guinea-pigs. They flamed red with a rash all over. Days later the skin scaled off the soles of the guinea-pigs' feet just as it peels off convalescent children. Every now and again the streptococcus poison pouring out of those agar jelly nests had enough of a wallop to kill those guinea-pigs. . . . Just as some children die, overwhelmed by the poison the rattlesnake microbe brews in their throats.

Meanwhile the Dicks (George and Gladys) of Chicago had the nerve to paint the throats of certain humans (who were still more nervy) with swabs soaked, teeming, with pure cultures of the hemolytic streptococcus they'd got from scarlet fever. Some of these volunteer human guinea-pigs just had sore throats; others flamed lobster-red with real scarlet fever. I don't know whether any came out of it with sick joints, or kidneys, or wrecked hearts. But it was a most instructive experiment.

IV

The events that now followed would have kicked up far more furor if scarlet fever were right now the terrible killer that it formerly was in our country, death rate thirty out of every hundred . . . sometimes wiping out whole families. Now hardly more than one dies where thirty died in the old days. It's only in Russia and China (where we think they're overcrowded anyway) that the red sickness now rages terribly. But none knows when the terror may stalk among us again, and even now scarlet fever has plenty of life-wrecking (if not spectacular) consequences.

1918 . . . two searchers, Schultz and Charlton, shot a bit of the blood serum of somebody just over scarlet fever into the lobster-red skin of another somebody sick with it. . . .

Right round where they'd shot that bit of recovered fellow's serum, the circle of red rash faded out, absolutely . . . leaving a pretty spot of perfectly healthy white skin. They had an entirely wrong explanation of why that happened but what they were right about was that here was a slick way to find out quickly whether or no anybody with a rash had scarlet fever. Over in England Dr. Mair got excited about this curious test. . . .

One of his patients—a youngster—helped him to get to the bottom of it, and to prophesy the cure of red sickness. . . .

This youngster's serum hadn't the power to douse scarlet fever rashes—till she came down with the red disease, then got better. Right after that the child's blood serum would blot out a scarlet fever rash presto—almost like turning a fire-extinguisher onto a fire. Mair now turned prophet, saying that whenever the real scarlet fever bug was found, you'd find it would make a poison giving folks a red rash. . . .

And that with that poison you'd be able to make an antitoxin to wipe the rash out!

Right then in New York (not knowing about Mair) Dochez was busy shooting doses of agar-agar under the skin of a horse. Then into that lump of solidified jelly he shot his special scarlet fever hemolytic streptococcus. Now to the disgust of the horse (who obviously felt awful) whose skin scaled off, who lost a lot of hair, Dochez kept injecting bigger and bigger doses of those rattlesnake bugs—for nine long months. Then at the Yale University Medical School, where kids were in hospital with scarlet fever, Dochez's serum fulfilled Mair's prophecy. It was in its way a small death-fighting miracle. . . .

A bit of the serum of this immune horse was shot into the hot, red skin of a scarlet fever patient. In six hours round that spot the lobster-red rash had faded. That was brilliant (scientifically) but wait . . . here was a boy very ill with the red sickness, his fever raging, with him soaked with the poison the hemolytic streptococcus was brewing in his throat, with him delirious. . . .

Into that boy's muscles went a big shot of the serum from the immune horse and what now happened was much more than scientifically brilliant because in a few hours his rash began fading—*all over*. In a day his skin was normal. His heart beat calmer as his fever began cooling and here he was, clear-eyed, out of his delirium.

It was the cure of acute scarlet fever.

v

It was the final proof that the rattlesnake microbe was the real cause of scarlet fever and it was like the antitoxin cure for diphtheria . . . only (alas) scarlet fever wasn't so simple, because the hemolytic coccus that grows in chains like a rattlesnake's was, though seemingly often innocent, a thousand times more treacherous. It was easy enough to put out the acute fire of the rash by getting antitoxin into sick kids early. But when the streptococcus took a notion to migrate from that child's throat into his ears, his neck glands, his blood— then all the serum in the world wouldn't stop this devil.

And that wasn't all, nor the worst of it. Even if this spreading of the rattlesnake bug didn't happen, even if it disap-

peared out of a child's throat (and whole body) completely
. . . strange disaster still threatened. A week or two after the
rash had faded, his urine might suddenly grow scanty, turn
bloody, his face become dropsical. Yet never a streptococcus
would you find in his kidneys.

Here's another child, a girl, and just when you thought
she'd recovered completely, she'd develop the fidgets, then
go into St. Vitus dance spasms. Surely her brain had been
damaged, but you'd never find a streptococcus in her brain—
should she die.

Or after a boy's scarlet fever was over, his joints might suddenly go hot, get terribly painful, stiffen, in a strange rheumatism migrating from joint to joint all over his body. A
little play might now turn him breathless, with his heart
hurting him horribly—with the muscle of his heart pump inflamed, degenerating. Yet if he died, you'd find none of these
scarlet fever hemolytic streptococci in his joints or his heart.

The whole business was mysterious: here for acute scarlet
fever you had a swell antitoxin against the poison of hemolytic streptococcus. Yet into such children dangerously down,
dying from these sudden after-effects you could shoot all the
antitoxin they'd hold . . . nothing doing. No go. What
were these mysterious breakdowns so often following scarlet
fever—and so much more serious than the red rash trouble?

At the Presbyterian Hospital in New York City, Stevens,
who is Dochez's right-hand man, asked this question. Dochez
(dreamer) keeps wondering . . .

From its nest in the throat it's now sure that the hemolytic
streptococcus sends its poison seeping through our bodies,
bringing the red rash, the fever.

But does it brew, besides, a more subtle, dangerous chemical, that lingers in the body after the microbe itself has vanished—a hidden poison getting in its deadly degenerating
licks long after?

Is there an unknown something that the streptococcus

leaves behind it, not dangerous to everybody who gets scarlet fever maybe . . . but torturing the joints, choking the kidneys, jangling the nerves, wrecking the hearts of folks who have the hard luck to be *born sensitive to it?*

It's unheard of in all death-fighting science. It's only a vague hunch in the brain of Dochez. It's entirely heretical—this notion that different chemical parts of one and the same microbe, acting on variously sensitive people, might cause a whole series of sicknesses hitherto thought distinct. Dochez the dreamer could be encouraged in his heresy from the ancient observations of certain sharp-eyed doctors in England. Hadn't Dr. Cheadle seen how often St. Vitus dance followed scarlet fever? And how often rheumatism hooked up with St. Vitus dance? Hadn't Dr. Symes noticed the dreadful danger of an attack of scarlet fever to children with rheumatic hearts?

Yet these ills couldn't be the same. Microbe-hunting lore was against Dochez's dream. Rheumatism caused by hemolytic streptococcus? Hardly a chance of it! Groping in the rheumatic mystery, microbe hunters had found bacilli and green streptococci . . . nasty little cousins, yet different from our streptococcus whose power to dissolve blood gives it the name *"hemolytic."*

It was 1926 now, and no answer yet to the enigma of rheumatic fever, rheumatic arthritis, with kidneys gone wrong and suddenly wrecked hearts. Only confusion, contradictions.

VI

The strange death fight that now started at the Presbyterian Hospital, New York City, began with defeat. It was impossible to cause anything like rheumatic fever in any species of laboratory animal. So how could you study it—scientifically? It was a licking that turned out to be lucky. Young Coburn—Dochez's helper—didn't realize how impossible this made it to unravel the rheumatic mystery; he was scientifically unsophisticated, from South Carolina, and more than a little naïve among the young doctors (cream of American medical graduates) at the Presbyterian Hospital. Not in any way trying to imitate him young Coburn was not a little like that big-footed Scot, the mender of hearts, James Mackenzie. Coburn now began watching sick human beings, rheumatic children, hardly experimenting, just looking and looking. . . .

With the help of that remarkable nurse, Lucille Miller, Coburn went into those sad warrens of poverty-plagued humanity in the East Side and the Bronx of New York City. There he watched miserable kids not quite sick enough for the hospital. He observed children too far gone to go there, past hope, dying. He watched others, before they were sick enough for hospital, and then observed them in their flare-ups that brought them to his ward. Late in the night, night after night, Coburn went soft-footed between rows of beds in the charity wards, asking questions in whispers of youngsters so sore-jointed that every move meant exquisite torture. He was back there, at seven next morning, listening to hearts so wrecked that the smallest exertion sent their bedridden owners into an agony of labored breathing. . . .

So these next years, Coburn soaked into him the subtle, numberless, furtive, doomful symptoms of three thousand rheumatic sufferers, in slums, in hospital, in convalescent homes in the country. He checked these against thousands of others—sick with every imaginable ill other than rheumatism. . . .

One thing certain, rheumatism picked out the poor ones: for one sick with it in the private hospital rooms of the well-off, you'd find twenty suffering with it in wards of the poor. . . .

Then Coburn sorted out one hundred and sixty-two rheumatic patients for a long, close watching—for a years-long following of the unrolling of their sickness, just as you'd watch

some grim drama in a movie not sugar-coated. These suffering people were really co-workers with Coburn. He had
picked them out for the brainy way they followed their own
sickness. It was remarkable, anyway, that children and young
folks fated for rheumatism seemed exceptionally intelligent.

Another thing was certain: each and every one showed a
movie of illness different from all of the others. While many
had fearful pains migrating from one joint to another, by no
means all had what's ordinarily called rheumatism. Instead,
some might complain of galling pain low down on their
right sides. Others broke out in a light red rash with deep
red margins. Some who had St. Vitus dance, but no joint
pains to speak of, had hearts inflamed and dangerously failing. Others, getting better, suddenly sickened with a strange
filling up of their lungs. They coughed up bloody foam.
Then they'd die of a microbeless peculiar pneumonia.

Many of them, after heart failure that seemed sure to be
fatal, up and got better. Others, improving, would suddenly
shoot a high fever, become maniacal, and die. The mortality
wasn't terrific, hardly more than three per hundred, yet all
seemed always in the shadow of a lurking danger.

There was no curing them. Great doses of aspirin might
relieve their pain. Even yanking out bad tonsils or teeth
didn't seem to lessen the rheumatic flare-ups or lower the
mortality. Indeed it was evident that these operations sometimes stirred up terrible explosive heart failure where the
trouble had been sleeping. But out of all his long sharp
looking one thing stood out. There was no mistaking it. . . .

Rheumatism, rheumatic heart failure, not only the flare-
ups but new cases as well, *followed colds and especially sore
throats.*

VII

Coburn wrinkled his brow over this peculiar succession of
events, this mystery. It was plain that rheumatic fever itself
wasn't contagious. No full-blown case coming into his ward

set new ones flaring. But just let one of your no-account epidemics of sore throat get going, and then . . .

But surely so distinct, so *specific* a disease as rheumatism couldn't be the same as sore throat. How many people have sore throats, with never a joint pain or a heart twinge following? It was ridiculous!

Yet, here was Coburn, woolgathering over the peculiar fate of a fourteen-year-old Italian boy. He was a tough lovable ragamuffin. His right fist was scarred and bigger than his left from the blows he'd given in the street brawls he loved to barge into. After a sore throat this waif had come down with sore joints, bad heart, and breathless. He'd got better, had gone back to his playing and fighting. . . . His heart (Coburn knew) was marked by the rheumatic stigma.

Then he'd come back to the hospital with terrible pneumonia. He had hovered for a week in coma and was saved by the oxygen chamber. Strange! During this week of the nearly disastrous assault of the pneumonia microbes, his heart (though so weak) never faltered. He'd hardly got better from his pneumonia when he suffered a severe crop of boils. Here were boil microbes, staphylococci, poisoning his body. Yet they never threatened his damaged heart. Then sore throat hit him. . . .

He was rushed to the hospital—a couple of weeks later, the sore throat was over. He had pains in his back. His urine was bloody. His face winced ever so little trying not to show the shattering pain over his galloping heart. In sixteen days he was dead . . . of rheumatism.

At the bottom of that mild sore throat was our rattlesnake friend—*hemolytic streptococcus.*

Pappenheimer the pathologist found this boy's heart, his blood vessels, his kidneys, all shot with the very peculiar, very characteristic signs of rheumatic sickness, yet in none of these places a trace of the rattlesnake microbe. Yet if that bug were really at the bottom of so explosive a sickness, it should be swarming all over . . . it shouldn't have vanished with that mild, departed sore throat.

It was at this moment the fashion among certain microbe hunters to accuse our rattlesnake's cousin, the green streptococcus, of rheumatic murder. This evil, green-growing bug was known for a heart-wrecker, was at the bottom of an entirely different, surely fatal heart disease called "sub-acute bacterial endocarditis." Now the woman microbe hunter, Ruth Pauli (Coburn's helper) fished these green-growing assassins from the blood of many people down with this desperate heart sickness. Coburn watched these folks dying—saw no hint of rheumatic fever.

Now with an endless number of combinations of extra· tasty microbe foods, Ruth Pauli tried to culture this green streptococcus from the blood of folks sick with rheumatism. Out of two hundred such experiments she found the green microbe only six times. It was no more than a happenstance. It wasn't the villain!

There was one picture Coburn couldn't get out of his head. That was the fatal heart failure in the tough little Italian boy—following swift on his mild sore throat. Now Coburn let the plain facts lead him . . . devil take all theories, all authority, that said impossible. The hard facts were these: That, in the sad movie of these one hundred and sixty-two rheumatic friends of his that he was watching, their rheumatic flare-ups, mild, severe, fatal . . . *all followed sore throats*. It was exactly the same with the student nurses of the Presbyterian Hospital, highly exposed as they were to sore throat infection. Many got rheumatism. Always—except in the case of one nurse—it followed sore throat. It was precisely alike with rheumatic girls convalescing in the country at Pelham Manor. They were much better off there than in their poor homes in the city but in spite of every care, occasional waves of sore throat got in among them sending them into rheumatic flare-ups, some dying.

By fifty thousand exact bacteriological examinations, Coburn and Pauli proved that any one of half a dozen different microbes could cause sore throat—with no danger.

But let hemolytic streptococcus show up: then in certain ones rheumatic explosion was sure to follow.

VIII

It was sad when Elsie from the Bronx first dragged herself to the Presbyterian Hospital to Coburn. What could he promise her? Born with heart sensitive to the streptococcus poison, what chance had this girl of the Ghetto to duck the thrusts of that terrible bug that all of us lucky ones—born healthy—can laugh at?

She was only seventeen, and Coburn tells in his wonderful book on the rheumatic state how Elsie had come to him, dressed like a little old woman with a shawl round her shoulders. Her face was haggard. . . .

"She was just a bundle of bones in pain," writes Coburn.

From that first sad day her sickness tossed her back and forth between hospital and her wretched tenement. In spite of her near unbearable headaches, her heart dangerously near failing, Elsie was happier in the hospital . . . they were all so kind to her.

The moment she was able to be up, she'd drag herself back home to her folks (most of them not quite so sick as she was) to help them keep bread on the table. Now it was May of 1928, and she'd just got home, and then she caught cold again. The nurse found Elsie, her father, her sister Rose, all in beds in the same room, and one and all of them down with rheumatic fever. Of all of them Elsie was worse than any, and now with shattering pain over her heart, she was rushed back to the hospital.

Now (writes Coburn) her life hung by a thread. Coming out of semi-coma, she looked up at him, bending over her. . . .

"If I could only go South . . ." Elsie whispered.

Coburn knew that many, near dying, pull through if only they have something to live for. If I tried to explain why this nearly dead girl longed for the South I would only be mystical. Coburn promised Elsie her trip South. He had reasons—hardly better than hunches. Yet they were more than idle promises made with him thinking her impending death would relieve him from fulfilling them.

For a long time, doctors had known that the dangerous time for all those cursed with the rheumatic stigma was the season from late February when the song sparrows foretell Spring's awakening, till late May when the wood thrush sings that Summer is coming.

Coburn, from South Carolina, where the strong sun would set meadow larks singing in February, knew that there rheumatic fever is rare. But, in New York, in those months following the darkest months—it's then the rheumatic terror wrecks its thousands. All over the North—in all countries—it kills its thousands before Summer sends it back into hiding.

Round the Presbyterian Hospital at the Medical Center in upper Manhattan lived many people who'd migrated from Porto Rico, where they'd never so much as heard of rheumatism. But—in their first Spring in New York—after they'd weathered the dark months of their first northern Winter, colds and sore throats hit many of these Porto Ricans. . . .

Then afterward, to some of these many, came tortured joints, wrecked hearts. . . .

These things Coburn knew, and he had heard of luckier people who, recovering from rheumatic fever, had moved to southern California and Florida, with never a return of their danger. Bad evidence, purely coincidental, your scientist might say. And yet . . .

What was there in the South (and in the northern Summer) that kept people from the rheumatic terror? Was there a gleam of hope here? For Elsie and uncounted thousands like her, there'd been, up till now . . . only tragedy. Born sensitive to the hemolytic streptococcus, what science could change the fundamental chemistry of the bodies nature had given them?

How could Elsie and the poor thousands like her dodge streptococcus that stalks invisibly in billions at the end of the dark months?

Coburn saw a gleam of hope—maybe. And Elsie lived for him to keep his promise.

IX

Years he'd been watching. Now at last he experimented. He took Elsie and the very sick boy, Eligio, and eight others —all rheumatic—to Porto Rico. For all of them death came knocking each Spring. He took them in January of 1929 just when their peril began looming. That was his experiment in a nutshell.

It was surface science. It was rough and primitive. From letters, from interviews with doctors in Europe, from the voyage of Dr. Feeley, who was now in the Tropics, this much seemed sure. . . .

Rheumatism rampant in the North fades off (geographically) as you go South till it's nearly unknown in the Tropics of Cancer and Capricorn.

So now Coburn took his ten threatened ones to Porto Rico where it was said there was no rheumatic fever. When they started, Eligio was nearly dead, bed-ridden. Others had to be helped aboard ship. Eight out of ten had sinister symptoms. Nearly all had hemolytic streptococcus lurking in their throats. All of this strange party were game, were in their way death-fighters, were certainly experimenters.

Coburn settled his ten sick ones in an open building looking northeast right by the ocean and exposed to the wind, the damp, and the rain. What he was doing (so he wrote) was all boiled down to "changing the cosmic forces of their environment." That was his broad way of putting it. He had no precise notion of what it was that was anti-rheumatic down there—if it was anything. Just the same, right away he got them to moving round outside as much as their tired hearts would let them. He put them into swimming suits. He exposed them as much to sun as was wise.

What happened now . . . Well, there was a lift to it, if you cared about folks going on living. The boy, Eligio, who (as Coburn said) at the age of eleven understood heart disease and talked like a sage . . . he was the worst off of all of them. Those first weeks down there they thought they were going to lose him. By X-ray his heart was enormous. He had nosebleeds. He was tormented by twitchings. When the pain gripped his heart, Eligio never whimpered, but just went white, began sweating. . . . Maybe one tear might glisten at the corner of his eye. Now in a little while his nosebleeds stopped and, yes, his pains were easier. . . .

Elsie at first couldn't walk at all, though, cheery imp that she was, she thought the whole experiment was a terrific picnic. They wheeled her out in the sun and it was curious how, by and by, her heart pain began to leave her. The ominous murmurs, the rubbing sounds in her chest began to die down. And, yes, you could see it . . . the look of agony in her face (Coburn reported) gave way to a strong expression. "For Elsie life began to be blissful," said Coburn. Her face filled out. She gained nine pounds. Now, finally, the best ear could hardly detect that her heart was rheumatic. . . .

Elsie's sister Rose gained ten pounds and grew two inches. Soon the very sick boy, Harry, had got so much better he could swim strongly without getting short-winded, and, yes, before six months were up, he'd gained ten pounds. . . .

So it went with all of them, all pain faded from over their hearts, from their joints; all were feverless now, and so under the tropic sun (and the other cosmic forces of that environment?) their rheumatism flickered, then faded away. This was, mind you, the very time of the year when one-third of the medical ward beds in the Presbyterian Hospital held patients acutely ill with this sickness. And these ten were picked for the worst, most threatened, most exquisitely susceptible. . . .

As their bodies filled out and they all felt the indescribable thrill of new strength rising in them, the hemolytic streptococcus vanished from their throats. From all but one it disappeared entirely. It was evident that the sub-visible rattlesnake didn't like Porto Rico. The able Dr. P. Morales Otero had shown that, too. Among his own people, native Porto Ricans, there were no epidemic hemolytic streptococcus infections. Not once was the rattlesnake microbe prominent in three thousand bacteriological examinations of the throats of twelve hundred people in thirteen months.

July, 1929 . . . and now there was a twinkle in Eligio's grave eyes. He could play like a strong boy now and was proud of his game cocks, and Elsie, too, at last could be up and about, and in short they were, all ten of them, changed people. . . .

Then they had to go home. The money generously given by Mr. and Mrs. Howell Van Gerbig was gone now. They all sailed away from the sun of Porto Rico to New York— where steamy, humid vapors so often obscure even strong Summer sun . . . where the heat is so often too oppressive to make use of the sun when it is shining.

X

So they sailed back toward their enemy the hemolytic streptococcus. It was amazing the way Eligio understood heart disease. . . .

Back again at Presbyterian Hospital this Autumn, even before the finest instruments could detect the perilous flutter of the auricles of his heart, Eligio would ask for his dose of digifoline. . . .

He bit his lips and tried to smile as his face twitched just before his convulsions. . . .

A few hours before he died he asked for morphine and oxygen.

Elsie lived a few months longer than Eligio.

But then during one of her heart attacks at the hospital, she broke a mirror, and that helped to take the fight out of her. . . .

With a gay red ribbon in her hair (so says Coburn) she had been the life of the hospital. . . .

They wanted to do a last-ditch surgical operation to try to save her but her old spirit had left her. . . .

It was so hard for her to breathe. She kept calling for air, air, more air. A little while before she left them (for good) she actually begged not to be saved but to die. . . .

It wasn't like the old Elsie.

The end of Coburn's experiment wasn't completely unhappy. There was Edward who went South with inflammation of every part of his heart, who'd been hopeless. But he'd gained twelve pounds, grew two and a half inches. When last heard from he'd had no return of his trouble. Two others of those ten have stayed well—even in dark New York and exposed to its billions of streptococci. One has gone back to Porto Rico to live and (of course) is now feeling fine. The rest, though they've had sore throats and flare-ups, are still living. . . .

That is to say, they were at Coburn's last writing.

This very last winter of 1932, this New York experiment has been marvelously confirmed by a Boston doctor who took a gang of heart-wrecked rheumatic kids to the strong sun of Miami.

Is it sun only? Is it more scientific to say it's the cosmic forces of the environment? What's the explanation of the life-giving power of the warmth and the sun and the open? It is still mysterious. Are the throats of these threatened people turned into tough places for the sub-visible rattle-snakes to scrape up a living? Are the hearts, joints, blood vessels, all the tissues of the sad souls born sensitive to this microbe . . . are they all made tougher, less sensitive to its poisons by reason of life in the sun and the open? These questions demand experiment. . . .

Is it again only a business of an upping of total condition that follows the mysterious touch of certain still not definitely known parts of the sunlight?

With millions sick, with hundreds of thousands wrecked, with thousands dying every year—these questions now shout for an answer by experiment.

For such experiments the men against death at Presbyterian Hospital now have no more money.[1] There are millions for obscure diseases in Asia but not a cent for the fight against streptococcus that's now known to cause ninety-nine percent of all heart disease in children . . . and most heart trouble of those in life's prime.

It's now sure that without hemolytic streptococcus, children can't be threatened with the rheumatic danger, and that (very possibly) grown-ups can't be tortured with rheumatic arthritis. But here's what's most remarkable: all of us are exposed to streptococcus, all of our throats may be bit by it . . . but the bodies of certain ones of us, only, are *sensitive* to its degenerating poison. It boils down to a three-cornered battle between yourself, hemolytic streptococcus, and the environment you live in.

It's nonsense to hope all rheumatism-sensitive kids of the northern cities can migrate (like robins and bluebirds going South at the start of the dark months) . . . to Porto Rico, or to Florida or California, which are nearer, and as sunny

---

1 Money to continue this work has been recently supplied by the W. K. Kellogg Foundation.

and healthy. It would be absolutely Utopic, with more than a touch of the communistic, to ask it.

To avoid a tragic end to this book of men against death, let's not look too closely at the horror of what is, compared to the happiness of what might be.

Are there ways to get round it? Long ago, Finsen the light hunter, invented his machine-sun in Denmark, where sunlight is dim. . . .

Today's light hunters at the Finsen Institute know that people tanned by *this particular* machine-sun's rays during the periods they're bathing in the carbon arc's light are remarkably free from colds and sore throat infections. . . .

Is there a gleam of hope here?

ENVOI

"Some day some tinkering fixer will learn to stave off the gradual tiring of the muscles of our hearts . . ." so I wrote at this book's beginning, long before I'd heard of this death fight of the men of the Presbyterian Hospital.

Before Dochez, Stevens, Coburn, and all the rest of them caught the sub-visible rattlesnake at its heart-wrecking deviltry, the tiring out of the hearts of the poor rheumatic youngsters was mysterious. But what of the tiring of the hearts and the degeneration of the blood vessels of the millions of us older ones?

Is their tiring inherent? Is it a pure wearing out? Is their degeneration intrinsic? Is death inevitably the consequence of life? Can life hardly be longer than it is now, as the scientifically pessimistic knife-wielders peering at dead bodies in the dead house want me to believe?

Or does the sub-visible rattlesnake—or other microbic marauders yet unknown—hasten that wearing out which might be much slower?

While I wait for men against death to unveil these mysteries, I'm not going to take chances, but instead will follow the rule of those three uncles whose example taught me to live the life of a civilized barbarian.

Are my three unscientific old uncles really so unscientific?

Isn't all of this only another example of the truth of what my three honorary uncles have taught me?

To grow old very slowly and stay young very long, what's better than living all I can in the wind and the rain and the sun?

INDEX

INDEX

359